# Community Water Systems
## SOURCE BOOK

by **JOSEPH S. AMEEN**, S.M., Sanitary Engineer

COMMERCIAL • INSTITUTIONAL • RESIDENTIAL
INDUSTRIAL APPLICATIONS

**FOURTH EDITION**

# TECHNICAL PROCEEDINGS

P. O. BOX 5041 • HIGH POINT, NORTH CAROLINA 27262

Printed in the United States of America

This book is DEDICATED to the

STAFF

SANITARY ENGINEERING DIVISION

NORTH CAROLINA STATE BOARD OF HEALTH

for unselfish dedication of their lives

to better environmental health.

# Acknowledgments

The compilation of much material for this handbook was made possible through the generosity of many contributors of such materials and suggestions of many of these contributors.

Among these contributors are:

A. M. Byers Company, Pittsburgh, Pennsylvania.

American Cast Iron Pipe Company, Birmingham, Alabama.

Badger Meter Manufacturing Company, Milwaukee, Wisconsin.

Cast Iron Pipe Research Association, Chicago, Illinois.

Darling Valve and Manufacturing Company, Williamsport, Pennsylvania.

James B. Clow & Sons, Incorporated, Chicago, Illinois.

Johns-Manville Corporation, New York, New York.

Mueller Company, Decatur, Illinois.

National Board of Fire Underwriters, New York, New York.

Naugatuck Chemical, Division of U. S. Rubber Company, Naugatuck, Connecticut.

Omega Machine Company, B-I-F Industries, Inc., Providence, Rhode Island.

Peerless Pump Division, Food Machinery & Chemical Corporation, Los Angeles, California.

Price Brothers Company, Dayton, Ohio.

Sanitary Engineering Division, North Carolina State Board of Health, Raleigh, North Carolina.

Steel Plate Fabricators Association, Chicago, Illinois.

Valve and Primer Corporation, Chicago, Illinois.

Wallace & Tiernan, Incorporated, Belleville, New Jersey.

Worthington Corporation, Harrison, New Jersey.

The author wishes to express his sincere thanks and appreciation to these contributors for their generosity and assistance.

# Preface To First Edition

Experience in the field of water supply over the years, has indicated a great need for a source book which provides basic information for design, operation, and economics within the field of Community Water Systems .

This handbook is written, setting forth criteria on water usage within communities including institutional, commercial, residential, and industrial usage. Such criteria is established from experience and may be accepted as being reasonable and adequate for actual design purposes.

The author has simplified the entire text so that persons without experience in the field of water supply may be enabled to use the information included. A vast amount of information within the text is also most valuable to the practicing architect and engineer in the field of water supply. It provides an accumulation of data which is most difficult to assemble from present literature.

The many tables within the text make it possible to establish estimates of a water system for a community without the vast expense of a detailed survey or study. Therefore, it is possible to evaluate the economic feasibility as to the practicality of the system for the proposed area to be served.

This handbook also provides a means of designing a system which will assure adequacy at completion of the community by setting forth aids in planning of the community. A properly designed system provides not only adequacy, but will operate more economically than a poorer designed water system.

In reading and interpreting the data included within the text, one should remember that information for small water systems is almost non-existent because of the high variance in the individual water usage which greatly alters accepted values of water usage.

Again, the author has tried to remove the highly technical details and has tried to get a workable and practical handbook that is usable in everyday practice without having to consult other handbooks and spend tedious hours working out the minute details which require a more complete knowledge of the subject.

It is suggested that the reader quickly review the entire contents of the text before applying any of the tables so that the relationship of the components of the system may be known and coordinated.

JOSEPH S. AMEEN

High Point, North Carolina
October 5, 1959

## Preface to Fourth Edition

It is the opinion of many authorities in the field of water supply that few technical changes have occurred since the First Edition was published.

Major changes, however, have been made in water quality standards set forth by the Public Health Service. Such changes of the "Drinking Water Standards of 1962" are included in the chapter on "Water Quality".

The term "part per million" is retained in general use throughout this Edition because its equivalent term, "milligram per liter" has not been widely accepted in general practice.

This Fourth Revision is necessary to update the economic factors brought about by the rising cost of water systems in the past three years.

High Point, North Carolina

August 22, 1967

Joseph S. Ameen

# About the Author

Joseph S. Ameen is Staff Sanitary Engineer for Burlington Industries, Incorporated. He received his Bachelor of Science Degree from the Georgia School of Technology, a Bachelor of Laws Degree from La Salle University, and the Master of Science Degree in Sanitary Engineering from Harvard University.

During World War II, he served with the Corps of Engineers, U. S. Armed Forces Far East, in the Southwest Pacific Areas. Following this tour of duty, Mr. Ameen served as Sanitary Engineer with the Fulton County Health Department, Atlanta, Georgia. From 1952 to 1966 he served in the capacity of Sanitary Engineer Consultant with the North Carolina State Board of Health in the fields of Air Pollution Control, Radiological Health, Water Supply and Sewage Treatment.

During 1955, Mr. Ameen served with the U. S. Public Health Service as Sanitary Engineer in the surveillance program for the Atomic Weapons Testing Program. He is also the author of a book, "Nuclear Radiation Protection," published in 1966.

Mr. Ameen is a Registered Engineer in the State of North Carolina. He is a member of many professional organizations to which he has presented numerous scientific papers.

# Table of Contents

# Summary of Tables

# Summary of Tables

# Appendix Summary

# CHAPTER I

# Basic Design Criteria

**General**

Water has become an important consideration in the modern way of living. The usage of water per person has more than tripled within the time period of 1945 to 1959. With the increased use of modern appliances, water is becoming the prime factor in the development of new communities. This modern way of living is based upon the desire for cleanliness and unlimited quantities of high quality water. The problem of meeting this demand of unlimited quantities of high qaulity water is facing each municipality, water company, developer, and individual concerned with public, semi-public, or private water supply. This problem is complicated by the lack of desired developmental property, the complexity of living conditions and the problem of environmental health of the community.

In the study of water usage or consumption within any community, one will discover that the variations in daily, weekly, and monthly usage are unique to that community and will differ somewhat from community to community. The standards of living within the different communities will account for much of the variations in per capita water consumption. As the increment of water usage becomes smaller, such as from daily to hourly, the fluctuations from community to community become greater. If one were to make a graph of water usage comparing a small community with a large community, the graph would be as illustrated in Figure 1. It can be

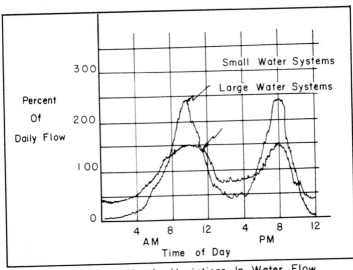

FIGURE I. Hourly Variations In Water Flow.

noted and explained that the individual habits of each consumer would influence the maximum and minimum values to an extent depending upon the size of the community being served. In other words, a small community would show greater variations throughout the 24-hour period, because of the influence of the individual users on the system. The graph clearly indicates that in the larger systems, the individual habits of the consumers will overlap to a much greater extent thus eliminating the influence as indicated within the smaller systems.

The prediction of water consumption, especially where small water systems are involved, is one of the most difficult problems in the field of water supply because of this individualism of consumers. Several other factors will also influence water usage or consumption within a community. Such factors as water quality, distribution system pressure and adequacy of the system, and water charges will have a defined effect upon this usage. If any of these factors are unsatisfactory to the consumers, the per capita water consumption will be much less than one predicts. The consumer, served by a community water system, demands a high quality water, but in many cases will tolerate a lower quality if circumstances are beyond the supplier's control for the production of water of desired quality. The water supplier should furnish the highest quality of water possible to consumers, not only because of his obligation to furnish such, but because the economics of his investment is made on the basis of receiving a fair return from "selling" his product.

Therefore, in the development of a community water system, every consideration should be given to making the product as attractive as possible so that expansion may proceed as in the original plans and so that the system will be more than adequate at all times for providing adequate service with as little maintenance and operation problems as possible. Such a system must return a reasonable profit if it is to provide adequate and uninterrupted service in exchange for proper operational maintenance required. In other words, a water system operating on a "shoe-string" budget cannot be expected to continuously provide satisfactory service for the community served. Details in planning and economics should be studied prior to the construction of a water system, so that adequate revenue for operation and amortization of the system may be had.

### Community Water Systems

In defining a community water system, it may be stated that community water systems are considered systems of water supply, which serve small populations within urban or rural areas. In many cases, such populations are located in areas, which are some distance from the limits of incorporated towns or water districts and from the standpoint of economics, cannot be served by such systems even though an extension from the municipality would certainly be the most desirable source of water supply. The communities are sometimes large enough to include shopping centers, schools, and even large industrial plants. The community water system should be designed to provide water service to all commercial, institutional, and industrial centers within the community.

Early in the planning stage of the development of a community, the question arises whether or not a community water system is economically feasible. Before this question can be answered, the problem must be studied in detail so that comparisons can be made of the cost and advantages of the community water system with those of the privately owned individual water systems for each residence, shopping center, school, and industrial plant. This preliminary study of the entire area to be developed would be a compilation of all data concerning growth, economics, etc., and then an evaluation of such data so that definite conclusions may be made. Such a preliminary study should include such factors as:

1. Area to be served by the community water system.
2. Estimates of water usage.
3. Sources of water supply available.
4. Proposed water system layout.
5. Economics of operation.

When a detailed study is made, many of the unforeseen problems may be easily eliminated or solved prior to final plans for the system are prepared.

In the comparison of the community system with the economics of individual water systems, other considerations should enter into the study, which are most important as far as the developer is concerned. One such factor, in favor of community water systems, is that community water systems will allow for smaller lots to be used in developments, because the additional area required within each lot for protection of individual water systems will not be necessary, in that the larger community wells replace these numerous individual wells. Another important factor to be considered is that the larger community wells, which are drawing water from the lower stratas of water, will less

likely be contaminated by the use of individual sewage disposal systems usually required in outlying communities because of the greater distances away from these sources of pollution. This greater distance between the source of water supply and sources of pollution allows for greater filtration of the sewage, as it seeks its course into the ground water table. A further consideration is from the standpoint of water quality and quantity. If the water within an area is undesirable due to a high concentration of an undesirable chemical such as iron, then the cost of treatment to remove the chemical to desired concentration can be done at a much more reasonable cost for the few community wells than for the numerous individual wells. Even if the problem is corrosion within the system due to a high content of carbon dioxide within the water, treatment on a large source can be accomplished more economically than on the small scale individual water system basis. Corrosion control equipment and application is also more economical and easily applied to the larger systems whereas it may be extremely expensive and troublesome for the individual systems. The application of Fluorides to a system, for aid in preventing dental caries in children's teeth, is impractical on individual water systems, because of the extreme accuracy with which the dosage must be applied.

Lastly, the quantity and dependibility of the supply must be considered. When failure occurs for the individual water system, there is not provision for reserve for long periods of time whereas with the community water system, sources and storage facilities are designed to provide a reserve which may be utilized during such emergency periods, or until such failure is overcome.

The cost of a community water system will vary depending upon the type of service to be rendered and provisions for adequacy. Figure 2 sets forth estimates of the cost of community water systems based upon this type of service to be rendered. This graph may be explained as follows:

*Curve A*—Community water systems, utilizing ground water source, providing domestic water service only. The water distribution system for this type system is designed to provide the needs for only domestic water and does not provide for fire service.

*Curve B*—Community water system utilizing ground water source providing domestic service and partial fire service. In other words, the storage facilities will provides some fire reserve, in addition to domestic storage. Also, the distribution system is designed to provide fire flows in certain areas, but in overall design, is not designed to provide fire flows.

*Curve C*—Community water system utilizing a ground water source, designed to provide adequate fire flows throughout the system. This type of system in its design, has proper storage facilities and large distribution lines, with properly spaced fire hydrants, to provide adequate fire protection.

*Curve D*—Community water system utilizing a surface water source, designed to provide adequate fire flows throughout the system as discussed for Curve C above. The filtration plant in this event is designed to provide 150% of the daily average flow of the community based on the usage of 100 gallons per day per person.

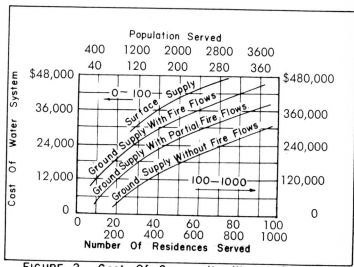

FIGURE 2. Cost Of Community Water Systems.

## 1. Area Study

A study of the area to be developed will provide basic information as to present and future potentials of a community water system. It is suggested that a plat plan of the area be made so that detail planning may be had. Such a plan will be a considerable help in estimating present or expected conditions as far as residential, commercial, and institutional requirements are concerned. Certain provisions should be made for future expansion within the development. It is most desirable to establish some definite limit for the area to be ultimately served in the future, so that the planning may include such areas. Such future areas to be developed may be several years hence, but the water system should be planned with this in view. In many communities inadequacy of the water supply is encountered within a few years because of poor planning due to lack of well defined boundaries and the continued enlargement of the system without a definitely defined permanent plan. Such inadequacies could include poor location of the source of supply, storage facilities, and/or distribution lines, which are too small to properly and adequately serve new areas which should have been included within the original plan but were omitted.

Within the proposed plan of the development, the location of all residences, multi-dwellings or apartment buildings, commercial and industrial establishments, and institutions should be clearly established as to size and location. If an area is reserved for a school or commercial use, the location and an estimate of size, type, future possibilities should be made so that water usage for the area may be estimated. This information

should be in the form that Tables II, III, and IV may be used to estimate the potential water requirements for the area in question. For these areas, it must be realized that the values so used are, only at best, estimates, therefore, it is not necessary to spend a great deal of time trying to get such values with great accuracy. In other words, if such future information is not available, a rough estimate should be made from the information at hand to determine the future requirements of the particular area involved. It should be remembered that for small water systems, estimates on water usage are extremely difficult to estimate with any degree of accuracy. Therefore, on the basis of knowledge of the community to be served, values set forth in Tables II, III, and IV are most satisfactory for most practical purposes. It should be stressed that it is important to make reasonable estimates of future water usage from predicted future land use. Thus, a definite basis is obtained for which the system may be designed.

## 2. Estimates of Water Usage

The water requirements for a community water system are the total of the combined water requirements for the domestic population, commercial and industrial, and institutional usage. Industrial process water requirements are beyond the scope of this text and should be given much greater consideration, because such requirements, in many cases, will exceed the total requirement of the entire community.

### A. Domestic Water Requirements

In determining domestic requirements, the basis for calculations may best be obtained from an estimate of population. Rather than try to obtain an actual count of population to be served, it is much more convenient to estimate the population on the basis of per dwelling unit from established criteria of population trends. Because of the movement of families in and out of the community, an estimation using this previous knowledge will be accurate enough for practical purposes. Therefore, knowing the number and type of dwellings to be served, an estimate of population may be had from Table II, which is based upon average values and will give dependable estimates for community populations.

In the early planning stage of many developments, it is difficult to make predictions of dwelling units, etc. However, a knowledge of the average proposed lot size and the total acreage to be developed, will provide basic information from which the population and water consumption may be estimated. From a knowledge of the average proposed lot width and depth, one may refer to Figure 3 and obtain the square footage of this average lot. With this information, Table I will provide an estimate of population density within the community on a per acre or per square mile basis.

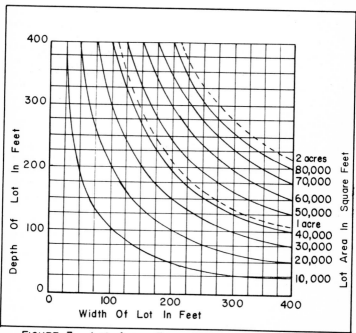

FIGURE 3.  Lot Areas From Width-Depth Dimensions.

## TABLE I
### Population Densities from Average Lot Area

| Average Area of Lot Within Development in Square Feet | Estimated Population Per Acre | Estimated Population Per Square Mile |
|---|---|---|
| 10,000 | 6.25 | 4,160 |
| 15,000 | 4.2 | 2,688 |
| 20,000 | 3.15 | 2,016 |
| 25,000 | 2.52 | 1,612 |
| 30,000 | 2.10 | 1,344 |
| 40,000 | 1.28 | 819 |
| 50,000 | 1.16 | 742 |
| 60,000 | 1.05 | 672 |
| 70,000 | 0.90 | 576 |
| 80,000 | 0.79 | 514 |

An estimate of total population may be obtained by multiplying the value obtained from Table I by the total number of acres or square miles to be developed:

Total Estimated Population = Population Density (from Table I) x Area to be Developed.

Studies of population trends for small communities to municipal populations of 100,00 indicate the population density will vary from a low of 2,400 persons per square mile to a maximum of 4,300 persons per square mile. Conditions, prevailing at the upper limit, indicate that the community is somewhat saturated and must expand its limits. When density is less than 2,400 persons per square mile, the problem of economical feasibility of water service becomes apparent. Further study of population trends for communities greater than 100,000, show that the population density will increase at the rate of 1,000 persons per square mile for each additional 100,000 population. Thus for a city of a population of 200,000, the population density will

range from some 3,400 persons per square mile to a maximum of 5,300 persons per square mile.

Utilizing these population densities for existing communities, an estimate of urban area development may be obtained from a prediction of population growth of the community. This prediction of population growth may be obtained by several methods as follows:

1. Comparison with other communities, which, in the past, have had similar growth characteristics. By making a graph of other communities (plotting years versus population), then extend graph of community under study to parallel such growth rates to obtain a predicted population.

2. Graphical projection of past community growth. By making a graph of past growth, a projection of the curve obtained, is extended using same growth rate to give future population.

3. Utilizing growth rate increments of the past and assuming that the future rate of growth will be similar. This method of predicting

population growth is achieved by calculating the growth increment per year for a period of ten years (Census Years), then projecting to the future year desired by multiplying the growth increment by the number of years hence.

4. Graphical representation of school enrollment growth applied as a trend to illustrate community growth.

5. Compilations of predictions of other agencies interested in community growth such as Chamber of Commerce, Gas and Telephone Utilities, Vital Statistics Section of the State Health Department, etc.

It should be remembered that mass population movements in and out of communities caused by influx or relocation of large industries will not be reflected in such studies of future populations but will be reflected in past population trends.

Upon obtaining a predicted population, the future urban area development of the community or extension of the community limits may be obtained by dividing the yearly esti-mated population by the present area of the community until a population density of some 4,300 persons per square mile is obtained. At that time, the area of the community should be increased so that the density of the population will be decreased to around 2,400 persons per square mile. This procedure is again repeated until the maximum of 4,300 is again reached. For communities over 100,-000, the density of population will vary as previously discussed.

In many new developments it is desirable to have an estimate of the number of residences which may be constructed prior to the actual subdividing of the property. From a knowledge of proposed lot size and acreage of the tract, Table I(a) supplements Table I so that the approximate number of residences may be roughly established. Table I(a) takes into consideration that a street right-of-way of 60 feet is to be provided for and that a certain percentage of the lots will not be suitable for construction because of topography.

## TABLE I(a)
## Estimated Number of Dwellings Per Area from Average Lot Size

| Average Lot Area in Square Feet | Estimated Number of Dwellings Per Acre | Estimated Number of Dwellings Per Square Mile |
|---|---|---|
| 10,000 | 1.56 | 1,040 |
| 15,000 | 1.05 | 672 |
| 20,000 | .78 | 504 |
| 25,000 | .63 | 403 |
| 30,000 | .52 | 336 |
| 40,000 | .32 | 204 |
| 50,000 | .29 | 186 |
| 60,000 | .26 | 167 |
| 70,000 | .22 | 144 |
| 80,000 | .19 | 121 |

## TABLE II
## Estimating Domestic Populations

| Type of Dwelling | Estimated Persons Per Dwelling |
|---|---|
| First-Class | 4 |
| Multi-Dwelling | |
|     One Bedroom Unit | 2 |
|     Two Bedroom Unit | 3 |
|     Three Bedroom Unit | 5 |
| Mobile Home | 2½ |

Table II provides estimates of populations for various types of residential housing facilities. These figures are based upon average values obtained from community study for various types of dwellings.

In determining domestic water usage, the daily usage must be based upon the maximum day of the week so that this quantity of water will be available for the community at all times. This maximum quantity of water necessary to furnish the need of the community will depend upon whether or not the system is metered. A system which is not metered will have a demand for water as great as 300 per cent of that community which is metered. For design purposes, the following values are accepted in general practice for water consumption for domestic populations:

On the basis of these accepted values, first class dwellings will have a daily usage of 500 gallons based upon the maximum day of the week for the system which is 100% metered. If the system is unmetered, the daily usage is expected to be around 1,000 gallons per day. The primary reason for this great difference in usage between the metered and unmetered systems is that a person on an unmetered system will use water freely and will not maintain his plumbing fixtures in good repair to prevent leakage. Also there will be a great deal more lawn watering on the system which has no meters. A further example of the use of Table II and Table III would be that the expected water usage of a multi-dwelling building with three two-bedroom units would be on the basis of nine persons

## TABLE III
## Domestic Water Consumption*

| Type of System | Daily Consumption Per Person |
|---|---|
| All Metered Services | 70-100-125 Gallons |
| Unmetered Services | 100-150-250 Gallons |

*The commonly accepted value for water usage for domestic populations is 100 gallons per day per person. Studies indicate that the combined average water usage for a community will vary from 69 to 109 gallons per person per day. Hence, for design of a community water system, the value of 125 gallons per day is the suggested value since it is a maximum per day usage per person.

with a usage of 1,125 gallons per day on a metered system or 2,250 gallons per day on an unmetered system.

**B. Institutional Water Requirements**

Water requirements for institutions may also be determined on the population basis as above. Such water consumption figures should be based upon the *future* enrollment of the school or institution, and upon future plans concerning changes in status of the type of the institution. Table IV suggests criteria on the per student or person basis and relates the type of institution to be served with this per person water usage.

it is impossible to predict with any degree of accuracy the potential success of the establishment. Therefore, Table V not only sets forth criteria for water consumption, but also is a simplified basis for the calculation of such requirements.

Upon the basis of water usage as given in Table V, the total daily water consumption can be calculated.

The total water requirements for a community would be the total as calculated, combining information from Tables II through V. To illustrate the use of these tables, an example would be, that a community, for which a water system is to be de-

## TABLE IV
## Institutional Water Consumption

| Type of Institution | Gallons Per Person Per Day |
|---|---|
| Boarding Schools, Elementary | 75 |
| Boarding Schools, Senior | 100 |
| Churches | 3 |
| Clubs, Country | 25 |
| Clubs, Civic | 3 |
| College, Day Students | 25 |
| College, Junior | 100 |
| College, Senior | 100 |
| Elementary Schools | 16 |
| Hospitals | 400 |
| Junior and High Schools | 25 |
| Nursing Homes | 150 |
| Prisons | 60 |
| Rooming Houses | 100 |
| Summer Camps | 60 |

**C. Commercial and Industrial Water Requirements**

Commercial and industrial water usage must be calculated on some other basis rather than either the patronage or per person usage because

signed has 60 first-class dwellings, a 200-student elementary school, a drug store with fountain service, a ready-to-wear shop, and a small super market, which has 5,000 square feet of floor area. From this information, it would be expected that this community

# TABLE V
## Commercial and Industrial Water Consumption Requirements

| Type of Establishment | Estimated Water Usage and Basis of Calculation |
|---|---|
| Barber Shop | 100 gallons per day per chair |
| Beauty Shop | 125 gallons per day per chair |
| Dentist Office | 750 gallons per day per chair |
| Department Store* | 40 gallons per day per employee |
| Drug Store | 500 gallons per day |
| With Fountain Service | Add 1,200 to 1,500 gallons per day |
| Serving Meals | Add 50 gallons per day per seat |
| Industrial Plant** | 30 gallons per day per employee |
| Laundry | 2,000-5,000-20,000 gallons per day |
| Launderette | 1,000 gallons per day per unit |
| Meat Market | 5 gallons per day per 100 sq. ft. floor area |
| Motel or Hotel | 125 gallons per day per room |
| Office Building* | 12 gallons per day per 100 sq. ft. floor area or 25 gallons per employee |
| Physicians Office | 200 gallons per day per examining room |
| Restaurant | 20-50-120 gallons per day per seat |
| Single Service | 500-1,500-2,500 gallons per day |
| Drive-In | 20 gallons per day per car space |
| Service Station | 600-1,000-1,500 gallons per day per wash rack |
| Theatre | 3 gallons per day per seat |
| Drive-In | 3 gallons per day per car space |
| Other Establishments*** | 500 gallons per day |

*Including customer service.

**Not including process water.

***Non-water using establishments. 500 gallons per day should be considered the minimum daily usage for any establishment.

would have a daily water usage or consumption as follows:

60 first-class dwellings with four persons per dwelling (Table II) will have a water usage of 125 gallons per day per person (Table III) = 30,000 gpd.

200-student elementary school with a water usage of 16 gallons per day per student (Table IV) = 3,-200 gpd.

One drug store with fountain service will have a daily water usage of 500 gpd plus 1,200 gpd (Table V) = 1,700 gpd.

One ready-to-wear shop will have a daily water usage of 500 gpd (other establishments—Table V) = 500 gpd.

One super market will have a daily usage based upon five gallons per 100 square feet of floor area (Table V), a usage of five gallons/100 square feet times 5,000 square feet = 250 gallons per day or from footnote for Table V, a usage of 500 gallons per day. Therefore, usage = 500 gpd.

A total requirement for water for this community is estimated to be 35,900 gallons per day. This will be the quantity of water required to meet the maximum daily requirements. The normal or average requirement for this community will be somewhat less than this, but is is necessary to provide this amount for the maximum day of the week.

There are several terms which are pertinent in expressing water usage. One term is daily average usage. This term is used to express the average used per day over a long period of time, in other words, the average of many days usage. This value would be 50 to 100 gallons per day per person, within any community, if referring strictly to domestic consumption.

Another term in general use is daily maximum water usage. This refers to the maximum usage for a 24-hour period. Peak flow relates somewhat to the daily maximum, but is intended to express the peak flow during a particular period. These values will exceed the average day by factors ranging from 125 to 300 per cent.

It is also common to express water usage in terms of hourly flow. The maximum hour, or hourly peak, is an expression to designate such peak flows during the 24-hour period. Refer to Figure 1 to see this variation for hourly flow during a typical 24-hour period.

Therefore, as a factor of safety, the daily maximum flow or usage should be used when selecting a source of supply and other appurtenances related to the daily water usage. Note that Table III, Table IV, and Table V give values of water consumption based on the maximum day. The hourly maximum water usage and other instanteous flows are used in the design of storage and pipelines in order that the instanteous demand of the community may be met. In any event, if definite information is lacking during the early stages of development, maximum values should be used, which are based on best available information, to assure adequacy of the system at some future time.

# CHAPTER II

# Sources of Water Supply

**General**

In the selection of sources of water supply, consideration must be focused on two main factors, *(1)* Quality of water, and *(2)* Quantity of water required. By quality of water is meant the chemical and physical characteristics of the water desired. For to be of high quality, the water must first of all be free of harmful bacteria or the index organisms which will indicate that pathogenic bacteria may find their way to the supply.

Second, the water must be free of objectionable taste and odors which may be caused by either undesirable chemicals or organisms. Third, it must be low in concentrations of troublesome minerals such as iron, sulphur, manganese, fluorides in high concentration, calcium and magnesium in high concentrations and other agents which will make the water unsuitable for use by excessive discoloration, hardness, or non-potable from the standpoint of high chemical content. Fourth, the water must be of a non-corrosive nature so that it will not react with plumbing fixtures or pipelines to cause failure of such lines, necessitating frequent replacement or cause the staining of plumbing fixtures.

The quantity of the available supply must be such that maximum daily demands of the community are satisfied at all times, even during extended periods of drought or pursuing years of community growth.

In the consideration of factors in the design and the construction of community water systems, the economic factor is of extreme importance. This indicates that the source of supply should be selected so that little maintenance for the operational factors will be required to furnish an adequate supply of water to the community. Even though surface water supplies, with proper treatment, are by far the more suitable from the standpoint of adequacy, yet the utilization of surface water supplies is confined to community water systems starting upwards at 50,000 gallons per day. Such surface supplies are utilized where water sources are immediately available. For smaller water systems, ground water sources are to be the first considered because of their being more practical and economical for many reasons which will be discussed in more detail.

## 1. Ground Water Sources

In the original planning of ground water supplies, little can be done about determining the chemical quality of the water because of the fact that the water will be obtained from several well-defined and different water-bearing geological layers or strata. The water contributed from each of these water-bearing formations or aquifiers will be of a chemical or mineral quality dependent upon the dissolution of material within the formation. Therefore, water withdrawn from any ground water source will be a composite of these individual aquifiers. Only by analyses after the completion of the construction of the well can the quality of water be determined and this is by actually sampling and then analyzing. However, much information can be obtained about ground water quality within a community by the experience of existing wells. Most well contractors will have a general idea as to what the quality of water is within an area because of their previous experience. Also, local and state health departments will have general and helpful information of water quality within their jurisdiction from analyses which have been made during the years. Most state geologists will also have information as to both quantity and quality of water within certain regions of their state. All such information is valuable and should be obtained when considering ground water sources of supply. All of the above officials will have the most reliable information regarding ground water characteristics.

Ground water, in most instances, will be the source of supply most readily available for development into community water systems because the ground water in most areas can be easily tapped to furnish the required quantity of water supply. Surface waters are usually not readily available in quantity and in many cases must be impounded for adequacy or must be piped some distance to serve the community. There is also the quality of the water to be considered when investigating surface waters, because of the gross pollution in many cases rendering available water unusuable for potable water supplies, even though complete treatment will be provided.

The ground water cycle or phenomenon is of interest to one concerned with the field of water supply to assist in the development of water sources[1]. This portion of the water cycle is included and is illustrated in Figure 4.

Ground water is an integral part of the hydrological cycle of rain and

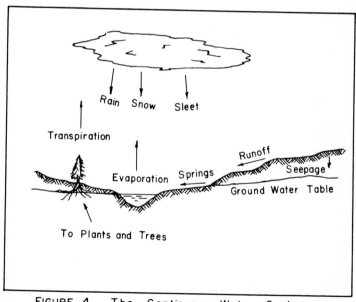

FIGURE 4. The Continuous Water Cycle.

evaporation of water between the earth's bodies of water and the vast moisture content of the atmosphere. The water content of the atmosphere precipitates from small nuclei and falls to the earth's crust in the form of rain, sleet, and snow. Approximately 70 per cent of this rain finds its way into the streams, rivers, and finally to the oceans. The remaining 30 per cent seeps into the earth and joins the ground water table. Some of this water returns as surface water from springs, flowing wells, etc., some is utilized as the water supply of plants and trees, and the remaining portion joins the ground water and appears in layers known as aquifers. The seepage of this water through the earth is dependent upon the soil and rock formations under the earth's surface. Seepage is much greater through porous type formations than the impervious formations. For example, water seeps much faster through sedimentary formations as sandstones than through metamorphic formations as gneiss or igneous formations as granite. Water seeps at much greater rates through fissures or cracks within the underlying formations. Ground water in the aquifers flows from higher elevations to lower elevations. Such data may be available from previous studies of geological investigations.

In the continuous cycle of water transportation from the earth to the atmosphere, water leaves the earth in the form of evaporation from bodies of water and transpiration from plant life, to return to the atmosphere where it is retained until again released in the form of rain, sleet, snow, etc. Replenishment of the ground water table may be accomplished to some extent by the location of ponds and lakes on watersheds. This phenomenon as relating to ponds and lakes is reversible as it supplements the ground water table during periods of drought and supplements stream flows during period of the wet season.

## A. Selection of Ground Water Sources of Supply

In the selection of a source of water supply, the availability, the economics, the adequacy of supply, the quality of the water, and the operational maintenance, govern the type of supply to be developed. The selection of a supply, which requires as little operational maintenance as possible for a continued production of a constant high quality water, is desired. To meet this requirement, first consideration would be given to a ground water supply of either springs, infiltration galleries, or wells. It is desired to meet the above criteria concerning the source of supply to be utilized. It is realized in almost each instance that the well is the most desirable of ground water sources. This is because the location of the well is the most flexible of the three types of ground waters. Also, the yield of the well will greatly exceed the other types of ground water sources. Springs and infiltration galleries are located usually in low areas. Therefore, large tracts of land are required for their protection from pollution. Even where the large tracts are available, in many cases it is impossible to provide the protection to these supplies to prevent pollution such as flooding, sewage contamination, etc. Factors such as this, when applied to the comparison of wells with other sources of ground water, usually favor the utilization of wells.

## B. Types of Wells[1]

Wells are classified in several ways: first, by the method of construction, and second by the depth. By the method of construction is meant how the well is constructed. This classification is as follows:

1. Dug well.
2. Bored well.
3. Punched well.
4. Drilled well.

By depth, wells are classified as follows:

1. Artesian or flowing wells.
2. Shallow well.
3. Deep well.

A description of each of these type of wells classified as to construction, is as follows:

1. The Dug Well. The dug well is constructed usually by manual labor. Its diameter varies from 30 to 36 inches and its depth may be to the layers of hard or bed rock but never more than 80 feet. The dug well being shallow, is usually not too dependable for large yields of water over long periods of time unless located in areas which have exceedingly high ground water tables. This type of well is the most difficult to protect from the standpoint of pollution if the well is located within a densily populated community. This difficulty in protection is due to the fact that water within the upper layers of the ground water table is utilized as the water supply and is more apt to be polluted. The protection of a dug well from surface contamination is illustrated in Figure 5.

2. The Bored Well. The bored well is constructed by the use of an auger which may either be operated manually or by machine. The diameter of the bored well may be from a few inches to approximately 20 inches. The depth will vary to a maximum at which bed rock is located. The characteristics of the bored well are similiar to those of the dug well, in that the yield is not too dependable for high yields or in drought seasons.

It cannot be easily protected from surface pollution in densily populated areas where individual sewage disposal systems are being used. Its protection from surface pollution is similiar to that given for the dug well.

3. The Punched or Driven Well. The punched or driven well is constructed by driving the well point and screen into the water vein by special equipment such as a pile driver or maul. Such wells are customarily located in areas where no hard or bed rock is found. These wells are usually of two inches in diameter and are to depths of somewhat greater than either the dug or bored well. The yield is not too great because of the small diameter of the well and the depth into the water strata which the well is driven. The protection of the driven well is similar to that for the drilled well as indicated in Figure 6.

4. The Drilled Well. The drilled well is constructed by pulverizing the soil, rock, etc., within the well hole, then jetting or bucketing the pulverized material out of the well hole. A well casing with a well shoe is then placed and imbedded in bed rock or the impervious layer. Drilled wells offer the greatest dependable yield of the four types of wells. They are more easily protected from unforeseen surface or underground pollution. Drilled wells range in diameter from two inches to a usual maximum of 12 inches with certain type gravel packed wells' diameters to 36 inches. From the standpoint of quality of water as relating to bacteria, the drilled well offers the highest quality of water of the four types of wells because of its drawing its water from these lower layers of water with depths ranging to 1,000 feet. The protection of the drilled well is illustrated in Figure 6.

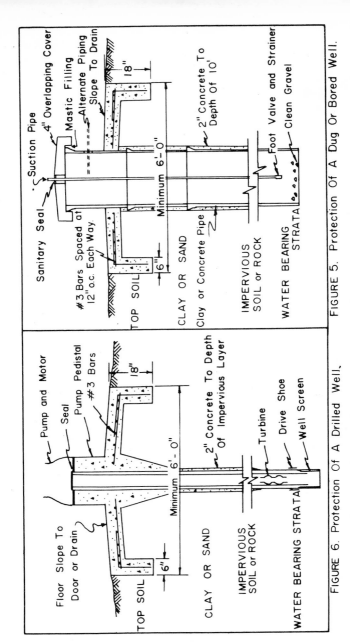

FIGURE 5. Protection Of A Dug Or Bored Well.

FIGURE 6. Protection Of A Drilled Well.

— 17 —

For the classification of wells according to the depth of the well, the following description of each type under that classification is as follows:

1. Artesian or Flowing Wells. Artesian type or flowing wells are considered those wells in areas where the ground water table is actually under pressure from overlying rock or other type impervious material. Therefore, when a well is constructed, the water will be forced out of the well casing by this hydrostatic force acting upon the ground water table. This impervious layer may extend for many hundreds of miles. The diameter of these wells vary from two to 12 inches. Their depth will vary from a few feet to many hundreds of feet, this depth varying with the depth and thickness of the impervious strata underground. Yields from this type of well will vary with the well diameter, pressure of the water layer, and depth of the water strata.

2. Shallow Wells. Shallow wells are considered those wells whose depth is 80 feet or less. All four types of wells, the dug, bored, driven, and drilled, may in certain areas be classified as shallow wells. Shallow wells in most cases, will be between 30 and 60 feet in depth.

3. Deep Wells: Deep wells are considered those wells which have depths greater than 80 feet. In most cases this will exclude all types of wells but the drilled well.

It is most desirable from economy and convenience to utilize a source of water supply which is conveniently located to the community to be served. Therefore, for all practical purposes, in the majority of the cases, the drilled type well will meet these requirements more satisfactorily than other sources of ground water. This can be explained by the fact that water obtained from drilled wells is from stratas below the bed rock. Therefore, it will be adequate to sustain long periods of drought. It can also be better protected from a sanitary standpoint because of the casing being imbedded in bedrock or other impervious type material providing a safer supply relative to the fact that sewage may within the area be disposed of by individual systems.

The size or diameter of a drilled well is governed by many factors, but can best be selected by the amount of water desired to be pumped from the well. This pumpage rate is important in relation to well diameter because of the creation of channel velocities within the different ground water aquifers. These channel velocities, if too great, will damage the well by closing the channel openings within the various stratas and will result in decreased yields. The circumference or "wetted area" of the well which is in contact with the ground water aquifers, is a function of the diameter of the well. Thus, the larger the diameter of the well, the less will be the flow per unit length of well casing diameter. The following table will act as a guide in the selection of the diameter of well to be drilled if the desired yield is known.

It must be realized that the cost of construction of a well is made in cost per linear foot or depth and varies greatly with the diameter. (Refer to Table XLII.) Care must be taken in the proper selection of the well site and well diameter.

Since from Table VI, the diameter of the well is selected from the desired well yield, it is necessary to calculate the yield from a knowledge of the quantity of water necessary to adequately supply the community. The desired well yield should be established on the basis that the

## TABLE VI
### Well Yield Versus Well Diameter

| Desired Daily Yield of Well | Recommended Diameter of Well |
| --- | --- |
| Flows up to 50,000 gpd | 6-inch |
| 50,000 to 100,000 gpd | 8-inch |
| 100,000 to 250,000 gpd | 10-inch |
| 250,000 to 500,000 gpd | 12-inch |
| 500,000 and over | Gravel-packed well* |

*Gravel-packed wells are advisable in certain localities.

pumping unit, used to withdraw water from the well, should not operate more than 18 hours per day or 75 per cent of the time. Therefore, after the quantity of water to meet community needs has been determined, then the desired well yield may be calculated by multiplying by a factor of 1.333. This may be shown by formulization as follows:

Desired well yield, gpd* = 1.5 to 2.0 x maximum daily requirements, gpd; or

Desired well yield, gpm** = 0.00104 to 0.0014 x desired well yield, gpd.

Desired well yield, gpm** = 0.00208 to 0.0028 x maximum daily requirements, gpd.

In large developments, it is desirable to provide several wells so that maintenance may be had without impairing the system to any great extent. In this case, the total water usage or requirement may be proportioned between the several wells on the system. Even in small community water systems, it is very desirable to have two such wells on the system, in the event of breakdown or repairs.

The depth of the well or wells in

*Desired yields based upon 12 to 16 hours well operation per day.
**Minimum well yield should not be less than 15 gpm.

the planning stage, can at best, only be estimated. However, it is advisable to discuss this problem with well drillers, health officials, geologists, etc., who are familiar with ground water problems within the general area, in order to get as much information as possible on depth and quantity of ground water. Contacts such as these will give dependable information as to what one may expect from wells in the general locality. Questions should pertain to depths and yields of existing wells, dependability of well yield during extended periods of drought, and chemical quality of the water. Information as to chemical quality of water, if not available from official sources, can usually be obtained from inquiries within the general locality with residents who utilize ground water supplies.

### C. Selection of Well Sites

Selection of the sites of wells is a most important consideration from the standpoint of sanitary protection of water quality. The site must provide protection of the well from not only existing pollution, but possible future pollution as the community grows. Well sites should be selected at as high elevation as possible within the community so that proper drain-

— 19 —

age may be had and to prevent flooding of the well installation. High elevations will also prevent the location of possible sources of pollution above the well site, thus eliminating any possible seepage into the ground water table of such pollution, which may find its way into the aquifer from which the water is to be drawn. Consideration should be given to the composition of the soil and rock layers for the depth to the aquifers from which the water is to be drawn. Certain types of formations, such as limestones will carry pollution in ground water for considerable distances. Also, experience has indicated that a high water table is found and high expected well yields are developed from tapping a ground water table where outcrops of flint or quartz are found.

As a general rule, all sources of pollution should be kept at least a horizontal distance of 100 feet from the well site and preferably on lower ground than the well site[2]. If it is necessary to locate a sewer within a 100 feet of the well, such pollution should be piped in cast iron pipe with leaded joints for any portion which is within the 100-foot radius of the well or ground water source. If at all possible, no pollution should be located within a reasonable distance above the well.

If more than one well is to be used for a water system, they should be located some distance apart to prevent interference between such wells. There is no set rule for the spacing of wells as the spacing depends upon the radius of influence around the well and the draw-down within the well. In many areas, well fields may be used because of the high ground water table and the availability of such ground water. In other areas, ground water is not too readily available. A rule of thumb for the spacing of wells may be stated for most areas where the ground water is not too readily available. This rule may be stated that the spacing of wells should be such that the distance between wells should be greater than three to five times the drawdown depth of the well. See Figure 7 for this in illustration.

## D. Selection of Pump and Controls

The selection of well pumps and controls for setting of depth and pressure are important considerations in every community water system because of the economics and performance efficiency concerned. Before the selection of the type and capacity of the pump is made, the well must be completed and a test made to determine the exact yield at various depths. This test should be made for a period of not less than 72 hours in order that the water-bearing cavities or channels within the water-bearing strata may be stabilized. In shorter testing periods, these channels will carry water at higher velocities and increased yields for short periods of time and will not give a true picture of the well because the stabilization of the water veins have not taken place during these shorter testing periods of greater yields.

Dependable information on the sustained yield of the well will be considerably more valuable regarding future operation of the well. Studies from the use of oberservation wells will render much information on the ground water situation within defined areas around the proposed well site. These observation wells will furnish information as to the rate of flow of ground water, the radius of influence, and the return and drawdown of the ground water for static and pumping conditions. Except in cases of very large systems, the use of test or ob-

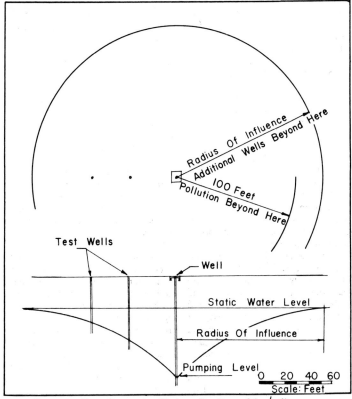

FIGURE 7. Ground Water-Radius Of Influence.

servation wells may not be economically feasible. Therefore, for small
water systems, the pumping test for
as long a period of time as practical
will furnish the information desired
to determine the exact characteristics
of flow so that a pump may be
selected for use.

The selection of the pumping
equipment will depend upon not only
the characteristics of the well, but the
actual quantity of water needed and
the discharge pressures necessary to
meet certain conditions of the system

at all times. One requirement in obtaining the pump and its controls, is
the selection of a dependable make
of pump and controls, preferably
from local representatives so that repair parts and service may be quickly
obtained in order that the installation
will be out of operation as short a
time as possible during failures.

Pumps are classified in several
ways. One method of classification is
according to purpose. The second
method of classification is according
to the principle of specific operating

— 21 —

chacteristics. The classification according to purpose may be stated as follows:

1. Low level.
2. High level or high service.
3. Standby, low or high service.
4. Booster.

The classification according to specific operating characteristics or principles may be as follows:

1. Jet.
2. Air lift.
3. Centrifugal or horizontal turbine.
4. Vertical turbine.
5. Plunger or sucker rod.

Pump manufacturers or their agents will be glad to assist in the design of the pump for each specific installation in order that the pump will give desired efficiency characteristics for a specific installation.

Common type of pumps used in small water systems are of the jet and turbine type. Plunger or sucker-rod pumps are also in common use, but the ease of installation and the greater discharge rate of the jet and turbine have caused these two types of pumps to replace the plunger-type in many installations. Jet pumps are most common in shallow wells and where not too high capacity is required. They are easy to install and to maintain. Their use in deep wells is limited because of the restriction in yield to increased depth. This is due to the method of operation of the jet-type pump. In its theory of operation, a small portion of the water is returned under pressure and is ejected through an orifice with extremely high pressure, thus forcing additional water under lower pressure and velocity back to the pump discharge. It can well be said that in the case of most small water systems, that the jet-type pump will be most economical from the standpoint of operation and maintenance.

The vertical centrifugal or commonly called vertical turbine pump operates on the principle of a screw-type propeller which operates at high velocity whereby the water is forced out of the well column or pump column.

In recent years, the use of submersible motors and pumps have come into common use. For deep wells with large capacities, the vertical turbine is the most commonly used type of pump. The horizontal centrifugal pump is used only in specific cases, such as, in the case where the water is to be pumped from the well into a large low level storage tank and is then to be pumped into the high service system. In this case, the centrifugal pump would be used to lift the water from the low level tank to the high service system. A comparison of types of pumps is given in Table VII.

## TABLE VII
## Comparison of Types of Pumps

| Type of Pump | Depth of Operation | Characteristics |
|---|---|---|
| Jet Pump | Shallow depth pumping level 60 to 120 feet. | At shallow depths high capacity and efficiency. |
| Turbine Pump | Deep well operation. | High capacity and efficiency. |
| Centrifugal Pump | Suction depth limited to 10 to 30 feet. | High capacity and efficiency. |

Before getting into specific operating characteristics of pumps, it is necessary to be familiar with the language used in the field of water works designating these characteristics. Water flowing through pipes is subjected to many interferences which will slow or decrease the flow rate as the length of the pipe increases. These interferences are known as losses and are expressed in terms of LOSS OF HEAD. Such losses are due to pipe age or corrosion, fitting friction, enlargements, constrictions, all of which, when totaled, are expressed as HEAD LOSS. Such losses are expressed in terms of FEET which is an expression of pressure head on the basis of 2.31 feet of water elevation will render a pressure of one pound per square inch, or one foot of water elevation will render a pressure of 0.4335 pounds per square inch. It should be remembered that each loss due to friction within a water system is known as a head loss and the sum of these losses is known as TOTAL HEAD LOSS. The STATIC HEAD is the elevation of water within a system when there is no movement or water flow within the facilities on the system. In this case the HEAD would be expressed exactly as the elevation of the system or storage. The DYNAMIC HEAD is the STATIC HEAD PLUS THE INDIVIDUAL LOSSES DUE TO FRICTION. The dynamic head may in other terms be expressed as the Total Head.

Each pump, having its own specific operating characteristics, must be studied to determine its feasibility for the job it must do[3]. Desired characteristics as far as the purchaser or user is concerned, are such items as:

1. Efficiency: High efficiency resulting in low power consumption and low cost of operation.

2. Durable material which is corrosion resistant and not readily subjected to deterioration by wear.

3. Design: Simple design for ease of operation and maintenance.

4. Replacement parts and service readily available.

5. Manufacturer of pump should be a reputable firm.

Pump selection is dependent upon three definite characteristics. These characteristics are:

1. Head-Capacity Relationship: The head and capacity of a pump are related to the extent that as the capacity or output is increased, the head or lift of the pump is reduced. This is not a direct relationship and will vary with each pump.

2. Capacity-Power Requirement Relationship: The capacity and the power requirement of a pump is related such that as the capacity or output of the pump is increased, the power requirement increases somewhat proportionately to a maximum. At this maximum point, the head decreases rapidly as the capacity increases and the power requirement levels off and begins to decrease.

3. Efficiency: Each pump will have its specific efficiency under varying conditions. The efficiency curve for each pump will indicate a maximum at a specific head and capacity for which it is designed.

These three pump characteristics are illustrated in Figure 8.

Two pertinent facts should be remembered concerning the use of the centrifugal-type pump used in water works. First of all, a pump's characteristics are dependent upon the speed of the pump. The head will vary as the square of the ratio of the speed of the pump. The capacity will vary directly with the ratio of the speed while the horsepower varies as the cube of the speed. Therefore, as the speed of the pump varies, all char-

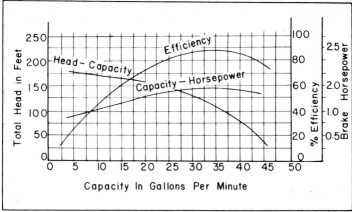

FIGURE 8. Specific Characteristics Of Pumps.

acteristics will vary according to the above. A second factor is that the dynamic head of a water system will vary according to high and low water elevations within the storage system. This varying head should be considered when selecting a pump and should be indicated on the specific characteristic curves of the pump under consideration.

The selection of the horsepower of the pump is determined by the total head that the water must be lifted and the quantity of water desired to be pumped. The total head is the sum of the individual heads, for which the water must be raised. The head of water is an expression of hydraulics, which is the pressure of water expressed in feet. It is based on the factor that 2.31 feet of water will give a pressure of one pound per square inch. An example of this would be that water in a tank which is 100 feet high will give a pressure of $\frac{100}{2.31} = 43.4$ pounds per square inch.

In calculating the total head of

water for pump calculations, the individual heads within the system would be totaled. These individual heads would be as follows:

1. Draw-down of pump suction line.

2. Friction loss through pump and fittings.

3. Height of elevated tank above ground surface.

4. Difference in ground elevation of pump and tank.

5. Friction loss in pipe line from pump to tank.

A discussion of each of these individual heads, represented in Figure 9, is as follows:

1. The draw-down head is the distance from the centerline of the pump to the jet, turbine, or suction end of the pump line. This depth is actually known in feet from previous knowledge of well test. In addition to the actual depth of the suction line, there would be friction loss within the suction line. This may be estimated on the following basis:

## TABLE VIII
## Approximate Estimations of Head Loss in Suction Lines*

| Pipe Diameter | Head Loss in Terms of Flow |
|---|---|
| 2-inch | 2.5 ft. per 100 ft. per 20 gpm |
| 3-inch | 2.5 ft. per 100 ft. per 60 gpm |
| 4-inch | 2.5 ft. per 100 ft. per 150 gpm |
| 6-inch | 2.5 ft. per 100 ft. per 400 gpm |
| 8-inch | 2.5 ft. per 100 ft. per 900 gpm |

* From Table X.

2. Friction loss through pump and fittings is relatively small but should be added into total head. This loss can be estimated to be 2.5 pounds per square inch or 5.77 feet. This is suitable for estimating purposes.

3. Height of elevated tank above ground surface is the distance in feet from the ground to the overflow pipe of the tank. The height of the tank will usually be such that an average pressure of 40 to 60 pounds per square inch is maintained on the system, or should be such that a minimum pressure of 30 pounds per square inch at the highest point within the community is maintained.

4. The difference in ground eleva-

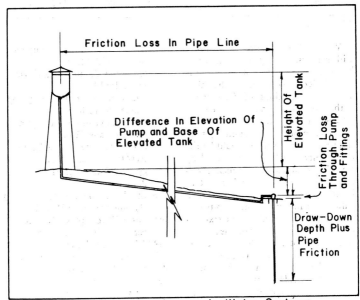

FIGURE 9. Friction Losses In Water Systems.

— 25 —

tion of the pump and the elevated tank is to be considered. For pneumatic storage where both are located together, this elevation is zero. For other cases, it can not be neglected.

5. Friction loss in pipe line from pump to tank is an important factor in calculating total head for which pump must discharge. For estimation purposes, Table XI provides data as to friction loss per 100 feet of pipeline in the relationship to flow of water through the pipe.

head, the calculations would be as follows:

1. Draw-down head of pump:
   a. Depth of suction line= 115 feet.
   b. Friction loss in suction line (Table VIII) 2.5 feet/100 feet times 115 feet/100 feet= 2.875 feet.
   c. Total draw-down head= 115 feet plus 2.875 feet= 117.875 feet.

## TABLE IX
## Approximate Estimations of Head Loss in Distribution Systems*

| Pipe Diameter | Head Loss in Terms of Flow in Pipe |
|---|---|
| 2-inch _____ | 2.5 feet per 100 feet per 20 gpm |
| 3-inch _____ | 2.5 feet per 100 feet per 60 gpm |
| 4-inch _____ | 2.5 feet per 100 feet per 150 gpm |
| 6-inch _____ | 2.5 feet per 100 feet per 400 gpm |
| 8-inch _____ | 2.5 feet per 100 feet per 900 gpm |

*From Table X.

Valves, bends, tees, and crosses within a system may be estimated as being equivalent to 100 feet of the size of pipe equal to size of the valve, bend, etc. Fractions of flow stated within this table may be used for estimation purposes.

An example of determining total head for a water system would be the community which is to be served by a well, which has a four-inch draw-down pipe and which is 115 feet in length. The pump discharge is 150 gallons per minute through a pipeline of a length of 1,000 feet of six-inch pipe to an elevated tank on the system. The tank site is 15 feet above the well site and the tank is 120 feet in height. The total head for this system would be calculated using the following methods. First of all for an approximate estimation of the total

2. Friction loss through pump and fittings=5.77 feet.
3. Height of elevated tank above ground=120 feet.
4. Difference in elevation of pump and tank=15 feet.
5. Friction loss in pipeline from pump to tank (Table IX) 2.5 feet/100 feet times 1,000 feet/100 feet times 150 gpm/400 gpm equals to 9.38 feet.

The total head would be (1) plus (2) plus (3) plus (4) plus (5) or 117.875 feet plus 5.77 feet plus 120 feet plus 15 feet plus 9.38 feet equals to 268.025 feet total head.

For more accurate determination of total head of this pump, Table X would be utilized as follows:

1. Draw-down head of pump:
   a. Depth of draw-down, 115 ft.

b. Friction loss in suction line (for four-inch line is based on 2.55 feet per 100 feet of pipe) 2.55 x 115/110 = 2.93 feet.

Total Suction Head = 117.93 feet.

2. Friction loss through pump and fittings (Table XI and Appendix):

   a. Equivalent length of pipe:

      *1.* Sudden contraction, 3.8 feet.

      *2.* Sudden Enlargement, 7.0 feet.

      *3.* 45-elbows (3) @ 6.2 feet, 18.6 feet.

      *4.* Gate valves (2) @ 2.1 feet, 4.2 feet.

      *5.* Check valve, 25.2 feet. Equivalent length of four-inch pipe = 58.8 feet.

   b. Friction loss through pump and fittings: Based on friction loss of 2.55 feet per 100 feet; 2.55 x 58.8/100 = 1.47 feet.

3. Height of elevated tank above ground = 120.0 feet.

4. Difference in elevation of pump and tank base = 15 feet.

5. Friction loss in pipe line from pump to tank: Based on friction loss of 2.55 feet per 100 feet of pipe; 2.55 x 1,000/100 = 25.5 feet.

Total head equals (1) plus (2) plus (3) plus (4) plus (5) or 117.93 plus 1.47 plus 120 plus 15 plus 25.5 = 279.90 feet.

The use of Tables VIII and IX should only be used for rough estimations in the early planning stages of a water system. Tables X and XI should be used for final analysis to get accurately the Total Head necessary for final pump selection.

After obtaining the Total Head for the water system, it is then possible to calculate the required horsepower for the pump installation. A simplified formula for the selection of horsepower is as follows:

$$\text{Theoretical Horsepower} = \frac{\text{Flow in GPM x Total Head in Feet}}{3960}$$

$$\text{Theoretical Horsepower} = \frac{\text{Flow in CFS x Total Head in Feet x Density}^*}{550}$$

The difference between the Theoretical Horsepower and the Actual Horsepower requirements of an installation, is the efficiency of the motor and the pump. In other words, the efficiency of the installation is less than 100% by the combined frictional and other losses of the motor and pump. Therefore, the above formula may be expressed as follows for Actual Horsepower:

$$\text{Actual Horsepower} = \frac{\text{Flow in GPM x Total Head in Feet}}{3960 \text{ x Motor Efficiency x Pump Efficiency}}$$

$$\text{Actual Horsepower} = \frac{\text{Flow in CFS x Total Head in Feet x Density}^*}{550 \text{ x Motor Efficiency x Pump Efficiency}}$$

$$\text{Actual Horsepower} = \frac{\text{Theoretical Horsepower}}{\text{Motor Efficiency x Pump Efficiency}}$$

*Density of water is 62.4 pounds per cubic foot.

# TABLE X
## Friction of Water in Pipes

### FRICTION of WATER in PIPES
#### LOSS OF HEAD IN FEET DUE TO FRICTION PER 100 FEET OF 15-YEAR-OLD ORDINARY CAST IRON OR WROUGHT IRON PIPE

| Gal per min | ½ inch Pipe | | ¾ inch Pipe | | 1 inch Pipe | | 1¼ inch Pipe | | 1½ inch Pipe | | 2 inch Pipe | | 2½ inch Pipe | | 3 inch Pipe | |
|---|---|---|---|---|---|---|---|---|---|---|---|---|---|---|---|---|
| | Vel | Fric | Vel | Fric | Vel | Fric | Vel | Fric | Vel | Fric | Vel | Fric | Vel | Fric | Vel | Fric |
| 1 | 1.05 | 2.1 | | | | | | | | | | | | | | |
| 2 | 2.10 | 7.4 | 1.20 | 1.9 | | | | | | | | | | | | |
| 3 | 3.16 | 15.8 | 1.80 | 4.1 | 1.12 | 1.26 | | | | | | | | | | |
| 4 | 4.21 | 27.0 | 2.41 | 7.0 | 1.49 | 2.14 | 0.86 | 0.57 | 0.63 | 0.26 | | | | | | |
| 5 | 5.26 | | 3.01 | 10.5 | 1.86 | 3.25 | 1.07 | 0.84 | 0.79 | 0.40 | | | | | | |
| 10 | 10.52 | 147.0 | 6.02 | 38.0 | 3.72 | 11.7 | 2.14 | 3.05 | 1.57 | 1.43 | 1.02 | 0.50 | 0.65 | 0.17 | 0.45 | 0.07 |
| 15 | | | 9.02 | 80.0 | 5.60 | 25.0 | 3.20 | 6.50 | | 3.0 | 1.53 | 1.08 | 0.98 | 0.36 | 0.68 | 0.15 |
| 20 | | | 12.03 | 136.0 | 7.44 | 42.0 | 4.28 | 11.0 | 3.36 | 5.2 | 2.04 | 1.82 | 1.31 | 0.61 | 0.91 | 0.25 |
| 25 | | | | | 9.30 | 64.0 | 5.36 | 16.6 | 3.94 | | 2.55 | 2.73 | 1.64 | 0.92 | 1.13 | 0.38 |
| 30 | | | | | 11.15 | 89.0 | 6.43 | 23.5 | 4.72 | 11.0 | 3.06 | 3.84 | 1.96 | 1.32 | 1.36 | 0.54 |
| 35 | | | | | 13.02 | 119.0 | 7.51 | 31.2 | 5.51 | 14.7 | 3.57 | 5.1 | 2.29 | 1.72 | | |
| 40 | | | | | 14.88 | 152.0 | 8.58 | 40.0 | 6.3 | 18.8 | 4.08 | 6.6 | 2.61 | 2.20 | 1.82 | 0.71 |
| 45 | | | | | | | 9.65 | 50.0 | 7.08 | 23.2 | 4.60 | 8.2 | 2.94 | 2.80 | 2.05 | 0.91 |
| 50 | | | | | | | | | 7.87 | | 5.11 | 9.7 | 3.27 | 3.32 | 2.27 | 1.15 |
| 75 | | | | | | | 15.01 | 113 | 11.02 | 53.4 | 7.66 | 20.9 | 4.58 | 6.21 | 3.4 | 2.57 |
| 100 | | | | | | | | | 15.74 | 102 | 10.21 | 35.8 | 5.51 | 7.1 | 4.54 | 4.96 |
| 125 | | | | | | | | | 18.89 | 143 | 12.75 | 54 | 5.84 | 16.8 | 5.67 | 7.6 |
| 150 | | | | | | | | | | | 15.32 | 76 | 8.16 | 18.2 | 6.8 | 10.5 |
| 175 | | | | | | | | | | | 17.85 | 102 | 9.80 | 25.5 | 7.94 | 14.0 |
| 200 | | | | | | | | | | | 20.4 | 129 | 11.3 | 33.8 | 9.08 | 17.8 |
| 225 | | | | | | | | | | | | | 13.61 | 43.1 | | 22.3 |
| 250 | | | | | | | | | | | | | 14.67 | 50.3 | 11.32 | 27.3 |
| 270 | | | | | | | | | | | | | 16.3 | 66 | | 31.3 |
| 275 | | | | | | | | | | | | | | | 12.50 | 32.5 |
| 300 | | | | | | | | | | | | | | | 13.62 | 38.0 |

—From Permission of Worthington Pump and Machinery Corporation.

# TABLE X
## Friction of Water in Pipes

| Gal. per min. | 4 inch Pipe Vel. | 4 inch Pipe Fric. | 5 inch Pipe Vel. | 5 inch Pipe Fric. | 6 inch Pipe Vel. | 6 inch Pipe Fric. | 8 inch Pipe Vel. | 8 inch Pipe Fric. | 10 inch Pipe Vel. | 10 inch Pipe Fric. | 12 inch Pipe Vel. | 12 inch Pipe Fric. | 14 inch Pipe Vel. | 14 inch Pipe Fric. | 16 inch Pipe Vel. | 16 inch Pipe Fric. |
|---|---|---|---|---|---|---|---|---|---|---|---|---|---|---|---|---|
| 40 | 1.02 | 0.22 | | | | | | | | | | | | | | |
| 45 | 1.17 | 0.28 | | | | | | | | | | | | | | |
| 50 | 1.28 | 0.34 | | | | | | | | | | | | | | |
| 70 | 1.79 | 0.63 | 1.14 | 0.21 | | | | | | | | | | | | |
| 75 | 1.92 | 0.73 | 1.22 | 0.24 | | | | | | | | | | | | |
| 100 | 2.55 | 1.22 | 1.63 | 0.41 | 1.14 | 0.14 | | | | | | | | | | |
| 120 | 3.06 | 1.71 | 1.96 | 0.58 | 1.48 | 0.25 | | | | | | | | | | |
| 150 | 3.84 | 2.55 | 2.45 | 0.88 | 1.71 | 0.38 | | | | | | | | | | |
| 175 | 4.45 | 3.44 | 2.86 | 1.18 | 2.00 | 0.48 | | | | | | | | | | |
| 200 | 5.11 | 4.40 | 3.27 | 1.48 | 2.28 | 0.62 | 1.60 | 0.22 | | | | | | | | |
| 225 | 5.77 | 5.45 | 3.67 | 1.86 | 2.57 | 0.74 | 1.70 | 0.25 | | | | | | | | |
| 250 | 6.40 | 5.72 | 4.08 | 2.24 | 3.03 | 0.92 | 1.73 | 0.27 | | | | | | | | |
| 275 | 7.03 | 7.99 | 4.50 | 2.72 | 3.06 | 1.15 | 1.90 | 0.32 | | | | | | | | |
| 300 | 7.66 | 9.30 | 4.90 | 3.14 | 3.40 | 1.29 | 2.20 | 0.42 | 1.80 | 0.21 | | | | | | |
| 350 | 8.90 | 12.30 | 5.72 | 4.19 | 3.98 | 1.75 | 2.90 | 0.54 | 1.92 | 0.24 | | | | | | |
| 400 | 10.21 | 16.00 | 6.54 | 5.40 | 4.54 | 2.21 | 2.00 | 0.74 | 1.94 | 0.25 | | | | | | |
| 450 | 11.50 | 19.40 | 7.35 | 7.22 | 5.49 | 2.90 | 3.07 | 1.34 | 2.04 | 0.28 | | | | | | |
| 475 | 12.77 | 23.00 | 7.76 | 7.76 | 5.55 | 2.95 | 3.10 | 0.76 | 2.25 | 0.33 | | | | | | |
| 500 | 12.90 | 24.00 | 8.17 | 8.12 | 5.60 | 3.30 | 3.20 | 0.82 | 2.46 | 0.39 | 1.42 | 0.11 | | | | |
| 550 | | | 8.99 | 9.60 | 6.16 | 3.93 | 3.52 | 0.97 | 2.86 | 0.46 | 1.57 | 0.14 | | | | |
| 600 | | | 9.80 | 11.30 | 6.72 | 4.70 | 3.84 | 1.14 | 3.06 | 0.50 | 1.85 | 0.19 | | | | |
| 650 | | | 10.62 | 13.20 | 6.78 | 5.00 | 4.16 | 1.34 | 3.28 | 0.59 | 2.00 | 0.22 | | | | |
| 700 | | | 11.44 | 15.10 | 7.84 | 7.00 | 4.46 | 1.54 | 3.48 | 0.67 | 2.13 | 0.24 | 1.37 | 0.09 | | |
| 800 | | | 12.26 | 17.30 | 8.00 | 8.13 | 4.80 | 1.74 | 3.68 | 0.75 | 2.27 | 0.27 | 1.47 | 0.10 | | |
| 850 | | | | | 9.08 | 9.00 | 5.12 | 1.97 | 3.88 | 0.83 | 2.41 | 0.31 | 1.58 | 0.11 | | |
| 900 | | | | | 9.58 | 8.95 | 5.48 | 2.28 | 4.08 | 0.91 | 2.56 | 0.34 | 1.69 | 0.13 | | |
| 950 | | | | | 10.30 | 10.11 | 5.75 | 2.46 | 4.29 | 1.00 | 2.70 | 0.38 | 1.79 | 0.14 | | |
| 1000 | | | | | 10.72 | 10.80 | 6.06 | 2.87 | 4.50 | 1.09 | 2.84 | 0.41 | 1.89 | 0.16 | | |
| 1050 | | | | | 11.30 | 13.04 | 6.40 | 3.02 | 4.71 | 1.20 | 2.98 | 0.44 | 2.00 | 0.18 | | |
| 1100 | | | | | 12.50 | 14.31 | 7.03 | 3.51 | 4.91 | 1.34 | 3.13 | 0.49 | 2.10 | 0.19 | | |
| 1150 | | | | | 12.95 | 15.60 | 7.35 | 3.84 | 5.11 | 1.46 | 3.27 | 0.53 | 2.31 | 0.22 | | |
| 1200 | | | | | 13.52 | 16.69 | 7.67 | 4.15 | 6.10 | 1.51 | 3.41 | 0.57 | 2.42 | 0.23 | 1.99 | 0.15 |
| 1250 | | | | | 14.10 | 18.50 | 8.00 | 4.45 | 8.10 | 1.90 | 3.55 | 0.82 | 2.52 | 0.25 | 2.39 | 0.21 |
| 1500 | | | | | | | 12.70 | 10.71 | 10.10 | 3.05 | 4.20 | 1.02 | 2.63 | 0.26 | 3.19 | 0.39 |
| 2000 | | | | | | | | | 12.10 | 5.33 | 5.60 | 1.43 | 2.95 | 0.35 | 3.99 | 0.56 |
| 2500 | | | | | | | | | 14.10 | 7.80 | 7.00 | 2.28 | 4.20 | 0.60 | 4.79 | 0.80 |
| 3000 | | | | | | | | | | 10.08 | 8.40 | 3.15 | 4.52 | 0.66 | 5.59 | 1.04 |
| 3500 | | | | | | | | | | | 9.80 | 4.10 | 5.25 | 1.01 | 6.38 | 1.34 |
| 4000 | | | | | | | | | | | 11.35 | 5.32 | 6.30 | 1.47 | 6.72 | 1.45 |
| 4500 | | | | | | | | | | | 12.78 | 6.30 | 7.35 | 1.81 | 7.20 | 1.65 |
| 5000 | | | | | | | | | | | 14.20 | 6.90 | 8.40 | 2.47 | 7.96 | 2.09 |
| 5500 | | | | | | | | | | | | 8.40 | 8.90 | 2.80 | 8.78 | 2.39 |
| 6000 | | | | | | | | | | | | | 9.45 | 3.22 | 9.56 | 2.90 |
| 6500 | | | | | | | | | | | | | 10.50 | 3.92 | 10.12 | 3.32 |
| 7000 | | | | | | | | | | | | | 11.55 | 4.65 | 11.50 | 3.68 |
| 7500 | | | | | | | | | | | | | 13.65 | 5.50 | 11.95 | 3.96 |
| | | | | | | | | | | | | | 14.70 | 7.15 | | 4.28 |

Vel. = Velocity feet per second.   Fric. = Friction Head in Feet.
For New Smooth Wrought Iron Pipe multiply values in tables by 0.71.
For Old Wrought Iron Pipe multiply values in tables by 1.52.
These figures are approximate only and will vary with kind of water and actual condition of pipe.
Data taken from more complete information in "Standards of Hydraulic Institute".

—From Permission of Worthington Pump and Machinery Corporation.

## TABLE XI
## Resistance of Fittings

EQUIVALENT LENGTH OF STRAIGHT NEW STEEL PIPE – FEET

| NOMINAL DIAMETER OF STANDARD PIPE | GATE VALVE FULLY OPEN | COMPOSITION DISC OR BEVEL SEAT GLOBE VALVE FULLY OPEN | PLUG DISC GLOBE VALVE FULLY OPEN | ANGLE VALVE FULLY OPEN | SWING CHECK VALVE | HORIZONTAL (LIFT) CHECK VALVE | BALL CHECK VALVE | REGULAR SCREWED 90° ELBOW |
|---|---|---|---|---|---|---|---|---|
| 1/2" | 0.20 | 11.3 | 14.4 | 4.3 | 2.4 | 16.4 | 111.0 | 1.2 |
| 3/4" | 0.28 | 16.1 | 20.6 | 6.1 | 3.4 | 23.5 | 159.0 | 1.8 |
| 1" | 0.39 | 22.2 | 28.5 | 8.4 | 4.7 | 32.5 | 219.0 | 2.4 |
| 1-1/4" | 0.55 | 31.5 | 40.2 | 11.9 | 6.7 | 46.0 | 310.0 | 3.5 |
| 1-1/2" | 0.67 | 38.4 | 49.0 | 14.5 | 8.1 | 56.0 | 378.0 | 4.2 |
| 2" | 0.92 | 52.3 | 66.8 | 19.8 | 11.1 | 76.3 | 515.0 | 5.7 |
| 2-1/2" | 1.1 | 65.0 | 83.1 | 24.6 | 15.8 | 94.8 | 640.0 | 7.1 |
| 3" | 1.5 | 85.0 | 109.0 | 32.2 | 18.0 | 124.0 | — | 9.3 |
| 4" | 2.1 | 119.0 | 152.0 | 45.0 | 25.2 | 173.0 | — | 13.0 |
| 5" | 2.7 | 156.0 | — | 59.4 | 33.2 | 228.0 | — | 17.1 |
| 6" | 3.4 | 194.0 | — | 75.6 | 41.1 | 283.0 | — | 21.2 |
| 8" | 4.8 | 272.0 | — | 103.0 | 57.5 | 396.0 | — | 29.7 |
| 10" | 5.9 | 337.0 | — | 128.0 | 71.3 | 492.0 | — | 36.9 |
| 12" | 7.8 | 443.0 | — | 168.0 | 93.9 | 647.0 | — | 48.5 |
| 14" | 8.5 | 483.0 | — | 183.0 | 102.0 | 706.0 | — | 53.0 |
| 16" | 10.1 | 578.0 | — | 219.0 | 125.0 | 843.0 | — | 63.3 |

—From Permission of Worthington Pump and Machinery Corporation.

## TABLE XI
### Resistance of Fittings

| NOMINAL DIAMETER OF STANDARD PIPE | LONG RADIUS SCREWED 90° ELBOW | RUN OF STANDARD SCREWED TEE | BRANCH TO LINE OF STANDARD SCREWED TEE | LINE TO BRANCH OF STANDARD SCREWED TEE | REGULAR SCREWED 45° ELBOW | SCREWED CLOSE RETURN BEND | SQUARE EDGED INLET | INWARD PROJECTING PIPE | FOOT VALVE |
|---|---|---|---|---|---|---|---|---|---|
| 1/2" | 0.66 | 0.66 | 2.5 | 1.8 | 0.59 | 2.4 | 0.85 | 1.3 | 24.7 |
| 3/4" | 0.94 | 0.94 | 3.6 | 2.5 | 0.85 | 3.5 | 1.2 | 1.9 | 35.3 |
| 1" | 1.3 | 1.3 | 5.0 | 3.5 | 1.2 | 4.8 | 1.7 | 2.6 | 48.7 |
| 1-1/4" | 1.8 | 1.8 | 7.1 | 5.0 | 1.7 | 6.8 | 2.4 | 3.7 | 68.9 |
| 1-1/2" | 2.2 | 2.2 | 8.6 | 6.0 | 2.0 | 8.3 | 2.9 | 4.5 | 83.9 |
| 2" | 3.1 | 3.1 | 11.7 | 8.2 | 2.8 | 11.3 | 3.9 | 6.2 | 114.0 |
| 2-1/2" | 3.8 | 3.8 | 14.6 | 10.2 | 3.4 | 14.0 | 4.9 | 7.7 | 142.0 |
| 3" | 5.0 | 5.0 | 19.1 | 13.4 | 4.5 | 18.3 | 6.4 | 10.0 | 186.0 |
| 4" | 6.9 | 6.9 | 26.6 | 18.7 | 6.2 | 25.6 | 8.9 | 14.1 | 260.0 |
| 5" | 9.1 | 9.1 | 35.1 | 24.6 | 8.2 | 33.7 | 11.8 | 18.5 | 343.0 |
| 6" | 11.3 | 11.3 | 43.5 | 30.6 | 10.2 | 41.8 | 14.6 | 23.0 | 425.0 |
| 8" | 15.9 | 15.9 | 60.9 | 42.7 | 14.3 | 58.5 | 20.4 | 32.1 | 594.0 |
| 10" | 19.7 | 19.7 | 75.5 | 52.9 | 17.7 | 72.6 | 25.3 | 59.8 | 738.0 |
| 12" | 25.9 | 25.9 | 99.5 | 69.7 | 23.3 | 95.5 | 33.3 | 52.5 | 970.0 |
| 14" | 28.2 | 28.2 | 108.0 | 76.1 | 25.4 | 104.0 | 36.4 | 57.2 | 1059.0 |
| 16" | 33.7 | 33.7 | 130.0 | 91.0 | 30.4 | 125.0 | 43.5 | 68.4 | 1265.0 |

MULTIPLY VALVES OF SCREWED FITTINGS BY:

FLANGED FITTINGS

Regular Flanged 90° Elbow. . . . . . . . . . . . . . . 0.34
Long Radius Flanged 90° Elbow. . . . . . . . . . . . 0.46
Long Radius Flanged 45° Elbow. . . . . . . . . . . . 0.53
Flanged Close Return Bend. . . . . . . . . . . . . . . 0.26
Long Radius Flanged Return Bend. . . . . . . . . . . 0.17

ADDITIONAL DATA IN APPENDIX.

—From Permission of Worthington Pump and Machinery Corporation.

Or for further simplification, the Actual Horsepower may be obtained from:

Actual Horsepower = (Factor†) x Theoretical Horsepower

Actual Horsepower = (Factor††) x Flow in GPM x Total Head in Feet

Factor† and Factor†† are to be obtained from Motor and Pump Efficiency as follows:

| Overall Motor and Pump Efficiency | Factor† | Factor†† |
|---|---|---|
| 100% | 1.00 | 0.000252 |
| 98 | 1.02 | 0.000258 |
| 96 | 1.04 | 0.000262 |
| 94 | 1.06 | 0.000268 |
| 92 | 1.09 | 0.000275 |
| 90 | 1.11 | 0.000280 |
| 88 | 1.14 | 0.000288 |
| 86* | 1.16 | 0.000292 |
| 84* | 1.19 | 0.000300 |
| 82* | 1.22 | 0.000308 |
| 80* | 1.25 | 0.000315 |
| 78* | 1.28 | 0.000323 |
| 76* | 1.31 | 0.000330 |
| 74* | 1.35 | 0.000340 |
| 72* | 1.39 | 0.000350 |
| 70* | 1.43 | 0.000360 |
| 68* | 1.47 | 0.000371 |
| 66* | 1.51 | 0.000381 |
| 64* | 1.56 | 0.000394 |
| 62* | 1.61 | 0.000406 |
| 60* | 1.66 | 0.000418 |
| 58* | 1.72 | 0.000434 |
| 56 | 1.78 | 0.000449 |
| 54 | 1.85 | 0.000467 |
| 52 | 1.92 | 0.000485 |
| 50 | 2.00 | 0.000505 |

*Actual Horsepower will be within the asterisk range as indicated.

It should be remembered that each pump operates on a specific curve of characteristics and final selection should be made only after study of this performance curve. Such a characteristic curve is illustrated in Figure 8.

An example for use of the above formulas can be shown in the following example. What will be the Horsepower requirement for an installation for which the discharge is 150 gallons per minute against a Total Head of 268 feet?

Theoretical Horsepower

$$= \frac{\text{Flow in GPM x Total Head in Feet}}{3960}$$

$$= \frac{150 \times 268}{3960}$$

$$= 10.15 \text{ Horsepower}$$

Assuming that the motor efficiency to be 90% and the pump efficiency to be 80%, the Actual Horsepower will be:

$$\text{Actual Horsepower} = \frac{\text{Flow in GPM x Total Head in Feet}}{3960 \text{ x Motor Efficiency x Pump Efficiency}}$$

$$= \frac{150 \text{ x } 268}{3960 \text{ x } 0.90 \text{ x } 0.80}$$

$$= 14.10 \text{ Horsepower; or}$$

$$\text{Actual Horsepower} = \frac{\text{Theoretical Horsepower}}{\text{Motor Efficiency x Pump Efficiency}}$$

$$= \frac{10.15}{0.90 \text{ x } 0.80}$$

$$= 14.10 \text{ Horsepower}$$

Simplified formulas using Factor† and Factor†† are as follows:

$$\text{Actual Horsepower} = (\text{Factor†}) \text{ x Theoretical Horsepower}$$

$$= 1.39 \text{ x } 10.15$$

$$= 14.10 \text{ Horsepower}$$

$$\text{Actual Horsepower} = (\text{Factor††}) \text{ x Flow in GPM x Total Head in Feet}$$

$$= 0.000350 \text{ x } 150 \text{ x } 268$$

$$= 14.10 \text{ Horsepower}$$

For most planning purposes, the estimates of overall efficiencies may be of 58% to 86%. It is advisable to select values within the low range or order to obtain reasonable cost data in such planning. For such purposes, 64% is assumed to be a reasonable value. Table XIII is set up on the basis of an overall efficiency of 64%.

Table XII provides information as to Theoretical Horsepower, as related to specific discharges and draw-downs. The discharge pressure is set at 60 pounds per square inch for these definite values of draw-down and discharge. No corrections are made for pipeline loss of the suction pipes, as such are estimated to be on the order of 10 to 25 per cent. This may not in all cases compensate for the loss which exists, but will provide adequate information for this table.

# TABLE XII
## Theoretical Horsepower for Discharge Pressure of 60 Pounds
### Per Square Inch at Given Discharges and Draw-downs

| Flow in GPM | 10 | 20 | 30 | 40 | 50 | 60 | 70 | 80 | 90 | 100 |
|---|---|---|---|---|---|---|---|---|---|---|
| | | | | | (Drawn-down in Feet) | | | | | |
| 10 | .37 | .40 | .42 | .45 | .47 | .50 | .52 | .55 | .57 | .60 |
| 20 | .75 | .80 | .90 | .95 | 1.00 | 1.05 | 1.10 | 1.15 | 1.20 | 1.2 |
| 30 | 1.1 | 1.1 | 1.2 | 1.3 | 1.3 | 1.4 | 1.5 | 1.6 | 1.6 | 1.7 |
| 40 | 1.5 | 1.6 | 1.7 | 1.8 | 1.9 | 2.0 | 2.1 | 2.2 | 2.3 | 2.4 |
| 50 | 1.8 | 1.9 | 2.1 | 2.2 | 2.3 | 2.5 | 2.6 | 2.7 | 2.8 | 3.0 |
| 60 | 2.2 | 2.4 | 2.5 | 2.7 | 2.8 | 3.0 | 3.1 | 3.3 | 3.4 | 3.6 |
| 70 | 2.6 | 2.8 | 2.9 | 3.1 | 3.3 | 3.5 | 3.6 | 3.8 | 4.0 | 4.2 |
| 80 | 2.9 | 3.1 | 3.4 | 3.6 | 3.8 | 4.0 | 4.2 | 4.4 | 4.6 | 4.8 |
| 90 | 3.3 | 3.5 | 3.8 | 4.0 | 4.2 | 4.5 | 4.6 | 4.9 | 5.1 | 5.4 |
| 100 | 3.7 | 4.0 | 4.2 | 4.5 | 4.7 | 5.0 | 5.2 | 5.5 | 5.7 | 6.0 |
| 125 | 4.6 | 4.9 | 5.5 | 5.9 | 6.2 | 6.5 | 6.8 | 7.0 | 7.2 | 7.5 |
| 150 | 5.6 | 5.9 | 6.3 | 6.7 | 7.1 | 7.5 | 7.8 | 8.2 | 8.6 | 9.0 |
| 175 | 6.5 | 6.9 | 7.4 | 7.8 | 8.3 | 8.7 | 9.2 | 9.6 | 10.1 | 10.5 |
| 200 | 7.5 | 8.0 | 9.0 | 9.5 | 10.0 | 10.5 | 11.0 | 11.5 | 12.0 | 12.5 |

In the planning of pneumatic water systems where the pressure tank is located adjacent to the well house and pump, more accurate planning can be had in estimating the capacity of pump required, as far as horsepower is concerned. The assumption that the overall efficiency of 64 per cent will provide dependable data along with the fact that the discharge pressure should range from 40 to 60 pounds per square inch. If plans are to design with a pressure of 60 pounds per square inch with an overall efficiency of 64 per cent, Table XIII may be used in the selection of the desired horsepower pump. For 64 per cent overall efficiency, the actual horsepower becomes:

Actual Horsepower = 0.000394 x Flow in GPM x Total Head in Feet

Table XIII may be used for other draw-downs than shown in this table and for other discharge pressures than 60 pounds per square inch. Such relationships will be as follows:

$$\text{Actual Horsepower} = \frac{\left(\begin{array}{c}\text{From Table XIII} \\ \text{Horsepower}\end{array}\right) \times \left(\begin{array}{c}\text{Draw-down} \qquad \text{Desired} \\ \text{In Feet} + 2.31 \times \text{Pressure in PSI}\end{array}\right)}{\text{Draw-down in Feet} + 138.60}$$

## TABLE XIII
## Assumed Actual Horsepower for Overall Efficiency of 64 Per Cent for Discharge Pressure of 60 Pounds Per Square Inch at Given Discharges and Drawdowns

| Flow in GPM | 20 | 40 | 60 | 80 | 100 | 120 | 140 | 160 | 180 | 200 | 250 |
|---|---|---|---|---|---|---|---|---|---|---|---|
| | | | | | (Draw-down in Feet) | | | | | | |
| 10 | .6 | .7 | .8 | .9 | 1.0 | 1.0 | 1.1 | 1.2 | 1.3 | 1.4 | 1.5 |
| 20 | 1.2 | 1.4 | 1.6 | 1.6 | 1.8 | 2.0 | 2.2 | 2.4 | 2.6 | 2.7 | 3.1 |
| 30 | 1.7 | 1.9 | 2.2 | 2.4 | 2.6 | 3.0 | 3.5 | 3.6 | 3.9 | 4.1 | 4.7 |
| 40 | 2.5 | 2.8 | 3.1 | 3.4 | 3.7 | 4.2 | 4.5 | 4.9 | 5.2 | 5.5 | 6.3 |
| 50 | 3.3 | 3.5 | 3.9 | 4.3 | 4.6 | 5.3 | 5.7 | 6.1 | 6.5 | 6.9 | 7.9 |
| 60 | 3.7 | 4.2 | 4.6 | 5.1 | 5.6 | 6.4 | 6.8 | 7.3 | 7.8 | 8.3 | 9.5 |
| 70 | 4.3 | 4.9 | 5.4 | 6.0 | 6.5 | 7.5 | 8.0 | 8.6 | 9.1 | 9.7 | 11.0 |
| 80 | 5.0 | 5.6 | 6.2 | 6.8 | 7.5 | 8.5 | 9.1 | 9.8 | 10.0 | 11.0 | 12.0 |
| 90 | 5.5 | 6.3 | 7.0 | 7.7 | 8.4 | 9.6 | 10.0 | 11.0 | 12.0 | 13.0 | 14.0 |
| 100 | 6.2 | 7.0 | 7.8 | 8.6 | 9.4 | 10.0 | 11.0 | 12.0 | 13.0 | 14.0 | 16.0 |
| 125 | 8.0 | 9.0 | 10.0 | 11.0 | 12.0 | 13.0 | 14.0 | 15.0 | 16.0 | 17.0 | 20.0 |
| 150 | 9.0 | 10.0 | 12.0 | 13.0 | 14.0 | 16.0 | 17.0 | 18.0 | 20.0 | 21.0 | 24.0 |
| 175 | 11.0 | 12.0 | 14.0 | 15.0 | 16.0 | 18.0 | 20.0 | 21.0 | 23.0 | 24.0 | 28.0 |
| 200 | 12.0 | 14.0 | 15.0 | 16.0 | 18.0 | 21.0 | 23.0 | 25.0 | 26.0 | 28.0 | 31.0 |
| 225 | 14.0 | 15.0 | 16.0 | 17.0 | 20.0 | 22.0 | 24.0 | 26.0 | 27.0 | 29.0 | 34.0 |
| 250 | 15.0 | 16.0 | 17.0 | 20.0 | 23.0 | 26.0 | 28.0 | 30.0 | 32.0 | 34.0 | 37.0 |
| 275 | 17.0 | 19.0 | 21.0 | 23.0 | 25.0 | 29.0 | 31.0 | 33.0 | 36.0 | 38.0 | 43.0 |
| 300 | 18.0 | 20.0 | 22.0 | 24.0 | 27.0 | 32.0 | 34.0 | 36.0 | 39.0 | 41.0 | 48.0 |

## 2. Surface Water Sources

For larger communities, surface water sources are used for water supply. Surface water sources of water supply are considered those waters which are derived directly from stream flow or which are stored prior to utilization. Many factors must be considered for utilization of surface waters other than the factor of quantity. Such factors include chemical and bacterial quality because these factors greatly influence the economics of water treatment and add to the problem of taste and odors.

Surface water supplies are divided into two distinct classifications, filtered and unfiltered. The difference of these surface water classifications is based upon the type of treatment necessary to produce a potable water and upon the quality of such waters prior to treatment.

### A. Unfiltered Surface Water Sources

In few instances a water supply is derived from a watershed area which is entirely owned or completely controlled by the water company or authority. The watershed is uninhabited and uncultivated, but is usually heavily covered with wooded areas. Controlled forestry, to prevent erosion and for the protection of water quality, is programmed to carry out procedures in thinning, replanting, construction of fire lanes, timbering, etc., so as to prevent high turbidity in run-off and other effects of lowering water quality. Hunting, hiking, and other forms of recreation are prohibited so that unnecessary pollution will be prevented because of the low or small amount of treatment provided to the water.

Requirements for treatment of water derived from such a controlled watershed, usually consist of coarse screening and continuous chlorination. Preferred treatment would consist of coarse to fine screening, pressure sand filtration, pH adjustment, corrosion control, and continuous chlorination. Patrolling of the areas is necessary to prevent unauthorized persons from entering and contaminating the watershed area.

With the unfiltered water supply, specific rules and regulations with enforcement of such are of utmost importance to regulate the use of the watershed area for every purpose. First of all, the water should be maintained at its highest quality. To achieve this, all types of habitation, cultivation, recreation, or other use must be prohibited. Secondly, a forest fire could very easily ruin the entire watershed area by destruction of the forest system thus leading to wide erosion problems making the water unsuitable unless complete treatment in the form of coagulation and filtration is used. Therefore, a well-planned forestry program should be inaugurated under the supervision of a trained forester to include timbering operations, thinning, reforestation, and maintenance of fire lanes throughout the entire watershed area. All such operational plans should include location and construction of logging roads, repair of equipment, refueling of equipment, and sanitation procedures for workers within the watershed area. Care should be taken so that the discharge of greases, oils, or other fuels will be avoided as much as possible. Sanitation rules involving the disposal of excreta and

garbage should be strictly enforced. Central stations for the disposal of excreta and garbage should be established preferably below the waterworks intake for use by workers. If such stations are located above the intake works, extreme care should be taken in their location and their use should be rigidly enforced. A third factor is the control of the area and water treatment. The entire area should be posted and properly patrolled. The frequency of patrol inspections will depend upon the potential hazards of pollution. If the area is more or less isolated, the frequency of inspecions may be monthly or quarterly whereas in other instances, constant patrolling is necessary. Water treatment facilities must be adequately supervised and maintained on a daily basis.

Suggestions for size of watersheds and yields to be expected from watershed areas will be discussed within the paragraphs pertaining to surface water supplies and will be applicable to both unfiltered and filtered supplies.

### B. Filtered Surfaces Water Sources

Surface water sources requiring complete treatment include those supplies which derive their waters from a source which is not entirely owned, supervised, or controlled by the water company or authority. In other words, it is a stream which is subjected to the normal environment of man. The water will contain normal bacteria content commonly associated with community life, excluding, of course, gross pollution from sewage or industrial wastes to the extent that the water, with proper treatment, will be of potable quality. Present bacterial standards state that the bacterial load should be less than 5,000 coliforms per 100 milliliter, but may be as great as 20,000[4]. Present day loadings indicate that complete treatment of the water, providing coagulation and super-chlorination, will capably treat bacterial loadings much greater than this. This water from man's environmental habitation, will contain high turbidity and possibly some taste and odor producing substances.

In the selection of a source of water for a surface supply, both the quality and the quantity of the water should be considered, and the final decision should be made with a balance between these two factors. Water quality includes such factors as bacteria, suitability for treatment, taste and odor producing substances, and the effect of future land use along the tributary streams from which the water is to be taken as a measure to assure a long obtainable, high quality of water. Water quantity should indicate that the source will be adequate many years hence to parallel expected community growth.

In the balance of quality and quantity of water sources, it is most desirable to locate on the largest watershed possible. However, in many cases, this is not possible because of the pollution of such a source. Therefore, to reach this balance, smaller watershed areas are developed by means of raw water impoundments, thereby meeting the requirements of a high water quality with an adequate water yield. This pollution problem of large water sources is becoming more apparent with community growth because these larger streams are more suitable for the receiving of sewage and industrial wastes from the standpoint of dilution and oxygen assimilating capacity, as well as economy of sewage and waste treatment. In view of the pollutional standpoint, the water quality of smaller streams will be the most suitable for water supply.

There are many methods of evaluating the yield of a watershed, storage requirements, and the draft upon such, to provide answers of the economical storage and the maximum draft upon a particular watershed area. These methods may be discussed as follows:

1. Mass Diagram. The mass diagram provides a method of utilization of past records of rainfall and runoff, or in other words, gauging station measurements of stream runoff. On the Mass Diagram, the accumulated stream measurement is plotted versus time. On the same Diagram, the maximum daily draft is plotted in the same manner (as accumulated values). The required amount of storage is equivalent to the largest depression or dip within the curve plotted from runoff and as measured down from a parallel of draft.

2. Applying information as to storage requirements from experience of other water companies within the same catchment basin. Such information will include such factors as draft, yield of watershed per square mile, and adequacy of present storage with figures indicating draw-down of these facilities during extended drought periods.

3. With a knowledge of average yield of a watershed, the maximum daily draft of the community supply, provides a reservoir with a storage of 180 days capacity with additional capacity for silting and evaporation.

A simplified method using a combination of the above methods along with accepted practice and experience, it is possible to derive certain basic and simplified equations, which will provide reliable information concerning watershed yield, maximum daily draft, and the required storage for known watershed areas and predesignated drafts. These relationships may be stated as follows:

1. For unimpounded streams where the water is taken directly from the stream flow by means of a small diversion dam, the draft will depend directly upon the minimum stream flow. Combining minimum stream flow, area of the watershed, and the maximum daily draft, it is possible to state a relationship as follows:

$$\text{Dependable Draft in MGD} = \text{Area of Watershed in Square Miles} \times \text{Minimum Yield of Watershed in MGD per Square Mile}$$

The unknown factors in this formula would be the Draft and the Area of the Watershed which must be worked out for each community. Experience has indicated that the minimum dependable yields for watershed areas will be approximately within the following values:

| Average Annual Rainfall, Inches per Year | Minimum Dependable Yield, MGD Per Square Mile |
|---|---|
| 30 | 0.0055 |
| 32 | 0.0062 |
| 34 | 0.0075 |
| 36 | 0.0088 |
| 38 | 0.010 |
| 40 | 0.012 |
| 42 | 0.014 |
| 44 | 0.016 |
| 46 | 0.020 |
| 48 | 0.023 |
| 50 | 0.026 |
| 52 | 0.030 |
| 54 | 0.035 |
| 56 | 0.040 |
| 58 | 0.048 |
| 60 | 0.056 |

It should be remembered that the Minimum Dependable Yield of a watershed may occur once in a short period such as five years or it may occur once during a long period of time such as 50 years. Therefore, in every case the water system should be designed as that the source will be dependable for the long periods of time. An example using the above would be the community located in an area where the annual rainfall is 46 inches per year. If the area of the watershed is 27 square miles, what would be the dependable draft available from this watershed?

$$\text{Dependable Draft in MGD} = \text{Area of Watershed in Square Miles} \times \text{Minimum Yield of Watershed in MGD per Square Mile from above table}$$

$$\text{Dependable Draft in MGD} = 27 \times 0.020 = 0.540 \text{ MGD}$$

2. For impounded streams. In many cases the watershed area is small and the minimum yield is not adequate to furnish the amount of water necessary to meet daily needs. Therefore, it is necessary to resort to storage to supply this additional amount of water in addition to the stream flow. The entire contents within any impoundment are not available for use because of such factors as evaporation, seepage into the soil, use by plant life, and the sedimentation of silt within the reservoir area, concentrating such objectionable matter as organic material, and compounds of iron, sulphur, and manganese.

A simplified formula may be derived for the determination of the amount of storage required to supply certain daily requirements from a known watershed area. This formula again relates back to the suggested values given as minimum dependable yield of watershed areas based on average rainfall data to the extent that an impoundment should not be expected to yield an average daily amount which is greater than 25 times the minimum dependable yield of the watershed area on which the impoundment is located. In other words, the maximum draft is a function of watershed area and watershed yield, and regardless of reservoir size, there is a maximum limit for the draft from the watershed. Therefore, it can safely be established to be some 25 times the minimum yield of the watershed area. With the draft governed by this upper limit, the following simplified formula may be applied to relate draft, area, and reservoir volume:

$$\text{Volume of Storage Required in Million Gallons}^* = 4.68 \times \left[\text{Draft in MGD} - \text{Minimum Dependable Yield, MGD per Square Mile} \times \text{Area of Watershed in Square Miles}\right]^2$$

---

For example, how much storage will be needed for a community in which the water demand or draft will be 24 million gallons per day? The area of the watershed is 75 square miles. The average rainfall is 46 inches per year.

$$\text{Volume of Storage, MG} = 4.68 \times \left[\text{Draft in MGD} - \text{Minimum Dependable Yield, MGD Per Square Mile} \times \text{Area of Watershed in Square Miles}\right]^2$$

$$= 4.68 \times [24 - 0.02 \times 75]^2$$

$$= 2{,}380 \text{ Million Gallons}$$

---

*Valid only where the Yield x Area exceeds 0.05 mgd.

By use of this same method of formation, it is possible to calculate the draft possible from an existing reservoir since the volume of storage, the minimum dependable yield of the watershed area, and the area of the watershed is known. Such formulation is as follows:

Maximum Draft
from
Reservoir in MGD =

$$\begin{pmatrix} \text{Minimum} \\ \text{Dependable} \\ \text{Yield, MGD} \\ \text{Per Square} \\ \text{Mile} \end{pmatrix} \times \begin{pmatrix} \text{Area of} \\ \text{Watershed} \\ \text{in Square} \\ \text{Miles} \end{pmatrix} + \sqrt{\begin{pmatrix} 0.214 \times \begin{matrix} \text{Volume of} \\ \text{Reservoir} \\ \text{in MG} \end{matrix} - 3 \times \begin{matrix} \text{Minimum} \\ \text{Dependable} \\ \text{Yield, MGD} \\ \text{Per Square} \\ \text{Mile} \end{matrix} \times \begin{matrix} \text{Area of} \\ \text{Watershed} \\ \text{in Square} \\ \text{Miles} \end{matrix} \end{pmatrix}}$$

3. Water treatment facilities. In the development of a water source for a potable water supply, the economic and operational factors influence the consideration of treatment facilities necessary to produce a high quality potable water. As the treatment facilities become more complicated and complete, the initial cost and operational maintenance greatly increase. It is therefore necessary to study the source of supply in the light of the treatment required.

## A. Ground Water Sources

Ground water sources are usually characterized by a water quality which has a pH of from 6.8 to 7.4, a low concentration of iron which varies from 0.1 to approximately 1.0 parts per million, and in some areas by the presence of Hydrogen Sulphide. With the low pH, the Carbon Dioxide concentration increases to create a definite corrosion problem. The range of Carbon Dioxide will range from about three to five parts per million at a pH of 7.4, to about 20 to 25 parts per million at a pH of 6.0. With the corrosion problem, the presence of Iron

and possibly Hydrogen Sulphide in ground water, the use of certain treatment is sometimes a must with ground water supplies. Treatment facilities involving the removal or prevention of such trouble will be discussed.

(1) Aeration. Aeration provides for the exchange of gases so that either removal or oxidation of matter will take place in the exchange interface of water and air. Aerators are used to eliminate Carbon Dioxide from the water, release Hydrogen Sulphide, aid in the decomposition of organic matter, control taste and odors, and in the oxidation of Iron and Manganese for removal of these troublesome compounds. Aerators are usually of the gravity type in which the water is discharged through nozzles into the air and allowed to trickle over cascades or perforated plates or trays with or without special type of media. Other types of aeration processes utilize the blowing of air through the water media.

Aerators should be designed so that adequate exposure time and contact may be had. With this as the basis

*Valid only where the Yield x Area exceeds 0.05 mgd.

of design, the aerator tower should be of a height of eight to 20 feet with 12 feet being preferable so that a contact time of one to five seconds will occur. The nozzle loading should be from 20 to 75 gallons per minute per nozzle with a spacing of from 40 to 150 square feet per nozzle. Nozzle pressures should vary from two to 10 pounds per square inch. It has been found that coke trays and spray fountains provide around 75 per cent removal of Carbon Dioxide. Hydrogen Sulphide is loosely held and is easily eliminated through the gaseous phase exchange of aerators.

*(2) Pressure Filters*[29]. Pressure filters utilizing sand and gravel media, have been used in the field of water treatment for swimming pools for many years. Their use in the treatment of ground water supplies is also common. Pressure filters utilizing sand and gravel, crushed pyrolusite ore (Natural Manganese Oxide), or ion exchange resins are in common use in special type of treatment and in conjunction with other treatment units. When used with aerators and sedimentation basins, they are effective in the removal of iron and manganese, or in conjunction with chemical treatment for the removal of excess hardness from the water.

For removal of Iron and Manganese, pretreatment in the form of aeration and pH adjustment to above 7.0 is required prior to sedimentation, which is followed by filtration. In this process, the Iron and Manganese is oxidized by aeration to form a precipitate which is settled and the filter in this case is used to remove the fine suspended matter which remains in suspension. The oxidation of the Iron and Manganese takes place as the water flows over a contact media of coke located on trays within the aerator:

Pumps $\rightarrow$ pH Adjustment $\rightarrow$
Aeration $\rightarrow$ Settling $\rightarrow$
Filtration $\rightarrow$ Pumps to System

The sedimentation basin in this case should be of capacity to provide at least a 45-minute detention period. Also the sand beds in this type of treatment, do not become effective until coated with the oxidizing compounds.

In many cases the procedure is to utilize an aerator, pH adjustment, and a filter which has been pretreated with Sodium Permanganate to retain the oxidized Iron and Manganese. In this case the settling basin is eliminated, as the Iron and Manganese in this case is retained by contact oxidatino with the filter media.

If the Iron and Manganese is loosely held as organic matter within the water, the filter media is treated or the use of a Sodium Zeolite is used as the filter media this acting as a contact bed in addition to being a filter media. Such beds must be cleaned and regenerated by the use of Sodium Permanganate:

Pumps $\rightarrow$ pH Adjustment $\rightarrow$
Contact Filter $\rightarrow$ Pumps to System

Pressure filters should be designed with proper piping for backwash water, waste lines, loss of head gauges, and sight glass indicators. Rates of filtration should be from two to three gallons per square foot of filter area per minute. Back wash rates should be from 10 to 15 gallons per minute per square foot of filter area. Pressure filters operate at pressures of from 20 to 45 pounds per square inch. It should be noted that if media other than sand and gravel is used, thtat the wash water rate as given above should be adjusted for the media used such for Anthrafilt, the wash water rate should be from eight to 10 gallons per minute per square foot of filter area.

Pressure filters may be used in the softening process of water in conjunction with either solids contact units or conventional coagulation treatment units utilizing the lime-soda or chemical precipitation process. In such cases, filters must be employed to provide for the removal of suspended matter from the water.

Special type of units utilizing filter boxes with zeolites in place of filter media, are used for the softening of water. In the ion exchange process, the ions of Magnesium and Calcium, components of hardness in a water, are exchanged within the ion exchange resins for the Sodium ion. In other words, the ions which cause hardness in water are removed and an ion which does not possess hardness characteristics is placed into solution in their place. When the resins become saturated with the Calcium and Magnesium ions, it is then necessary to regenerate the resins by use of salt brines to remove the Calcium

Pump — Lime (CaO) — Mixing — Settling — Filtration — Pumps to System
Soda ($Na_2CO_3$)

and Magnesium and discharge these ions to waste by the replacement of such with the Sodium. These processes may be described as follows:

| Water with Hardness | Pumps | Zeolite Exchange Charged with Sodium Ion | Exchange of Sodium Ions for Calcium and Magnesium Ions | Soft Water, Pumps to System |
|---|---|---|---|---|

The regeneration cycle as follows:

| Spent Ion Exchange Resin Saturated with Calcium and Magnesium Ions | Treatment with Salt Brine | Removal of Calcium and Magnesium Ions and Discharge to Waste | Regenerated Resin Saturated with Sodium Ions Ready for Use Again |
|---|---|---|---|

*(3) Corrosion Control and Chlorination.* Other equipment commonly used in the treatment of ground water supplies deals with the problem of corrosion control of the pump and distribution system and the application of chlorination and fluorides to the water in proper dosage. The dosages of these materials are relatively small, therefore in most cases are applied in solution form. All such solution feeders should be of dependable make and should be of such capacity to provide chemical dosages up to some 10 parts per million considering the per cent of solution strength available and the discharge rate of the source.

## B. Surface Water Sources[2]

The treatment facilities for surface water sources are more complex from both the design, as well as the operational standpoint, because of the lower quality of the raw water to be treated. Such treatment facilities include intake works, impoundments for raw water, raw water conduits, and the treatment plant facilities.

*(1) Intake Works.* The intake works are structures which are used to divert and lift the water from a stream or impoundment to the treatment works. Intake structures may be of concrete in the form of towers with multiple ports located at different elevations or as a crib weighted down within a stream channel. When intakes are located in stream channels, it is important to protect from flood waters or damage from floating debris. If possible the intake structure should be located in the quiescence portion of a stream rather than the highly turbulent portion if at all possible. The location and the design of the structure will minimize the entrance of sand, silt, fish, and debris. Rough or coarse screening is necessary and should be provided with bars, which are spaced from one to three inches apart, with the area of the openings restricting the entrance velocity to less than 20 feet per minute. If a diversion dam is utilized within the stream channel, provisions should be made for the removal of silt and sediment from behind this dam.

All raw water pumping facilities should be provided in duplicate. Standby or auxiliary gasoline driven pumps should also be provided for large installations. All installations should be easily served by all weather roads for proper maintenance of equipment.

The intake structure for raw water impoundments should be located within the deeper portions of the reservoir. Inlets for the intake structure should be located at various levels, depending on the mean and low water levels and depth of the water at this location. Surface waters are subject to algae growths, whereas the lower waters are loaded with organic matter, silt, and high concentrations of iron, manganese, and sulphides. Coarse screening or gratings should be provided and designed as mentioned for stream intakes.

All piping or tunnels for intake structures should be designed at velocities of from two to four feet per second in order to be self-cleansing. Fine screens are desirable for the protection of pumps from grit and other debris.

*(2) Raw Water Impoundments.* The capacity of the raw water reservoir should be calculated in accordance with formulae given in previous paragraphs. Certain basic requirements should be followed concerning the preparation of the reservoir.

(a) An adequate amount of land should be purchased in addition to that acquired for the water area so that proper controls may be had regarding the prevention of pollution from use of the land along the water's edge. The additional strip of land should be measured from the high water margin of the reservoir. It will also be usable in the patrolling and in the reservoir maintenance program.

(b) An area of two feet above the high water margin and five feet below the mean level of the reservoir should be cleared and grubbed of all growth. This will prevent the creation of a satisfactory environment for the breeding of insects.

(c) The entire area below the five-foot level from mean water elevation should be cleared and grubbed of all growth. It may be desirable to cut off stumps, of six inches and larger, at ground level. All such material should be burned or removed from the reservoir area to prevent organic decay over long periods of time, thus leading to taste and odor problems. Care should be taken in the planning of the clearing and grubbing program for large reservoirs because the long period of time involved in construction of the dam, spillway, and intake structures, will provide ample time for the vegetation to regrow thus necessitating the clearing and grubbing of the reservoir a second time.

(d) Of extreme importance is the preparation of the areas along the entrance of the tributary streams to the reservoir, as these areas will usually be somewhat swampy. Therefore, either islands should be constructed to give deeper water areas, or the material dredged entirely from the reservoir. In many cases, small impoundments are constructed within these areas so that it is possible to control the breeding of mosquitoes by fluctuation of the water level within the small impoundment. The smaller impoundment must be constructed with the toe of the dam within the larger reservoir in order to prevent the existence of a shallow water area. It will also serve a second purpose in that it will not only provide some additional storage, but will act as a settling basin for incoming silt from the watershed area.

(e) *Raw Water Pipelines.* All pipes or tunnels used for intake conduits should be designed at velocities of from two to four feet per second in order to be self-cleansing. An adequate number of blow-off valves and air relief valves should be provided along all pipelines for maintenance purposes of cleaning.

*(3) Water Treatment Plant*[2]. The water treatment plant provides chemical treatment in the form of coagulation of suspended solids, screening or filtering by use of gravity-type rapid sand filters, corrosion control, and chlorination, thus producing a high quality, potable water. The principle of operation is that the water enters the plant, chemicals are added, mixing, sedimentation, and filtration follow, then final adjustment of the water is provided for corrosion control and disinfection. Details of design of these appurtenances are as follows:

*(a) Mixing Process.* One of the most important processes in water treatment is the mixing process whereby the added chemicals are mixed in proper dosage to the incoming water thus causing precipitation to occur. Mixing facilities may be done by hydraulics or by mechanical equipment.

(1) *Baffle Mixing.* Accepted practice for a baffle mixing basin, either around-the-end or over-and-under, is that a velocity of 1.5 feet per second be maintained for the first third of the basin, a velocity of 0.75 feet per second through the second third, and 0.4 to 0.5 feet per second through the last third. In many cases, a flash mechanical mixer at the entrance of the baffled basin will assist in the coagulation process. The flash mixer should have a shaft speed of 350 to 750 rpm and the time of the mix should be from one minute to five minutes.

(2) *Mechanical Mixing.* Mixing should be adequate to thoroughly disperse the chemicals in the raw water prior to its entrance into the flocculator basin. If the mix is done by high velocity mixers such as by a pump or turbine-type mixer, the velocity should be five feet per second or greater, and the retention time should be one minute more or less. If a flash mixer is used, it should be as discussed above under baffle mixing.

Paddle-type mixers, equipped with variable speed regulators, should provide a peripheral speed of one to three feet per second and a retention time of not less than five minutes.

Air mixing devices provide benefits in addition to agitation or mixing of the chemicals. Air being blown through the basin, provides this additional treatment in the removal of taste and odors from the water. It also provides oxidation of Iron and Manganese to aid in their removal. Air mixing units should be designed to provide three stages of agitation—violent, intermediate, and quiescent. The requirement of the air supply is at least 0.5 cubic feet of air per square foot of tank area or 0.05 to 0.20 cubic feet of air per gallon of water. The time of aeration contact of the water should be from 10 to 30 minutes. Air mixing devices may be used in conjunction with either baffle or mechanical mixers.

The final step in mechanical mixing is that of mechanical flocculation, that is, the slow agitation of the fine floc to hold it in suspension so that the size may build up before the sedimentation process. Mechanical flocculators should be of variable speed, with the peripheral speed of the paddles being from 0.5 to 2.0 feet per second. The basin should be sized to provide a detention period of from 20 to 40 minutes.

All conduits, carrying coagulated water to the sedimentation basin, should be designed to provide a velocity of 0.5 to 1.0 feet per second. Less than 0.3 feet per second, the floc will settle while greater than 1.0 feet per second it will be broken up. Therefore, the 0.5 feet per second is considered the optimum velocity for coagulated water.

*(4) Sedimentation Basin.* The sedimentation basin is provided for the removal of the floc from the coagulation process. In a well-operated plant, the majority of the purification process takes place in this coagulation process. Therefore, the design of this basin is of importance. The sedimentation basin consists of a diffusion wall and the basin itself. The diffusion wall acts to diffuse the floc over the entire width of the basin. It should be located from five to 10 feet from the end of the basin. The size and number of the slots within the wall should be based upon a velocity of 0.4 to 0.8 feet per second through the slots and to provide uniform distribution and velocity across the basin. This diffusion wall may be omitted, provided that other methods are used to give this uniformity of distribution.

The sedimentation basin should provide a theoretical detention period of at least four hours. The velocity of flow through the basin should be from 0.3 to a maximum of 1.0 feet per minute. The length to width ratio of the basin should be from two to one to a maximum of three to one. The depth of the basin should be from 10 to 16 feet.

The bottom of the basin should be sloped to a drain which is sized to empty the basin within a period of four hours. An independent overflow should be provided for each basin. The outlet device for settling tanks should be either of the submerged weir-type or large openings to prevent high velocities.

*(5) Solids Contact or Up-Flow Units.* Within recent years, the solids contact or up-flow unit has come into use. This compact unit provides chemical mixing and sedimentation in a manner in which the settled floc is recirculated to mix with the newly formed floc thus providing a heavy floc for settling. This type of unit also provides for continuous sludge removal by automatic timing device. Even though these units have been utilized in the water softening processes for a large number of years, their application to clarification of turbid waters for community systems requires greater care in design and operation.

The maximum rise rate for the clarification of water should be in the range of one to 1.25 gallons per minute per square foot of clarification area. In certain instances where the quality of raw water contains a high concentration of hardness, the rise rate may be increased to 2.25, but in doing so in design, considerable study should be made of the year-round water quality.

The detention period for this type of treatment unit should not be less than two hours with the mixing and flocculating zone averaging not less than 35 minutes. At the greater rise

rates, the detention period may be lowered accordingly, but not less than one hour. The mixing device should be a variable speed type agitator with a ratio of two to one and should be designed so that there will be no dead space in the bottom of the zone of mixing. Sludge removal from the unit should be somewhat continuous with the sludge removal mechanism controlled by an adjustable automatic timer. The effluent weir of the unit should provide for uniform collection of the clarification area at a loading not to exceed seven gallons per minute per foot of weir length.

*(6) Rapid Gravity Sand Filters.* Sand filters provide the final treatment for the removal of suspended matter from the water. Filtration as a treatment process, provides greatest efficiency when a layer of floc creates a mat on the sand surface for the water to filter through. Sand filters are designed on the basis of filtration rate and backwash rate. The filtration rate is established at two gallons per minute per square foot of filter area. In certain instances, this rate may be increased to three gallons per minute per square foot of filter area, in which case the plant design and operation must be extremely good. The backwash water rate is established at 24 inches rise per minute. This will give a flow of 15 gallons per minute per square foot of filter area. When Anthrafilt is used, the backwash rate should be around 18 inches rise per minute. To meet these two flow conditions, the filter under-drain and other controls must be properly designed.

For proper operation of a filter, proper controls and gauges must be installed on the filter. These include rate of flow controllers, loss of head gauges, rate of flow gauges, and wash water rate gauges. Filter bottoms must be of adequate capacity to provide filtration and backwash water flows. Bottoms may be either cast iron manifolds, concrete cast in place, or in the form of precast plates or blocks. Surface agitators or sweeps are very desirable for proper cleaning of the filter media during the washing cycle.

Filter sand should be of the following specifications:

Effective Size—0.35 to 0.55 millimeters.

Uniformity Coefficient—1.70 or less.

Dust Content—Less than 0.5 per cent.

Depth of Sand—24 to 30 inches.

If Anthrafilt is used as the filter media, the Effective Size should range from 0.65 to 0.75 millimeters and the Uniformity Coefficient should be 1.7 or less. The Wash Water Rate should also be adjusted to give 18 inches rise per minute.

Supporting gravel for the filter media should consist of:

First three-inch layer—⅝ to one inch size stone.

Second three-inch layer—⅜ to ⅝ inch size stone.

Third three-inch layer—3/16 to ⅜ inch size stone.

Fourth three-inch layer—Number 10 to 3/16-inch stone (Torpedo Sand).

To provide for proper expansion of the filter media during the washing cycle, the minimum distance from the top of the wash water trough to the top of the media should be at least 27 inches. Wash water troughs should be of adequate dimensions to carry the maximum wash water rate. The spacing of such troughs should be not greater than five to seven feet.

*(7) Chemical Feed Equipment.* Chemical feed equipment should be of dependable make and of accuracy to provide correct dosages. They should be sufficient in number so that split dosage is unnecessary for any one machine except the chlorinator which is best operated from a panel and has several points of application. Dry chemical feeders should have capacities ranging from 50 to 100 pounds per hour per million gallons of water treated. The upper limit should be provided for the coagulant feed machines.

Chlorinators and chlorine cylinders should be kept in separate rooms from the other feeders because of safety and leakage of chlorine gas will react with dampened metal surfaces to cause corrosion. The chlorinator room should be provided with an exhaust fan located approximately six inches above the floor and with a capacity sufficient for two complete air changes per minute. The fan control should be located outside the chlorinator room. A gas mask should also be stored outside the room.

Where fluoride compounds are added to the water, the storage of the fluoride chemicals should be kept separate from other chemical storage so as to eliminate the danger of mixing this chemical with other water treatment chemicals.

*(8) Several other items* noteworthy of mentioning regarding water treatment plants are as follows:

(a) *Laboratory.* The laboratory for proper operation and control, should be adequately equipped for daily bacterial and chemical analysis of water quality.

(b) *Chemical Storage.* Storage areas for treatment chemicals, should be ample to store at least a month's supply of chemicals. It is preferable to have several months of storage area so that the chemicals may be bought in bulk quantity. All chemical storage areas should be located in the driest portion of the plant to prevent moisture difficulties.

(c) *Finished Water Storage* (Clear well or clear water storage). The reservoirs used for storage of finished water should provide at least 10 to 12 hours' storage. Together with elevated storage, the total storage facilities of clear water should be one day's supply and preferably not less than 75,000 gallons. The clear wells should be constructed of concrete or fabricated steel. These reservoirs should be covered and have access watertight manholes. They should be well ventilated and contain adequate overflow pipes and drains. All such outlets or openings should be screened with at least a 16-mesh screening. The inlets and outlets should be arranged so that circulation of water is provided.

(d) *Finished Water Pumping*. Finished water pumping facilities should consist of duplicate pumping units. A generator driven by a gasoline or diesel engine should be available as auxiliary power for the plant and pump operation. For larger installations, pumps should vary in number and capacity from 100 to 150 to 250 per cent of plant capacity.

## 4. Combination Utilization of Water Sources

In many instances, it is desirable to utilize more than one of the above sources of water supply for a community system. Example of this would be a community utilizing wells and a surface water treatment plant, a well and an unfiltered surface supply, or an unfiltered surface supply and a surface water treatment plant. In such instances, the overall design would be based upon the development of the individual sources in accordance with what has been previously discussed.

# CHAPTER III
# Storage Requirements

## General

Storage of water is provided on a water system so that the instantaneous and daily demand for water may be furnished to consumers at all times. Such storage may therefore be considered "equilizing' storage because it provides for equalizing flow in accordance with daily demand to meet maximum and minimum requirements for the 24-hour period. It is estimated that the peak or maximum requirements by consumers on a water system will range from 150 to over 300 per cent of the daily average demand. This equilizing storage may be provided in several ways such as low pressure or ground storage under atmospheric pressure, or in standpipes, or as high pressure storage, or combinations of storage facilities. A description of storage facilities is as follows:

1. Low Pressure Storage. Low pressure storage of water is considered that storage of water that is located under atmospheric or zero gauge pressure, and that is immediately available to the distribution system. By means of a high capacity, high lift or service pump, this water may be placed into the high pressure or elevated storage facilities located on the distribution system. Low pressure storage is economical as a means of providing large quantities of storage. A typical layout of low pressure storage is illustrated in Figure 10.

2. High Pressure Storage. High pressure storage is storage of water that provides and maintains pressure on the water distribution system. This storage may be at ground elevation in the form of pneumatic or pressure storage tanks, or in standpipes on higher elevations, or in elevated tanks located within the distribution grid. Desirable pressure limits for a water system should be based on a desired pressure of not less than 20 pounds per square inch at the highest plumbing fixture in multi-story buildings, or,

Maximum
> 60 to 75 pounds per square inch

Minimum
> 30 pounds per square inch

Average
> 45 pounds per square inch

A typical layout of high pressure storage facilities is illustrated in Figure 11.

### 1. Small Water Systems Utilizing Ground Water Sources

Requirements for storage for a water system depend not only upon the type of water consumers being served, but also upon the maximum demand for water, which the consumers place upon the system for short periods of time, and the replenishment of this water to the storage facilities by the source of water supply so that the service will be uninterrupted.

Due to the individualism of users as discussed in Chapter I, the calculation of storage is made somewhat difficult. Therefore, in order to simplify the problems involved, certain assumptions are made governing conditions which may exist within a community water system. These assumptions are based upon such conditions that the instantaneous water requirement for a community will be a percentage of the total number and type

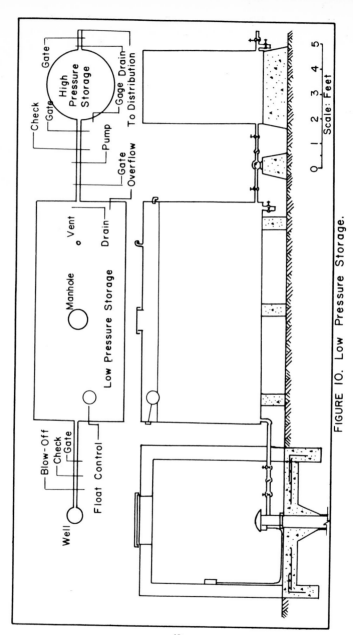

FIGURE 10. Low Pressure Storage.

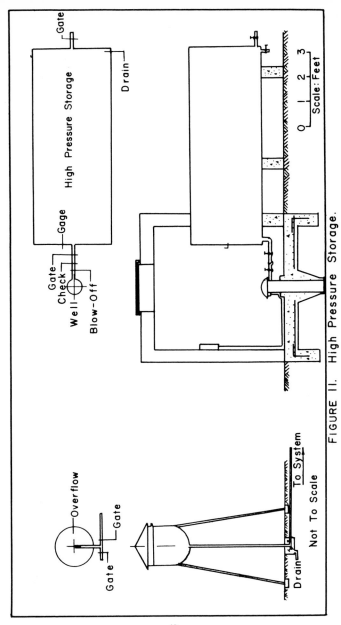

FIGURE II. High Pressure Storage.

of plumbing fixtures located within the community will be in operation at the same time. This fact is recognized by plumbing codes and manuals. This instantaneous water demand will cause a greater flow within the system for that particular time. As the community increases in size, the instantaneous water requirement will decrease accordingly because of the individualism of consumers which tend to average out the percentage of fixtures operating at the same instant, thereby causing a decrease in the sharp fluctuations of instantaneous usage.

## A. Storage Requirements

Storage requirements are based upon average daily consumption and the maximum instantaneous flows within the community. The occurrence of instantaneous flows so greatly exceeds the average flows and requirements of the community that it is necessary to calculate these maximum or instantaneous flows within a community water system in order that storage and pumping facilities may be properly designed. Tables XIV, XV, and XVI provide information and data by which these calculations may

be made. These tables set forth criteria for instantaneous flow demands for residential, commercial, and institutional areas.

The flow demand of institutions must be considered in the light of the time for which the institution is used per day. For example, day schools are operated for a period of six to eight hours per day, while other institutions such as colleges and hospitals are operated for 24 hours. The flow demand with this consideration is given in Table XVI.

Apartment buildings are to be considered as individual residential units within Table XIV and each apartment unit is thereby counted as a separate residence.

By considering the breakdown of the individual type of users in accordance with the above tables, it is possible to determine the individual instantaneous flows and the total instantaneous flows required for a water system. This total instantaneous flow is the demand upon storage facilities which may be expected to occur instantaneously during a 24-hour period. The total average daily demand

## TABLE XIV
### Instantaneous Water Demands for Residential Areas

| Total Number of Residences Served | GPM Per Residence | Total Number of Residence Served | GPM Per Residence |
|---|---|---|---|
| 5 | 8.0 | 90 | 2.1 |
| 10 | 5.0 | 100 | 2.0 |
| 20 | 4.3 | 150 | 1.6 |
| 30 | 3.8 | 200 | 1.3 |
| 40 | 3.4 | 300 | 1.2 |
| 50 | 3.0 | 400 | 0.9 |
| 60 | 2.7 | 500 | 0.8 |
| 70 | 2.5 | 750 | 0.7 |
| 80 | 2.2 | 1,000 | 0.6 |

## TABLE XV
## Instantaneous Water Demands for Commercial Areas

| Type of Establishment | Basis of Flow Demand |
| --- | --- |
| Barber Shop | 1.5 gpm per chair |
| Beauty Shop | 1.5 gpm per chair |
| Dentist Office | 2.0 gpm per chair |
| Department Store* | 0.5-1.0-1.5 gpm per employee |
| Drug Store | 3.0 gpm |
|    With Fountain Service | add 3.0 gpm |
|    Serving Meals | add 1.0 gpm per seat |
| Industrila Plant** | 0.5 gpm per employee |
| Laundry | 20.0-40.0-60.0 gpm |
| Launderette | 5.0 gpm per unit |
| Meat Market, Super Market | 1.0 gpm per 100 square feet floor area |
| Motel, Hotel | 2.0 gpm per unit |
| Office Building* | 0.2 gpm per 100 square feet floor area |
| Physician's Office | 2.0 gpm per examining room |
| Restaurant | 1.0 gpm per seat |
|    Single Service | 3.0-6.0-10.0 gpm |
|    Drive-In | 0.5-1.0-3.0 gpm per car space |
| Service Station | 3.0-5.0-8.0 gpm per wash rack |
| Theatre | 0.3-1.0-2.0 gpm per seat |
|    Drive-In | 0.4 gpm per car space |
| Other Establishments*** | 0.3-1.0-3.0 gpm per employee |

\* Including customer service.
\*\* Not including process water.
\*\*\* Non-water using establishments.

for water may be obtained from Table II, III, IV, and V.

An example of determining total flow which would occur instantaneously within a community would be in the case of a water system which is to serve a community of 80 residences and a commercial center comprised of a ready-to-wear shop, a drug store which has fountain service, a television repair shop, and a super market of 3,000 square feet floor area. The breakdown of individual flows and the total instantaneous flow for this community, would be as follows:

```
80 Residences at 2.2 gpm per residence (Table XIV) . . . . . . . . . . .  176 gpm
 1 Ready-to-wear shop at 1.0 gpm (Table XV) . . . . . . . . . . . . . .    1 gpm
 1 Drug Store (3.0 gpm) with fountain service (3.0 gpm)
       (Table XV) . . . . . . . . . . . . . . . . . . . . . . . . . . . . . . . . . . . . .    6 gpm
 1 Television repair shop at 1.0 gpm (Table XV) . . . . . . . . . . . . .    1 gpm
 1 Super Market at 1.0 gpm/100 square feet x 3,000 square feet . .   30 gpm
                                                                         _____
       Total Instantaneous Flow . . . . . . . . . . . . . . . . . . . . . . . .  214 gpm
```

## TABLE XVI
## Instantaneous Water Demands for Institutions

| Type of Institution | Basis of Flow Demand |
|---|---|
| Boarding Schools, Colleges | 1.0 gpm per student |
| Churches | 0.2 gpm per member |
| Clubs, Civic | 0.4 gpm per member |
| Clubs, Country | 0.6 gpm per member |
| Hospitals | 4.0 gpm per bed |
| Nursing Homes | 2.0 gpm per bed |
| Prisons | 1.0 gpm per prisoner |
| Rooming Houses | 1.0 gpm per roomer |
| Summer Camps | 0.2 gpm per camper |

### SCHOOLS: DAY, ELEMENTARY, JUNIOR, SENIOR

| Number of Students | GPM Per Student | Number of Students | GPM Per Student |
|---|---|---|---|
| 0-50 | 1.0 | 800 | 0.68 |
| 100 | 0.97 | 900 | 0.66 |
| 200 | 0.94 | 1,000 | 0.60 |
| 300 | 0.90 | 1,200 | 0.52 |
| 400 | 0.86 | 1,400 | 0.46 |
| 500 | 0.82 | 1,600 | 0.41 |
| 600 | 0.78 | 1,800 | 0.38 |
| 700 | 0.72 | 2,000 | 0.35 |

The maximum demand upon this water system would be 214 gpm. Therefore, the combined yield of the well or low pressure pumping facilities and the storage facilities must be adequate to supply this flow to the community. The total daily demand for this system would be 51,200 gallows per day. Therefore, the well system and storage facilities should be ample to provide 51,200 gallons per day and an instantaneous flow of 214 gallons per minute.

### B. High Service Storage

It is highly desirable to provide all high service storage in the form of elevated storage and in the quantity of at least one day's supply. However, in many cases this is not practical from the standpoint of economy. Therefore, in these cases it is necessary to provide this high service storage in the form of pneumatic or pressure storage tanks on the distribution system. In such cases, these facilities, in combination with the flows from the wells or low pressure storage and pumping facilities, should provide an equilizing flow for a period of at least 20 minutes to meet the instantaneous flow demand. Since this demand occurs for a short period of time, experience has indicated that the 20-minute time period suggested is ample for small water systems. This storage is based on the maximum distribution requirements from individual requirements according to type of user and is considered that storage above operating pressures set forth for the distribution system as given on Page 47.

On this basis, the high pressure storage requirement for a system may be calculated as follows:

| High Pressure Storage Requirement, Gallons | = | Maximum Flow Demand For Distribution System For 20-minute Time Period | — | Yield of Wells For a Time Period of 20 Minutes |
|---|---|---|---|---|

To illustrate this by example, the problem stated above indicated that a maximum distribution flow of 214 gallons per minute is required by the 80 residences and the commercial center. If this system is supplied by two wells of 20 gpm and 30 gpm each, then the requirement for high pressure storage would be:

| High Pressure Storage Requirement, Gallons | = | Maximum Distribution System Flow Demand | x 20 — | Total Yield of Well or Wells | x 20 |
|---|---|---|---|---|---|

$$= 214 \times 20 - (20 + 30) \times 20$$

$$= 3,280 \text{ gallons}$$

In sizing pneumatic storage tanks, it must be remembered that approximately 25 per cent of the total capacity of the tank is available for use at pressures above the minimum of 30 pounds per square inch. Therefore, in the above example, it is necessary to provide four times the capacity or $4 \times 3,280$ to give 13,120 gallons.

Table XVII is given to provide information on actual tank capacities from a knowledge of the equilizing flow. It is only necessary to calculate the instantaneous demand and from this, the equilizing flow is obtained by substracting the yield of the well or wells. In other words:

Equilizing Flow, GPM = Instantaneous Demand — Total Yield of Wells

# TABLE XVII
## Pneumatic Storage Tank Requirements

| Equilizing Flow for 20-Minute Period, Instantaneous Demand less Yield of Wells on System (in gpm) | Required Actual Capacity of Tank on System (in gallons) |
|---|---|
| 25 | 2,000 |
| 40 | 3,200 |
| 60 | 4,800 |
| 80 | 6,400 |
| 100 | 8,000 |
| 120 | 9,600 |
| 140 | 11,200 |
| 160 | 12,800 |
| 180 | 14,400 |
| 200 | 16,000 |
| 225 | 18,000 |
| 250 | 20,000 |
| 275 | 22,000 |
| 300 | 24.000 |
| 350 | 28,000 |
| 400 | 32,000 |
| 500 | 40,000 |

Minimum pneumatic storage capacity should not be less than 20 times the yield of pump.

After this is obtained, consult Table XVII to obtain the actual capacity of the tank required to give the 20-minute required storage.

The above pertains to total storage requirements for water systems. However, in many cases, especially where several wells are concerned, it is more desirable from both the economical and efficiency standpoint, to divide the storage between the wells and place smaller tanks at each well installation. This dividing or proportioning the storage between more than one well can best be done on the actual yield or pumping rate of the specific wells in question. This proportioning should be done so that the larger storage will be located at the well which has the largest yield. In the above example, a total storage capacity of 11,200 gallons is required. If this were proportioned between the two wells, the division of this storage would be on the ratio basis as follows:

$$\text{High Pressure Storage At Well of 20-gpm Yield} = 11,200 \ \text{x} \ \frac{\text{Well Yield}}{\text{Total Yield of Wells}}$$

$$= 11,200 \ \text{x} \ \frac{20}{20 \ + \ 30}$$

$$= 11,200 \times \frac{20}{50}$$

$$= 4,480 \text{ gallons}$$

High Pressure Storage
At Well of 30-gpm Yield $= 11,200 \times \dfrac{\text{Well Yield}}{\text{Total Yield of Wells}}$

$$= 11,200 \times \frac{30}{20 + 30}$$

$$= 11,200 \times \frac{30}{50}$$

$$= 6,720 \text{ gallons}$$

Therefore, it may be formulated for a system which has any number of wells, that the proportioning of the storage between these wells will be as follows:

High Pressure Storage at any Well in System (in gallons) $=$ Total Storage Required for The System $\quad$ times $\quad \dfrac{\text{Yield of that Well}}{\begin{array}{l}\text{Total Yield of All}\\ \text{Wells Within the}\\ \text{System}\end{array}}$

This formula should be applied to all wells within the system so that the total storage at each well will equal the total required for the entire system.

### C. Low Level Storage in Combination with Service Storage

In many cases, it is desirable from the standpoint of economy as well as operation, to utilize low pressure storage in combination with high pressure storage. Examples of where this would be desirable, would be in instances where the yield of the well supply slightly exceeds the daily de-mand of the community so that it is necessary to operate the pumping unit some 20 or more hours per day to meet the demand. Or in the case where large communities are being served, it may be desirable to have such large storage available to the distribution system, yet it may not be economically feasible to put all the storage into the air in the form of elevated storage. Other examples of this would be in cases where wells within an area have small yields, yet located on the system are large water users such as a school requiring a large quantity of water in a relatively short period of time. Therefore, low pressure storage may be the most feasible method to supplement the pneumatic storage on the distribution system.

Low pressure storage is located usually at the well site and at atmospheric pressure (zero gauge pressure). By means of a high capacity pump, water is supplied from the low pressure storage to the distribution storage system. The pump used for raising the water into the high service system should be so sized that it will not be operated on short repeated cycles, but on operating cycles of from 15 to 60 minutes. In the design of the pumping facilities, the question of high pressure storage again must be considered because the capacity of the pumping unit is related to this storage capacity. It should be remembered that the suction lift of this pump will be very small, so that a low horsepower pump may be used.

Low pressure storage capacity, when used within a water system, makes it possible to utilize the maximum potential of the sources of supply. Low pressure should be based on two factors: well yield and daily demand of water by the community. Minimum capacities for low level storage tanks should be based on requirements given in Table XVIII.

The high service storage facilities to be used in conjunction with this low level storage should be adequate to meet the 20-minute flow demands as given on Page 52. The high capacity, high service pump which lifts the water from the low level storage tank to the high service storage system should have a capacity to supply a flow equal to 30 to 40 per cent of the instantaneous demand of the system. For example, assume that the daily demand of a community is 40,000 gallons per day. The instantaneous demand is 200 gpm. One well with 35-gpm yield supplies the system. The well will furnish over a 24-hour period 35 gpm times 1,440 minutes per day or 50,400 gallons of water. Therefore, the well must operate some $\frac{40,000}{50,400} = 0.794$ or 79.4 per cent of the day. The time interval of operation will be 79.4 times 24 hours or 19.1 hours per day to furnish this demand. Referring to Table XVIII, a low pressure storage tank equivalent in capacity to 60 per cent of the total daily water usage must be provided. Therefore, the capacity

## TABLE XVIII
## Low Level or Low Pressure Storage Requirements*

| Hours Per Day of Well Operation to Supply Demand | Percentage of Total Day for which Well Must be Operated | Percentage of Total Daily Demand Required in Low Pressure Storage |
|---|---|---|
| 16 | 66 | 30 |
| 17 | 71 | 40 |
| 18 | 75 | 50 |
| 19 | 79 | 60 |
| 20 | 83 | 80 |
| 21 | 87 | 100 |
| 22 | 91 | 120 |
| 23 | 95 | 130 |
| 24 | 100 | 150 |

*Provisions made for eight-hour pump repair.

of the low pressure storage tank will be in the amout of 60 per cent times 40,000 or 24,000 gallons.

The high service pump operating between the low pressure tank and the high pressure tank will have a capacity of 40 per cent of the instantaneous demand of 200 gpm. This will be:

Pump Capacity =
0.3 to 0.4 x Instantaneous Demand

or in this case will be 40 per cent times 200 gpm or 80 gpm. The equilizing flow in order to determine the capacity of the high service pressure tank for this system will be the instantaneous demand less the capacity of the high service pump or 200 gpm less 80 gpm equals to 120 gpm. From Table XIV is found that the actual capacity of the high service tank required is 9,600 gallons.

### D. Elevated Storage

Elevated storage is the most desirable type of storage for a community water system. This is because the water is readily available to the water system even in the event of power or mechanical failure of equipment. In the selection of the capacity of elevated storage for a water system, it is usually desirable to provide storage in the amount of from 50 to 100 per cent of daily usage. Elevated storage may be used in lieu of low pressure or high service pneumatic storage. It is customary to discharge the well water directly into the distribution system and to provide no other type of storage where adequate elevated storage is provided.

Of importance is the selection of the site for elevated tanks. These tanks should be located at high elevations within the system from the economics standpoint. Also the tanks should be located near the center of

the system or near the congested or large consumption areas so that there will be a tendency to equilize varying flow requirements and pressure differentials during the peak periods. As the community increases in size, then it will be necessary to utilize additional elevated tanks within the system. An elevated tank which is properly located will act as an additional well during peak periods when the draft on the system is exceptionally heavy.

### 2. Surface Water Sources

Storage requirements for surface water sources must be considered in view of the type of source and treatment being utilized for the water system.

### A. Unfiltered Water Sources

Where unfiltered water sources are utilized as water sources of supply, it is sometimes possible to use the raw water impounded storage as supplemental elevated storage provided that gravity flow is available. The total quantity of storage should be as previously discussed under ground water sources with the exception that further consideration should be given to the utilization of the raw storage.

### B. Surface Treatment Plants

Filtration plants are utilized in areas where there is a scarcity of ground water, or where the ground water is of inferior water quality, and in communities where the population or water-using industries have large water demands and thus can economically develop a surface supply. It can be roughly estimated that where community populations exceed 900 persons, that a surface water and treatment plant is economically feasible provided that the source of water supply is available. Storage for such communities is in the form of low-level or clear-water storage and elevated or high-service storage.

*(1) Low level or Clear-water Storage.* Low-level or clear-water storage for a filtration plant is usually located adjacent to the plant and finished water pumping station. The capacity of this storage reservoir should not be less than 50 per cent of the daily rated capacity of the filtration plant. The clear-water storage reservoir serves two purposes: First, it acts as a reserve for distribution storage, being readily available for use. Second, it serves as a factor in the planning of daily plant operation. In many areas, power costs are influenced by the charges based upon a power factor which means that it is more economical to operate the plant and pumping station during certain periods of the day when the power consumption of the community is at its lowest. Therefore, such operation can be adjusted and regulated in accordance with the storage available.

*(2) Elevated Storage.* Elevated storage is located in the distribution grid in relation to the water demand and fire protection. The total storage facilities of the clear water reservoir plus the elevated tanks should be equal to at least one day's storage. As much of the storage as is economically feasible, should be placed in elevated tanks. With the purpose of storage as follows, 25 per cent for emergency purposes, 15 per cent for equilizing purposes, and 60 per cent for fire reserve, the quantity of elevated storage should equal from 25 to 50 per cent of the total storage with an average suggested quantity of 40 per cent. Referring to Figure 12, it can be noted that 75,000 gallons

elevated storage is the recommended quantity to provide for fire protection for small communities. This rule should be that the elevated storage should be based on at least 75,000 gallons or one day's supply, which ever is greater, for small communities[2].

*(3) Fire Storage.* When fire flows are considered in the design or layout of water systems, two important factors enter into the picture. One of these factors is the ability of the distribution system to adequately carry the required flow of water to the desired areas where the flow is needed. The second is the adequacy of storage to provide the sustained flow for the period of time necessary to protect other property in addition to fighting one fire. Both of the above are dependent upon the population served by the water system and the value of the area to be served. Based on the population served, it can be assumed that the required flow will vary from around 500 gpm to several thousand gallons per minute, depending upon the population served. The curve represented in Figure 12 may be used for estimating storage on the population basis assuming that there will be several fire streams for a short period of time or one fire stream over a long period of time.

If the area is heavily industrialized, the National Bureau of Fire Underwriters Tables should be consulted[5].

When considering storage for fire flows, it is advisable to provide such storage in the form of elevated tanks so that it will be readily available to the system at all times.

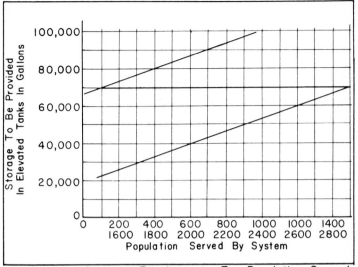

FIGURE 12.  Storage  Requirements  For  Population  Served.

## TABLE XIX
### Hydrant Distribution for Fire Flows

| Fire Flow Required GPM | Average Area Per Hydrant Square Feet | Fire Flow Required GPM | Average Area Per Hydrant Square Feet |
|---|---|---|---|
| 1,000 | 120,000 | 7,000 | 70,000 |
| 2,000 | 110,000 | 8,000 | 60,000 |
| 3,000 | 100,000 | 9,000 | 55,000 |
| 4,000 | 90,000 | 10,000 | 48,000 |
| 5,000 | 85,000 | 11,000 | 43,000 |
| 6,000 | 80,000 | 12,000 | 40,000 |

—From Permission of the National Board of Fire Underwriters.

## TABLE XX
## Required Flows for Fire Protection

| Population | Required Fire Flow for Average City (gpm) | Duration of Fire Flow (hours) |
|---|---|---|
| 1,000 | 1,000 | 4 |
| 1,500 | 1,250 | 5 |
| 2,000 | 1,500 | 6 |
| 3,000 | 1,750 | 7 |
| 4,000 | 2,000 | 8 |
| 5,000 | 2,250 | 9 |
| 6,000 | 2,500 | 10 |
| 10,000 | 3,000 | 10 |
| 13,000 | 3,500 | 10 |
| 17,000 | 4,000 | 10 |
| 22,000 | 4,500 | 10 |
| 27,000 | 5,000 | 10 |
| 33,000 | 5,500 | 10 |
| 40,000 | 6,000 | 10 |
| 55,000 | 7,000 | 10 |
| 75,000 | 8,000 | 10 |
| 95,000 | 9,000 | 10 |
| 120,000 | 10,000 | 10 |
| 150,000 | 11,000 | 10 |
| 200,000 | 12,000 | 10 |

—From Permission of the National Board of Fire Underwriters.

NOTE6: Over 200,000 population, a flow of 12,000 gallons with a reserve of 2,000 to 8,000 gallons per minute additional for a second fire is necessary. In residential areas, the required fire flows necessary are dependent upon the character and congestion of the buildings. In sections where low buildings predominate, flows of not less than 500 gallons per minute are needed. In sections where large buildings are located, up to 1,000 gallons per minute with four fire streams are required. Hotels, high value residences, etc., in densely congested areas, 1,500 to 3,000 gallons per minute are required to a maximum of 6,000 gallons per minute for the high value, densely congested areas.

# CHAPTER IV

# Distribution System

## General

This distribution system is as vital a part of the water system as either the source of supply or storage facilities. It is the part of the water system, which carries the finished product, water under pressure, to each consumer. In order to provide water to all consumers at all times, the distribution system must be properly designed to carry maximum instantaneous flows of the community. Inadequately designed systems may permit negative pressures to exist, allowing pollution to be siphoned or drawn into the system. An adequately designed system will always maintain positive pressures throughout the system to prevent the occurrence of back-siphonage.

The design and layout of the distribution system is the most complicated part of the entire water system. This difficulty arises from the fact that in small water systems, the individual habits of each consumer enter into the design criteria. Therefore, each water distribution system must be treated as an individual case so as to take into consideration the individualism of the consumer. Large water systems are much easier to design because of the fact that the instantaneous water using habits of the consumers tend to smooth out the great variations, therefore dependable criteria has been established on a per capita basis. Another important criteria concerning the design of large water systems is the fact that the facilities such as storage, pumps, distribution, etc., are designed to provide large and extensive fire flows throughout the entire community tend to make the individual domestic flows insignificant as far as variations in the instantaneous flows. This is not true in the case of the smaller water systems, for the individualism of each consumer creates large sources of error which may enter into calculations of design. The distribution system must therefore be designed to take in every possible variation, so that it will be adequate without over-designing from the economical standpoint. It is the intent of this chapter to set forth such design criteria and procedures so that in all cases the system will be approximately correct without the effect of grossly over-designing and the cost factors involved will not be unreasonable. Such design criteria is suggested below and may be applied to each individual layout to provide an adequate system. Procedure for using this criteria is as follows:

## 1. Small Water Systems with Domestic Water Only

In many instances, the developer of an area wishes to supply domestic water without any provisions for fire protection. The procedure for the design of such a system is as follows:

*Step 1.* The design of the distribution system should start with the service which is located fartherest from the source of supply or storage or supply service, and the design of pipe sizes should be calculated back to this point of supply from this extreme service location. This method enables

## TABLE XXI
## Maximum Instantaneous Flows for Residential Areas

| Number of Residences Served | Flow Per Residence in GPM | Number of Residences Served | Flow Per Residence in GPM |
|---|---|---|---|
| 1 (First) | 15.0 | 91-100 | 2.0 |
| 2-10* | 5.0 | 101-125 | 1.8 |
| 11-20** | 4.0 | 126-150 | 1.6 |
| 21-30 | 3.8 | 151-175 | 1.4 |
| 31-40 | 3.4 | 176-200 | 1.3 |
| 41-50 | 3.2 | 201-300 | 1.2 |
| 51-60 | 2.7 | 301-400 | 1.0 |
| 61-70 | 2.5 | 401-500 | 0.8 |
| 71-80 | 2.2 | 501-750 | 0.7 |
| 81-90 | 2.1 | 751-1,000 | 0.5 |

*Second, third, etc., through tenth residence served.
* *Eleventh, twelfth, etc., through twentieth residence served.

## TABLE XXII
## Maximum Instantaneous Flows for Commercial Areas

| Type of Business | GPM on Basis Shown |
|---|---|
| Barber Shop | 3.0 gpm per chair |
| Beauty Shop | 3.0 gpm per chair |
| Dentist Office | 4.0 gpm per chair |
| Department Store* | 1.0-2.0-3.0 gpm per employee |
| Drug Store | 5.0 gpm |
| With Fountain Service | add 6.0 gpm per fountain area |
| Serving Meals | add 2.0 gpm per seat |
| Industrial Plants** | 4.0 gpm plus 1.0 gpm per employee |
| Laundry | 30.0 gpm per 1,000 pounds clothes |
| Launderette | 8.0 gpm per unit |
| Meat Market, Super Market | 6.0 gpm per 2,500 sq. ft. floor area |
| Motel, Hotel | 4.0 gpm per unit |
| Office Building | 0.5 gpm per 100 sq. ft. floor area or 2.0 gpm per employee |
| Physicians Office | 3.0 gpm per examining room |
| Restaurant | 2.0 gpm per seat |
| Single Service | 6.0 to 20.0 gpm total |
| Drive-In | 2.0 to 7.0 gpm total |
| Service Station | 10.0 gpm per wash rack |
| Theatre | 0.2 gpm per seat |
| Drive-In | 0.2 gpm per car space |
| Other Establishments*** | Estimate at 4.0 gpm each |

*Including customer service.
* *Not including process water.
* * *Non-water using establishments.

an ample supply to the system extremities.

*Step 2.* The desired water flow for the fartherest residence or service should be in accordance with calculations of Tables XXI, XXII, and XXIII. The quantity of 15 gallons per minute and an available pressure of at least 30 pounds per square inch at the street service connection.

*Step 3.* Water usage within the community should be based upon the maximum instantaneous flows and the distribution system design should be based on this criteria using these maxima values. Maximum instantaneous flows within a community for which the distribution system should be based, are given in Tables XXI, XXII, and XIII.

*Step 4.* As water flows through a pipeline, the roughness and other characteristics of the pipe will decrease the velocity and the discharge of the quantity of water. This interference of flow is known as pipe "friction." It may be said that friction within the pipe causes "drag" along the pipe walls thus decreasing the velocity, pressure head, and discharge. Friction within the smaller pipes is much more significant because of the smaller carrying capacity of the pipe due to its small area. Friction loss within a pipe is usually expressed in terms of feet loss per 1,000 feet of length of pipe. Calculations are then made concerning the pressure head, total head loss and discharge of pipe.

## TABLE XXIII
## Maximum Instantaneous Flows for Institutions

| Type of Institution | Basis of Flow, GPM |
|---|---|
| Boarding Schools, Colleges | 2.0 gpm per student |
| Churches | 0.4 gpm per member |
| Clubs: Country, Civic | 0.6 gpm per member |
| Hospitals | 4.0 gpm per bed |
| Nursing Homes | 2.0 gpm per bed |
| Prisons | 3.0 gpm per inmate |
| Rooming Houses | Same as Residential* |

### SCHOOLS: DAY, ELEMENTARY, JUNIOR, SENIOR HIGH

| Number of Students | GPM Per Student | Number of Students | GPM Per Student |
|---|---|---|---|
| 0-50 | 2.00 | 800 | 1.38 |
| 100 | 1.90 | 900 | 1.32 |
| 200 | 1.88 | 1,000 | 1.20 |
| 300 | 1.80 | 1,200 | 1.04 |
| 400 | 1.72 | 1,400 | 0.86 |
| 500 | 1.64 | 1,600 | 0.70 |
| 600 | 1.56 | 1,800 | 0.54 |
| 700 | 1.44 | 2,000 | 0.40 |

*Each unit of an apartment building should be considered as an individual residence.

However, to simplify calculations, Tables XXIV, XXV, XXVI, and XXVII are given to indicate flows in gallons per minute for known lengths of different diameter pipes under varied pressures ranging from 30 to 60 pounds per square inch. The flows given in these Tables are for pipes which are 20 years old, thus taking into consideration the additional friction loss which tends to decrease the flow through the pipe over that designated period due to corrosion, encrustation, increased pipe roughness, etc.

To utilize these tables, two factors must be established; and first of all, is the pressure for which the system is to be operated. In other words, the desired operating pressure of the system, whether 30, 40, 50, or 60

pounds per square inch, which may be stated in terms of the height of the elevated tank above the highest plumbing fixture or the gauge setting for pneumatic storage tank. The relationship between pressure and height of water elevation is as follows:

| Pressure in Pounds Per Square Inch | Height in Feet Above Datum Plant |
|---|---|
| 30 | 69.30 |
| 40 | 92.40 |
| 50 | 115.50 |
| 60 | 138.60 |

If the storage is not located at the height point, then for a known pressure, the height of the elevated tank may be calculated as follows to give the desired pressures on the system:

$$\begin{array}{l}\text{Height of} \\ \text{Elevated Storage} \\ \text{Tank, Feet}\end{array} = 2.31 \times \begin{array}{l}\text{Desired} \\ \text{Pressure} \\ \text{in PSI}\end{array} + \begin{array}{l}\text{Difference} \\ \text{in Ground} \\ \text{Elevation of Tank} \\ \text{Site and} \\ \text{Highest Point}\end{array} + \begin{array}{l}\text{Height of} \\ \text{Building} \\ \text{Plumbing at} \\ \text{this Highest} \\ \text{Point}\end{array}$$

---

An example to illustrate the use of this formula is as follows: A water system is to be designed to operate under a pressure of 40 pounds per square inch. The ground elevation of the tank site is 100 feet. The highest ground elevation within the community is 120 feet. At the highest point, a multi-story building is to be located with the height of the plumbing fixtures in the building to be 24 feet. At what elevation should the operating level of the tank be constructed?

$$\begin{array}{l}\text{Height} \\ \text{of Elevated} \\ \text{Tank, Feet}\end{array} = 2.31 \times \begin{array}{l}\text{Desired} \\ \text{Pressure}\end{array} + \begin{array}{l}\text{Difference in} \\ \text{Ground Elevation} \\ \text{of Tank Site and} \\ \text{Highest Point}\end{array} + \begin{array}{l}\text{Height of} \\ \text{Plumbing Fixtures} \\ \text{at Highest} \\ \text{Point}\end{array}$$

$$= 2.31 \times 40 \quad + \quad 20 \quad + \quad 24$$

$$= 136.4 \text{ Feet}$$

(Note: Reduction in Pipe Discharge due to pipe friction is considered in Tables.)

If instead of elevated storage facilities, a pneumatic storage tank is to be used at the tank site, the operating pressure for this tank would be:

$$\text{Average Operating Pressure of Pneumatic Storage Tank, PSI} = \frac{\text{Height of Elevated Tank as Calculated}}{2.31}$$

$$= \frac{136.4}{2.31}$$

$$= 59 \text{ Pounds Per Square Inch}$$

A second factor is the consideration of pipe composition. Pipes of various compositions have different flow characteristics. These are variations in pipe smoothness, corrosive qualities, tuberculation, etc., all of which to some extent influence the carrying capacity of pipes. For use with Tables XXIV, XXV, XXVI, and XXVII are the following coefficients by which corrections may be made if one so desires:

Pipe Coefficients

| Pipe Material | Coefficient |
|---|---|
| Metallic Pipe, Coated | 140 |
| Metallic Pipe, Uncoated, New | 140 |
| Metallic Pipe, Uncoated, 20 years | 100 |
| Non-metallic Pipe | 140 |

These coefficients, when multiplied by the flows given within the following tables, will give the approximate corrected flow. If one uses the flows given within these tables, the additional factors of safety are the differences within the proper coefficients.

## TABLE XXIV
### Pipe Discharges in Gallons Per Minute for Different Diameter Pipe for Known Lengths and Under a Pressure of 30 Pounds Per Square Inch (Age of Pipe = 20 Years)

| Pipe Size Inches | Length of Pipe in Feet | | | | | | | |
|---|---|---|---|---|---|---|---|---|
| | 100 | 200 | 300 | 400 | 500 | 600 | 700 | 800 |
| 1½ | 85 | 54 | 44 | 37 | 34 | 31 | 30 | 29 |
| 2 | 170 | 110 | 85 | 74 | 64 | 59 | 56 | 54 |
| 2½ | 255 | 178 | 135 | 118 | 102 | 94 | 89 | 85 |
| 3 | 510 | 348 | 275 | 246 | 212 | 198 | 186 | 173 |
| 4 | 1,018 | 618 | 482 | 415 | 348 | 322 | 297 | 280 |
| 6 | 2,710 | 2,030 | 1,440 | 1,230 | 1,100 | 1,000 | 926 | 850 |
| 8 | 6,020 | 3,980 | 3,050 | 2,460 | 2,200 | 1,950 | 1,780 | 1,700 |
| 10 | 11,000 | 6,950 | 5,260 | 4,420 | 3,730 | 3,390 | 3,050 | 2,900 |
| 12 | 15,680 | 9,500 | 7,460 | 6,180 | 5,350 | 4,750 | 4,325 | 4,060 |

| Pipe Size Inches | Length of Pipe in Feet | | | | | | | |
|---|---|---|---|---|---|---|---|---|
| | 900 | 1,000 | 1,200 | 1,400 | 1,600 | 1,800 | 2,000 | 2,200 |
| 1½ | 28 | 27 | 25 | 23 | 22 | 20 | 18 | 17 |
| 2 | 51 | 48 | 43 | 39 | 36 | 33 | 30 | 27 |
| 2½ | 80 | 75 | 67 | 60 | 52 | 48 | 44 | 38 |
| 3 | 161 | 153 | 131 | 115 | 102 | 91 | 83 | 73 |
| 4 | 260 | 250 | 238 | 220 | 204 | 186 | 170 | 157 |
| 6 | 805 | 746 | 678 | 628 | 560 | 509 | 458 | 416 |
| 8 | 1,610 | 1,528 | 1,356 | 1,185 | 1,060 | 975 | 890 | 797 |
| 10 | 2,770 | 2,540 | 2,290 | 2,120 | 1,860 | 1,700 | 1,525 | 1,355 |
| 12 | 3,810 | 3,650 | 3,400 | 3,050 | 2,800 | 2,540 | 2,290 | 2,030 |

| Pipe Size Inches | Length of Pipe in Feet | | | | | | | |
|---|---|---|---|---|---|---|---|---|
| | 2,500 | 2,750 | 3,000 | 3,500 | 4,000 | 4,500 | 5,000 | 5,500 |
| 1½ | 15 | 14 | 12 | — | — | — | — | — |
| 2 | 25 | 23 | 21 | 18 | 15 | 12 | — | — |
| 2½ | 36 | 32 | 29 | 25 | 21 | 18 | 15 | 12 |
| 3 | 67 | 60 | 56 | 46 | 40 | 32 | 26 | 20 |
| 4 | 144 | 131 | 119 | 97 | 81 | 68 | 55 | 43 |
| 6 | 365 | 331 | 297 | 241 | 199 | 161 | 131 | 102 |
| 8 | 712 | 636 | 585 | 458 | 374 | 306 | 255 | 221 |
| 10 | 1,185 | 1,060 | 975 | 788 | 670 | 525 | 440 | 381 |
| 12 | 1,780 | 1,570 | 1,480 | 1,140 | 975 | 780 | 660 | 560 |

| Pipe Size Inches | Length of Pipe in Feet | | | |
|---|---|---|---|---|
| | 6,000 | 6,500 | 7,000 | 8,000 |
| 1½ | — | — | — | — |
| 2 | — | — | — | — |
| 2½ | — | — | — | — |
| 3 | 17 | 14 | — | — |
| 4 | 40 | 32 | 27 | 19 |
| 6 | 93 | 76 | 68 | 45 |
| 8 | 195 | 170 | 135 | 76 |
| 10 | 313 | 252 | 212 | 148 |
| 12 | 465 | 398 | 339 | 237 |

## TABLE XXV
## Pipe Discharges in Gallons Per Minute for Different Diameter Pipe for Known Lengths and Under a Pressure of 40 Pounds Per Square Inch (Age of Pipe = 20 years

| Pipe Size Inches | Length of Pipe in Feet | | | | | | | |
|---|---|---|---|---|---|---|---|---|
| | 100 | 200 | 300 | 400 | 500 | 600 | 700 | 800 |
| 1½ | 100 | 64 | 52 | 44 | 40 | 37 | 36 | 35 |
| 2 | 200 | 130 | 100 | 86 | 76 | 70 | 66 | 64 |
| 2½ | 300 | 210 | 160 | 140 | 120 | 110 | 105 | 100 |
| 3 | 600 | 410 | 325 | 290 | 250 | 235 | 220 | 205 |
| 4 | 1,200 | 730 | 580 | 490 | 410 | 380 | 350 | 330 |
| 6 | 3,200 | 2,400 | 1,700 | 1,450 | 1,300 | 1,180 | 1,090 | 1,000 |
| 8 | 7,100 | 4,700 | 3,600 | 2,900 | 2,600 | 2,300 | 2,100 | 2,000 |
| 10 | 13,000 | 8,200 | 6,200 | 5,200 | 4,400 | 4,000 | 3,600 | 3,300 |
| 12 | 18,500 | 11,200 | 8,800 | 7,300 | 6,300 | 5,600 | 5,100 | 4,800 |

| Pipe Size Inches | Length of Pipe in Feet | | | | | | | |
|---|---|---|---|---|---|---|---|---|
| | 900 | 1,000 | 1,200 | 1,400 | 1,600 | 1,800 | 2,000 | 2,250 |
| 1½ | 33 | 32 | 30 | 27 | 26 | 23 | 22 | 20 |
| 2 | 60 | 57 | 51 | 46 | 43 | 39 | 36 | 32 |
| 2½ | 94 | 88 | 79 | 71 | 62 | 57 | 52 | 45 |
| 3 | 190 | 180 | 155 | 136 | 120 | 108 | 98 | 86 |
| 4 | 310 | 300 | 280 | 260 | 240 | 220 | 200 | 185 |
| 6 | 950 | 880 | 800 | 740 | 660 | 600 | 540 | 490 |
| 8 | 1,900 | 1,800 | 1,600 | 1,400 | 1,250 | 1,150 | 1,050 | 940 |
| 10 | 3,200 | 3,000 | 2,700 | 2,500 | 2,200 | 2,000 | 1,800 | 1,600 |
| 12 | 4,500 | 4,300 | 3,900 | 3,600 | 3,300 | 3,000 | 2,700 | 2,400 |

| Pipe Size Inches | Length of Pipe in Feet | | | | | | | |
|---|---|---|---|---|---|---|---|---|
| | 2,500 | 2,750 | 3,000 | 3,500 | 4,000 | 4,500 | 5,000 | 5,500 |
| 1½ | 18 | 17 | 15 | — | — | — | — | — |
| 2 | 30 | 27 | 25 | 21 | 18 | — | — | — |
| 2½ | 42 | 38 | 35 | 30 | 25 | 21 | 18 | — |
| 3 | 79 | 71 | 66 | 55 | 47 | 38 | 31 | 24 |
| 4 | 170 | 155 | 140 | 115 | 96 | 80 | 65 | 51 |
| 6 | 430 | 390 | 350 | 285 | 235 | 190 | 155 | 120 |
| 8 | 840 | 750 | 690 | 540 | 440 | 360 | 300 | 260 |
| 10 | 1,400 | 1,250 | 1,150 | 930 | 790 | 620 | 520 | 450 |
| 12 | 2,100 | 1,850 | 1,750 | 1,350 | 1,150 | 920 | 780 | 660 |

| Pipe Size Inches | Length of Pipe in Feet | | | |
|---|---|---|---|---|
| | 6,000 | 6,500 | 7,000 | 8,000 |
| 1½ | — | — | — | — |
| 2 | — | — | — | — |
| 2½ | — | — | — | — |
| 3 | 20 | — | — | — |
| 4 | 48 | 38 | 32 | 23 |
| 6 | 110 | 90 | 80 | 54 |
| 8 | 230 | 200 | 160 | 110 |
| 10 | 370 | 310 | 250 | 175 |
| 12 | 550 | 470 | 400 | 280 |

## TABLE XXVI
### Pipe Discharges in Gallons Per Minute for Different Diameter Pipe for Known Lengths and Under a Pressure of 50 Pounds Per Square Inch (Age of Pipe = 20 Years)

| Pipe Size Inches | Length of Pipe in Feet | | | | | | | |
|---|---|---|---|---|---|---|---|---|
| | 100 | 200 | 300 | 400 | 500 | 600 | 700 | 800 |
| 1½ | 113 | 72 | 59 | 50 | 45 | 42 | 41 | 39 |
| 2 | 227 | 147 | 113 | 97 | 86 | 80 | 75 | 73 |
| 2½ | 340 | 238 | 181 | 159 | 136 | 125 | 119 | 113 |
| 3 | 682 | 455 | 370 | 330 | 284 | 267 | 250 | 232 |
| 4 | 1,360 | 830 | 657 | 556 | 465 | 432 | 397 | 374 |
| 6 | 3,630 | 2,720 | 1,930 | 1,645 | 1,475 | 1,340 | 1,238 | 1,138 |
| 8 | 8,060 | 5,340 | 4,100 | 3,300 | 2,960 | 2,620 | 2,390 | 2,280 |
| 10 | 14,800 | 9,300 | 7.040 | 5,900 | 4,990 | 4,540 | 4,080 | 3,750 |
| 12 | 21,000 | 12,700 | 9,975 | 8,280 | 7,150 | 6,350 | 5,785 | 5,450 |

| Pipe Size Inches | Length of Pipe in Feet | | | | | | | |
|---|---|---|---|---|---|---|---|---|
| | 900 | 1,000 | 1,200 | 1,400 | 1,600 | 1,800 | 2,000 | 2,200 |
| 1½ | 37 | 36 | 34 | 30 | 29 | 26 | 25 | 22 |
| 2 | 69 | 64 | 58 | 52 | 48 | 44 | 40 | 36 |
| 2½ | 106 | 99 | 89 | 80 | 70 | 64 | 59 | 51 |
| 3 | 215 | 204 | 176 | 154 | 136 | 122 | 111 | 97 |
| 4 | 351 | 340 | 318 | 295 | 272 | 248 | 226 | 210 |
| 6 | 1,075 | 996 | 905 | 840 | 748 | 680 | 612 | 555 |
| 8 | 2,150 | 2,040 | 1,815 | 1,585 | 1,418 | 1,305 | 1,190 | 1,060 |
| 10 | 3,630 | 3,400 | 3,160 | 2,830 | 2,495 | 2,270 | 2,040 | 1,815 |
| 12 | 5,100 | 4,870 | 4,430 | 4,080 | 3,740 | 3,400 | 3,040 | 2,720 |

| Pipe Size Inches | Length of Pipe in Feet | | | | | | | |
|---|---|---|---|---|---|---|---|---|
| | 2,500 | 2,750 | 3,000 | 3,500 | 4,000 | 4,500 | 5,000 | 5,500 |
| 1½ | 20 | 19 | 17 | 15 | 12 | — | — | — |
| 2 | 34 | 30 | 28 | 24 | 20 | 15 | 12 | — |
| 2½ | 47 | 43 | 39 | 34 | 28 | 24 | 20 | 16 |
| 3 | 89 | 80 | 75 | 62 | 53 | 43 | 35 | 27 |
| 4 | 193 | 176 | 159 | 131 | 109 | 91 | 73 | 58 |
| 6 | 488 | 433 | 397 | 323 | 267 | 216 | 176 | 136 |
| 8 | 955 | 852 | 784 | 614 | 500 | 408 | 340 | 295 |
| 10 | 1,590 | 1,420 | 1,305 | 1,055 | 897 | 704 | 590 | 510 |
| 12 | 2,380 | 2,100 | 1,985 | 1,530 | 1,305 | 1,045 | 885 | 750 |

| Pipe Size Inches | Length of Pipe in Feet | | | |
|---|---|---|---|---|
| | 6,000 | 6,500 | 7,000 | 8,000 |
| 1½ | — | — | — | — |
| 2 | — | — | — | — |
| 2½ | 12 | — | — | — |
| 3 | 22 | 17 | 12 | — |
| 4 | 54 | 43 | 36 | 26 |
| 6 | 125 | 102 | 90 | 61 |
| 8 | 261 | 227 | 183 | 125 |
| 10 | 420 | 352 | 284 | 198 |
| 12 | 625 | 534 | 454 | 318 |

## TABLE XXVII
### Pipe Discharges in Gallons Per Minute for Different Diameter Pipe for Known Lengths and Under a Pressure of 60 Pounds Per Square Inch (Age of Pipe = 20 Years)

| Pipe Size Inches | Length of Pipe in Feet | | | | | | | |
|---|---|---|---|---|---|---|---|---|
| | 100 | 200 | 300 | 400 | 500 | 600 | 700 | 800 |
| 1½ | 122 | 78 | 63 | 53 | 48 | 45 | 44 | 42 |
| 2 | 244 | 158 | 122 | 105 | 93 | 85 | 80 | 78 |
| 2½ | 366 | 256 | 195 | 171 | 146 | 134 | 128 | 122 |
| 3 | 732 | 500 | 395 | 354 | 305 | 286 | 268 | 250 |
| 4 | 1,460 | 890 | 706 | 596 | 500 | 463 | 427 | 403 |
| 6 | 3,900 | 2,920 | 2,070 | 1,770 | 1,585 | 1,440 | 1,330 | 1,220 |
| 8 | 8,650 | 5,830 | 4,380 | 3,540 | 3,170 | 2,805 | 2,560 | 2,440 |
| 10 | 15,820 | 9,980 | 7,550 | 6,340 | 5,370 | 4,880 | 4,380 | 4,030 |
| 12 | 22,500 | 13,650 | 10,750 | 8,900 | 7,680 | 6,830 | 6,250 | 5,850 |

| Pipe Size Inches | Length of Pipe in Feet | | | | | | | |
|---|---|---|---|---|---|---|---|---|
| | 900 | 1,000 | 1,200 | 1,400 | 1,600 | 1,800 | 2,000 | 2,250 |
| 1½ | 40 | 39 | 36 | 33 | 31 | 28 | 26 | 24 |
| 2 | 73 | 69 | 62 | 56 | 52 | 47 | 44 | 39 |
| 2½ | 114 | 107 | 96 | 86 | 75 | 69 | 63 | 55 |
| 3 | 232 | 219 | 189 | 166 | 146 | 132 | 119 | 105 |
| 4 | 372 | 366 | 341 | 316 | 243 | 268 | 244 | 226 |
| 6 | 1,160 | 1,075 | 975 | 905 | 807 | 743 | 661 | 598 |
| 8 | 2,320 | 2,200 | 1,955 | 1,712 | 1,528 | 1,406 | 1,284 | 1,148 |
| 10 | 3,910 | 3,670 | 3,300 | 3,060 | 2,690 | 2,445 | 2,200 | 1,955 |
| 12 | 5,500 | 5,260 | 4,770 | 4,280 | 4,030 | 3,670 | 3,300 | 2,930 |

| Pipe Size Inches | Length of Pipe in Feet | | | | | | | |
|---|---|---|---|---|---|---|---|---|
| | 2,500 | 2,750 | 3,000 | 3,500 | 4,000 | 4,500 | 5,000 | 5,500 |
| 1½ | 22 | 20 | 18 | 15 | — | — | — | — |
| 2 | 36 | 33 | 30 | 25 | 22 | 17 | — | — |
| 2½ | 51 | 46 | 42 | 36 | 30 | 25 | 21 | 17 |
| 3 | 96 | 86 | 80 | 67 | 57 | 46 | 38 | 29 |
| 4 | 208 | 189 | 171 | 140 | 117 | 97 | 79 | 62 |
| 6 | 525 | 476 | 426 | 346 | 285 | 232 | 189 | 146 |
| 8 | 1,025 | 916 | 843 | 670 | 538 | 440 | 366 | 317 |
| 10 | 1,710 | 1,525 | 1,405 | 1,135 | 966 | 758 | 634 | 548 |
| 12 | 2,570 | 2,260 | 2,140 | 1,650 | 1,405 | 1,125 | 950 | 805 |

| Pipe Size Inches | Length of Pipe in Feet | | | |
|---|---|---|---|---|
| | 6,000 | 6,500 | 7,000 | 8,000 |
| 1½ | — | — | — | — |
| 2 | — | — | — | — |
| 2½ | — | — | — | — |
| 3 | 24 | 18 | — | — |
| 4 | 58 | 46 | 39 | 28 |
| 6 | 134 | 110 | 97 | 67 |
| 8 | 280 | 244 | 195 | 134 |
| 10 | 452 | 378 | 305 | 213 |
| 12 | 670 | 572 | 488 | 341 |

The four-step procedure as previously outlined may be applied to any community water system as follows:

1. Make a complete layout of the community. This layout should be to a scale of approximately 100 feet equal to one inch so that scaling may be used for estimation purposes. On this layout, the residences, businesses,

XXIII, and place this usage on plan as made in *Step 1* above starting with the fartherest lot from the source of supply or storage if large storage tanks are provided on the system. Therefore, the example in Number 1 above would be as follows:

From Table XXI: Lot Number 7 would have a usage of 15 gpm; Lots

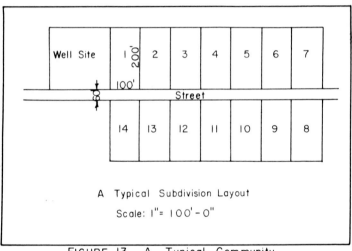

Well Site | 1 | 2 | 3 | 4 | 5 | 6 | 7
200'
100'
60'
Street
14 | 13 | 12 | 11 | 10 | 9 | 8

A Typical Subdivision Layout

Scale: 1" = 100'-0"

FIGURE 13. A Typical Community.

streets, proposed well sites, proposed storage sites, etc., should be indicated. An example of this would be the community shown in Figure 13. In this community are to be 14 lots, each lot to be sized 100 feet by 200 feet depth and fronting on a 60-foot street easement which provides for sidewalk areas.

2. Indicate water usage for each lot from Tables XXI, XXII, and

6, 5, 4, 3, 8, 9, 10, 11 will have a water usage of five gpm each; and Lots 2, 1, 12, 13, 14 will have a water usage of four gpm each.

3. Place this water usage on a scale of 100 feet equal to one inch starting with the fartherest service and working back to the source of supply. At each 100 foot interval, indicate the total water requirement to that point.

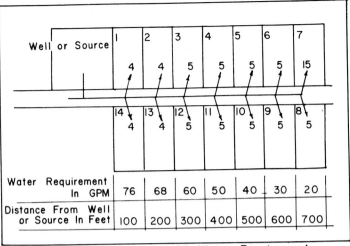

FIGURE 14. Summary Of Water Requirements.

4. Using Table XXV, determine the size of pipe required for this subdivision.

| Distance from Well Site or Source of Supply | 0' | 100' | 200' | 300' | 400' | 500' | 600' | 700' |
|---|---|---|---|---|---|---|---|---|
| Water Requirements at above known distances from Well or Source of Supply in GPM | 76 | 76 | 68 | 60 | 50 | 40 | 30 | 20 |
| Trial and Error Selection of Pipe Size. A two-inch pipe will supply the following flow expressed in GPM at known distance from Well or Source of Supply | | 200 | 130 | 100 | 86 | 76 | 70 | 66 |

A two-inch pipe will be more than adequate to supply this water system. Typical layout for this water system is given in Figure 15.

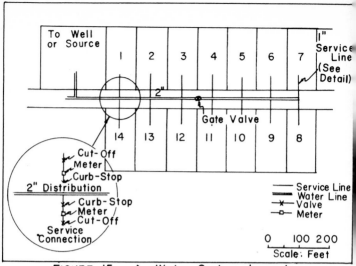

FIGURE 15.   A  Water  System  Layout.

If the above community were divided into 200-foot lots rather than 100-foot lots, then the solution would be, following the same steps as outlined above, as follows:

1. Layout of community subdivision to a scale of 100 feet equal to one inch:

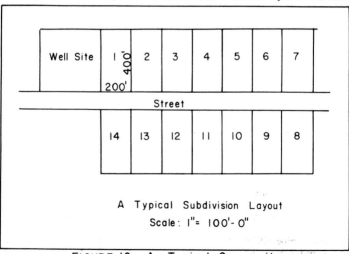

A  Typical  Subdivision  Layout
Scale:  1"= 100'- 0"

FIGURE 16.   A  Typical  Community.

2. Water requirements to be calculated from Tables XXI, XXII, and XXIII. In this case will be the same as above example.

3. Placing requirements on layout of 100 feet equal to one inch.

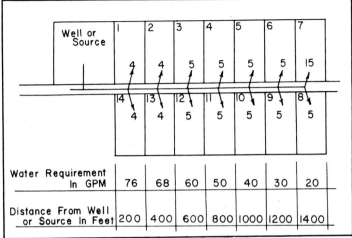

FIGURE 17. Summary Of Water Requirements.

4. Selection of Pipe Size to use from Table XXV:

| Distance from Well Site or Source of Supply | 0' | 200' | 400' | 600' | 800' | 1,000' | 1,200' | 1,400' |
|---|---|---|---|---|---|---|---|---|
| Water Requirements at above known distances from Well or Source of Supply in GPM | 76 | 76 | 68 | 60 | 50 | 40 | 30 | 20 |
| Trial and Error Selection of Pipe Size. A two-inch pipe will supply the following flow expressed in GPM at known distances from Well or Source of Supply | | 130 | 86 | 70 | 64 | 57 | 51 | 46 |

Therefore, it can be seen that a two-inch pipe is adequate to supply this community water system. It is suggested that for community water systems, that the two-inch pipe be used as a minimum pipe size where it is not desired to provide fire protection. The two-inch pipe should be minimum because of its large carrying capacity with smaller loss during the periods of high demand.

To illustrate a system where a change in pipe size is warranted to adequately supply the demand, the following example will indicate such:

1. Layout of community:

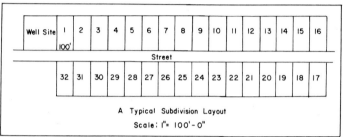

FIGURE 18. A Typical Community.

2. Water requirements from Table XVI:
Lot 16 ........................................ 15.0 gpm
Lots 15, 14, 13, 12, 17, 18, 19, 20, 21 ............... 5.0 gpm each
Lots 11, 10, 9, 8, 7, 22, 23, 24, 25, 26 ............... 4.0 gpm each
Lots 6, 5, 4, 3, 2, 27, 28 29, 30, 31 ................. 3.8 gpm each
Lots 1, 2 ..................................... 3.4 gpm each

3. Indicating water requirements on scaled layout:

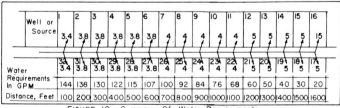

FIGURE 19. Summary Of Water Requirements.

4. Selection of pipe sizes for use from Table XXV:

| Distance from Well Site or Source of Supply | 0' | 100' | 200' | 300' | 400' | 500' | 600' | 700' | 800' | 900' | 1,000' | 1,100' | 1,200' | 1,300' | 1,400' | 1,500' | 1,600' |
|---|---|---|---|---|---|---|---|---|---|---|---|---|---|---|---|---|---|
| Water Requirements at above known Distances from Well Site or Source of Supply, In GPM | 144 | 144 | 138 | 130 | 122 | 115 | 107 | 100 | 92 | 84 | 76 | 68 | 60 | 50 | 40 | 30 | 20 |
| **Trial and Error Selection of Pipe Size:** | | | | | | | | | | | | | | | | | |
| Supply in GPM of two-inch pipe from Point 0' | | 200 | 130 | Not Adequate | | | | | | | | | | | | | |
| Supply in GPM of two-inch pipe from Point 100' | | | 200 | 130 | 100 | Not Adequate | | | | | | | | | | | |
| Supply in GPM of two-inch pipe from Point 200' | | | | 200 | 130 | 100 | Not Adequate | | | | | | | | | | |
| Supply in GPM of two-inch pipe from Point 300' | | | | | 200 | 130 | 100 | Not Adequate | | | | | | | | | |
| Supply in GPM of two-inch pipe from Point 400' | | | | | | 200 | 130 | 100 | 86 | Not Adequate | | | | | | | |
| Supply in GPM of two-inch pipe from Point 500' | | | | | | | 200 | 130 | 100 | 86 | 76 | 70 | 66 | 64 | 60 | 57 | 51 |
| Supply in GPM of three-inch pipe from Point 0' | 600 | 410 | 325 | 290 | 250 | 235 * | | | | | | | | | | | |

It can be seen that the two-inch pipe is adequate to supply the needs of the community starting at a distance of 500 feet from the Well Site or Source of Supply. At that point, the two-inch is capable of supplying the 107 gpm which is adequately supplied by the three-inch pipe.

The three-inch pipe is adequate to provide the necessary flow from the Well or Source of Supply to a point 500 feet from Well Site or Source of Supply.

*Note: At this point, the larger pipe should be adequate to supply the maximum flow of the smaller pipe which in this case is 200 gpm.

Therefore, this water system will be layout as indicated in Figure 20.

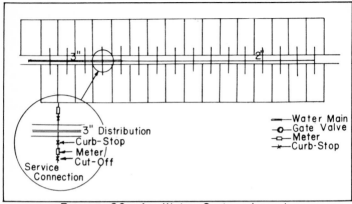

FIGURE 20. A Water System Layout.

## A. Complex Distribution Systems

Water distribution systems may be considered complex, because it is possible to loop and reinforce the system so that water may be fed to one point from more than one direction.

The Loop is considered a means of providing a greater flow to specific locations within the distribution system. The loop is formed in a distribution system when the system is laid out in such a way that the supply may be brought to the consumer from more than one direction. The hydraulic design of this type system is very complicated. Therefore, for simplicity of design, certain basic assumptions are made concerning adequate flow to the central portion of the distribution system. These assumptions are that (1) the last residence or consumer may receive water flow from each direction, and (2) the last residence or consumer served within the loop as in (1) above is considered to be the end of each system as far as design purposes are concerned even

though the system is continuous. In reality, the flow and direction of flow within such a system may be from either or both directions and are dependent upon many factors. Therefore, for simplicity, loop systems are designed on the basis of two independent distribution systems.

There are several advantages to providing loops in water systems. The first is that the loop provides a greater flow at all times throughout the system. Second, it eliminates dead ends within the system thus preventing stagnation or deterioration of the water quality at the extreme ends of the system. And third, it allows for uninterrupted water service in large systems during periods of repairs, breaks, etc., at which time only small sections may be taken out of operation until repairs are completed.

The design of the loop system is suggested as follows:

*Step 1.* A detailed layout of the subdivision or community to be served should be made.

*Step 2.* Select a point so that it may be assumed that the water may be provided by each leg or portion of the loop.

*Step 3.* Design each leg or portion of the loop as if it were a separate system.

The following illustration for a community is given and the above steps are followed in the design of the water system:

*Step 1.* Detailed layout of community to be served by system.

*Step 2.* Select Lot Number 26 as the consumer to be supplied from

each portion of the loop. The design of the water system will then be along the following steps:

    Pipeline C to B.
    Pipeline C to D.
    Pipeline E to D.
    Pipeline D to B.
    Pipeline B to A (Well or
        Source of Supply).

It must be remembered that the pipelines must be designed from the fartherest point with progression to the well or source of supply so that adequate flows along the pipeline may be had.

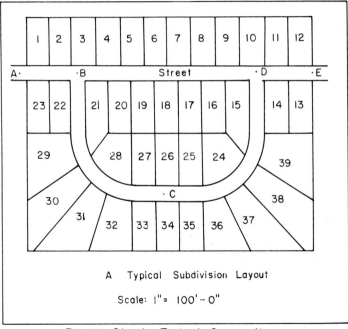

A Typical Subdivision Layout

Scale: 1" = 100' - 0"

FIGURE 21. A Typical Community.

*Step 3.* Layout to scale and design each pipeline individually as outlined in Step 2.

    a. Layout Scale of Point B to Point C at one inch equal to 100 feet.

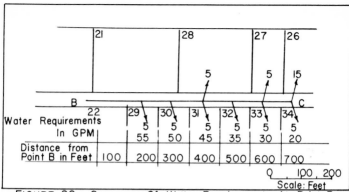

FIGURE 22. Summary Of Water Requirements At Point B.

b. Determine water requirements at distances from Point B to Point C on the following basis:

Lot 26 . . . . . . . . . . . . . . . . . . . . . . . . . . . . . . @ 15.0 gpm = 15.0 gpm

Lots 34, 27, 28, 33, 32, 31, 30, 29 . . . . . . . . . @ 5.0 gpm each = 40.0 gpm
_____

   At Point B . . . . . . . . . . . . . . . . . Total Water Requirement = 55.0 gpm

Determine Pipe Size:

| Distance from Point B, Feet | 0' | 100' | 200' | 300' | 400' | 500' | 600' | 700' |
|---|---|---|---|---|---|---|---|---|
| Water Requirements at Above Distances from Point B in GPM | 55 | 55 | 55 | 50 | 45 | 35 | 30 | 20 |
| Supply of two-inch Pipe Starting at Point B for Above Distances, Flow in GPM | | 200 | 130 | 100 | 86 | 76 | 70 | 66 |

A two-inch pipe is adequate to supply this section of the system.

c. Layout to scale of one inch equal to 100 feet, Point D to Point C.

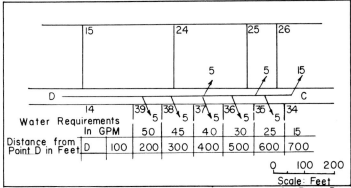

FIGURE 23. Summary Of Water Requirements At Point D

d. Determine water requirements at distances from Point D to Point C on the following basis:

| | |
|---|---|
| Lot 26 ................................. @ 15.0 gpm | = 15.0 gpm |
| Lots 25, 35, 36, 24, 37, 38, 39 ............... 5.0 gqm each | = 35.0 gpm |
| Total Water Requirement to Point D .................. | = 50.0 gpm |

Determine Pipe Size:

| Distance from Point D, Feet | 0' | 100' | 200' | 300' | 400' | 500' | 600' | 700' |
|---|---|---|---|---|---|---|---|---|
| Water Requirements at Above Distances from Point D in GPM | 50 | 50 | 50 | 45 | 40 | 30 | 25 | 15 |
| Supply of two-inch pipe starting at Point D for above Distances Follow in GPM | | 200 | 130 | 100 | 86 | 76 | 70 | 66 |

A two-inch pipe is adequate to supply this section of the system.

For Pipeline D to E, only four services, requiring a total flow of 30 gpm, are to be served. Therefore a two-inch pipeline will adequately serve this short section of the distribution system without going into greater detail.

e. Layout to a scale of one inch equal to 100 feet, pipeline section indicated as Point B to Point D.

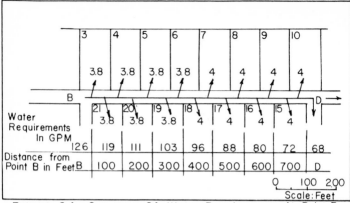

FIGURE 24. Summary Of Water Requirements At Point B.

Water flowing through the pipeline from Point B to Point D, must not only supply the water requirements along this segment, but must also supply the requirements of Pipelines D to C and D to E.

f. Determine water requirements at distances from Point B to Point D on the following basis:

It is necessary to recalculate the totals to Point D of Pipelines D to C and D to E because of the fact that the over-all water usage will decrease as the total number of users increase. Therefore, beyond Point D, there are 12 residences to be served. From Table XXI, the water usage will be:

First residence . . . . . . . . . . . . . . . . . . . . . . . . . . . . . . . . . . . . . . . = 15.0 gpm
Next nine residences . . . . . . . . . . . . . . . . . . @ 5.0 gpm each = 45.0 gpm
Next two residences . . . . . . . . . . . . . . . . . . . @ 4.0 gpm each =  8.0 gpm
                                                                         _____
At Point D . . . . . . . . . . . . . . . . . . Total Water Requirement = 68.0 gpm

Lots 10, 9, 8, 7, 15, 16, 17, 18 . . . . . . . . . . . . @ 4.0 gpm each = 32.0 gpm
Lots 6, 5, 4, 3, 19, 20, 21 . . . . . . . . . . . . . . . @ 3.8 gpm each = 26.6 gpm

The total water requirement at Point B from the B to D Segment will be the totals of 68.0 gpm, 32.0 gpm, and 26.6 gpm which is 126.6 gpm.

Determine Pipe Size:

| Distance from Point B, Feet | 0' | 100' | 200' | 300' | 400' | 500' | 600' | 700' | Point D |
|---|---|---|---|---|---|---|---|---|---|
| Water Requirements at Above Distances from Point B in GPM | 126 | 119 | 111 | 103 | 96 | 88 | 80 | 72 | 68 |
| Supply of two-inch pipe starting at Point B for above distances, Flow in GPM | | 200 | 130 | 100 | 86 | Not Adequate | | | |
| Supply of two-inch pipe starting at distance of 100 feet from Point B, Flow in GPM | | | 200 | 130 | 100 | 86 | 76 | Not Adequate | |
| Supply of two-inch pipe starting at distance of 200 feet from Point B, Flow in GPM | | | | 200 | 130 | 100 | 86 | 76 | 70 |

A two-inch pipe is adequate to supply the need starting at a distance of 200 feet from Point B.

| Supply of three-inch pipe starting at Point B for above distances, Flow in GPM | 600 | 410 | 325* | 290 | 235 |
|---|---|---|---|---|---|

A three-inch pipe is adequate from Point B to a distance of 200 feet where it is connected to the above two-inch pipeline.

---

*Note: The three-inch pipe flow at this point must be greater than the flow of the two-inch pipe as noted above.

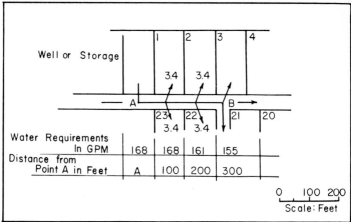

FIGURE 25. Summary Of Water Requirements At Point A.

g. Layout to a scale of one inch equal to 100 feet, pipeline section indicated as Point A to Point B.

Water flowing through this pipeline from Point A to Point B, must not only supply the water requirements along this segment, but must also supply the requirements of Pipelines B to D and B to C.

h. Determine water requirements at distances from Point A to Point B on the following basis:

It is again necessary to recalculate the totals to Point B of Pipelines B to D and B to C because the total number of users change, thus changing the total instantaneous water requirements.

Beyond Point 8, there are 35 residences. From Table XXI, the water requirements will be:

First residence . . . . . . . . . . . . . . . . . . . . . . . . . . @ 15.0 gpm =   15.0 gpm
Next nine residences . . . . . . . . . . . . . . . . . @ 5.0 gpm each =   45.0 gpm
Next 10 residences . . . . . . . . . . . . . . . . . . . @ 4.0 gpm each =   40.0 gpm
Next 10 residences . . . . . . . . . . . . . . . . . . . @ 3.8 gpm each =   38.0 gpm
Next five residences . . . . . . . . . . . . . . . . . . @ 3.4 gpm each =   17.0 gpm
                                                                        ─────────
At Point B . . . . . . . . . . . . . . . . Total Water Requirement = 155.0 gpm
Lots 22, 23, 1, 2, . . . . . . . . . . . . . . . . . . . @ 3.4 gpm each =   13.6 gpm

The total water requirement at Point A will be the totals of 155.0 gpm at Point B plus 13.6 for the Segment of A to B or 168.6 gpm.

Determine Pipe Size:

| | | | | |
|---|---|---|---|---|
| Distance from Point A, Feet | 0' | 100' | 200' | 300' |
| Water Requirements at above distances from Point A, in GPM | 168 | 168 | 161 | 155 |
| Supply of three-inch pipe starting at Point A for above distances, Flow in GPM | | 600 | 410 | 325 |

A three-inch pipeline is adequate to supply the need starting at Point A and connecting to the three-inch pipe at Point B.

Therefore, the completed water system will be as follows:

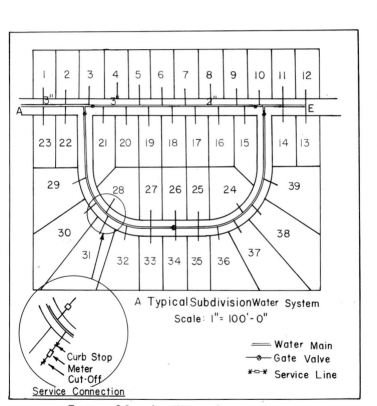

A Typical Subdivision Water System
Scale: 1"= 100'-0"

Water Main
Gate Valve
Service Line

Service Connection

FIGURE 26. A Water System Layout.

Distribution systems may be further reinforced to provide better water service to the consumers. What is meant by reinforcing a distribution system is this: to provide inter-connecting mains within the system to form a grid effect by the many loops thus created. Therefore as in the loop system, the water to the many consumers will be from several directions within the system and not from one single direction as in the case of a long single feed line. The one real advantage of the reinforced system is that it is possible to make repairs or to isolate certain portions without affecting the water service within the entire system. Also as in the loop system, are advantages of greater flow to all points and the elimination of dead ends.

An example of a complex water system is given in Figure 27.

In the design of this water system as a typical case, one would select Points F and E as the starting points as being farthest from the source of supply, well fields, or storage. The design would continue as follows:

*Pipeline CF.* From Point F, assuming that Lot 44 may receive its water through this pipeline as well as through Pipeline BF and DF, design to Point C.

*Pipeline DF.* From Point F, again assuming that the water to Lot 44 is through this pipeline, start at Lot 44 and design to Point D.

*Pipeline BF.* From Point F, assuming as above, that the water to Lot 44 is through this pipeline, design to Point B.

*Pipeline DE.* Assuming that Lot 16 is the fartherest service within this segment, design back to Point D.

*Pipeline CD.* Totalizing the flow

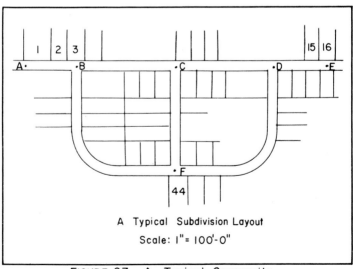

A Typical Subdivision Layout

Scale: 1"= 100'-0"

FIGURE 27.  A Typical Community.

to Point D for all services from F and E (Table XXI) and picking up additional services on Pipeline CD, design to Point C.

*Pipeline BC.* Totalizing the flow to Point C for all services from D and F, design to Point B.

*Pipeline AB.* Totalizing the flow to Point B for all services from F and C, design to Point A.

Reinforced systems may work into very complex systems. In case of extremely large developments, several loops may exist within the system. The following example will illustrate such a case:

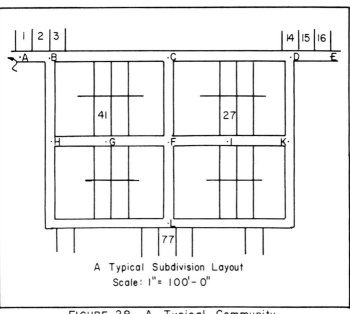

A Typical Subdivision Layout
Scale: 1" = 100'-0"

FIGURE 28. A Typical Community.

In this design, Lots 16, 27, 41, and 77 should be considered as those points fartherest away from the source of supply, well field, or storage facilities, and will have a water requirement of 15 gallons per minute each (Table XXI). The requirement of Lot 77 will be supplied equally by three water lines. The water requirement of Lots 41 and 27 will each be supplied by two water lines.

Calculations for design of this system will proceed with the design of the individual pipelines according to the following schedule:

  Pipeline FL.
  Pipeline FG.
  Pipeline FI.
  Pipeline CF—accumulated flows of FL, FG, and FI.
  Pipeline KL.
  Pipeline KI.

Pipeline DK—accumulated
flows of KL and KI.
Pipeline DE.
Pipeline CD—accumulated
flows of DE and DK.
Pipeline BC—accumulated flows
of CD and CF.
Pipeline HL.
Pipeline HG.
Pipeline BH—accumulated
flows of HG and HL.
Pipeline AB—accumulated
flows of BC and BH.

## 2. Storage on the Distribution System

In the design of distribution systems, the pipelines are designed to carry maximum flows from the storage facilities to all parts of the system. Where large quantities of storage are provided, it is necessary that they be properly located and that the water mains be located so as to provide the most adequate service to the community. Economics is a prime factor in the location of such storage on a distribution system.

## 3. Large Systems with Fire Flows

Of importance in any water system, is the importance of providing fire flows. In large systems, it is highly desirable to design for fire flows because this additional service provided by the water system is an asset to the community. Providing of fire protection will of course mean that larger distribution lines must be installed. Therefore, with the exception of very large systems, from the standpoint of design, it is not necessary to calculate

the individual water requirements for domestic usage from Table XXI because the systems when designed for greater fire flows, will be adequate for domestic usage. This does not apply to commercial or industrial or institutional water requirements because these requirements are within concentrated areas and therefore their flows must be taken into consideration in addition to fire flows. An example as given for the community problem on Page 77 is given in Figures 29 and 30.

Fire flows are determined by the value of the property to be protected. As the value of the property increases from residential to commercial to industrial, the requirement for the number of fire streams also changes from one to several. Tables have been established by the Board of Fire Underwriters for the determination of the number of fire streams in relation to the population served and the duration of such flows. See Tables XIX and XX.

As a rough estimate for fire flows, it is suggested that for residential areas that a minimum of 500 gallons per minute, with spacing of fire hydrants, so that each residence will be within 400 feet of a fire hydrant be established. Higher flow values should be used for commercial, industrial, and institutional areas. Also hydrants should be located much closer together to provide this additional amount of water. As a rule of thumb, a minimum of 1,000 gallons per minute should be provided for each $100,000 of property value.

---

*In most communities, it is only necessary to provide in design procedures, fire flows to the fartherest hydrant which will in turn provide adequate flows to other hydrants.

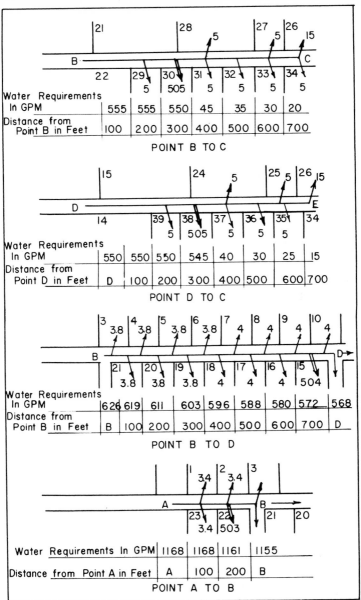

**POINT B TO C**

| Water Requirements In GPM | 555 | 555 | 550 | 45 | 35 | 30 | 20 |
|---|---|---|---|---|---|---|---|
| Distance from Point B in Feet | 100 | 200 | 300 | 400 | 500 | 600 | 700 |

**POINT D TO C**

| Water Requirements In GPM | 550 | 550 | 550 | 545 | 40 | 30 | 25 | 15 |
|---|---|---|---|---|---|---|---|---|
| Distance from Point D in Feet | D | 100 | 200 | 300 | 400 | 500 | 600 | 700 |

**POINT B TO D**

| Water Requirements In GPM | 626 | 619 | 611 | 603 | 596 | 588 | 580 | 572 | 568 |
|---|---|---|---|---|---|---|---|---|---|
| Distance from Point B in Feet | B | 100 | 200 | 300 | 400 | 500 | 600 | 700 | D |

**POINT A TO B**

| Water Requirements In GPM | 1168 | 1168 | 1161 | 1155 |
|---|---|---|---|---|
| Distance from Point A in Feet | A | 100 | 200 | B |

FIGURE 29. Summary Of Water Requirements.

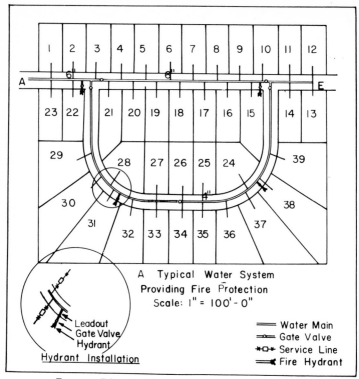

A Typical Water System
Providing Fire Protection
Scale: 1" = 100'-0"

Hydrant Installation
Leadout
Gate Valve
Hydrant

═══ Water Main
═□═ Gate Valve
✳□➤ Service Line
══◄ Fire Hydrant

FIGURE 30. A Water System Layout.

### 4. Distribution System Pipe Composition and Joints

#### A. Pipe Composition

Water pipe is available in many different type materials such as cast iron, cement-asbestos, concrete pressure, copper, plastic, steel and wrought iron. The selection of the type of pipe to be used within a system depends upon such design criteria and data such as: working pressures, water hammer, tensile and bursting strength, corrosion properties of the water to be handled, durability, economics, the particular use

within the system, and obstacles in laying and construction conditions. Concerning the above conditions, one type of pipe may be more suitable than others in order to meet some specific condition.

Classification of pipe strength is based upon certain accepted designations set forth by the American Water Works Association and the American Standards Association[7]. These accepted designations classify pipe according to average working pressures stated by letter or number. For example, a Class B pipe is designated

— 88 —

with a working pressure of 86 pounds per square inch or 200 feet of head. Certain allowances are made for water hammer and other safety factors such that factory tests are made on the pipe considerably greater than the 86 psi or 200 feet of head. The alternate method of pipe pressure designation is by number such that the number gives the working pressure of pipe in pounds per square inch. For example, a pipe with a designation of 150 means that the pipe is designed to within a working pressure of 150 pounds per square inch. Table XXVIII sets forth these generally accepted designations.

A discussion of the different types of pipe follows:

1. Asbestos-Cement Pressure Pipe[8]. Asbestos-Cement Pressure Pipe is composed of an intimate mixture of asbestos fibers, silica and portland cement. The silica is added to combine chemically with the free lime during the special curing process thereby forming more stable compounds which add to the pipe's inherent corrosion resistance. This material is tough and durable. Asbestos-Cement Pipe is available in diameters ranging from four inches to 36 inches and in lengths (commercially available) of 13-foot sections. Asbestos-Cement Pipe is easily tapped for all sizes of service lines. It is resistant to corrosion by reaction of natural waters and waters of low pH. Since it is non-metallic, electrolysis by either association of different pipe materials, stray currents, or electrical grounds, is negligible. Therefore, the carrying capacity of asbestos-cement is no reduced by tuberculation and will remain high during the lifetime of the pipe.

2. Cast Iron Pipe[7]. Cast iron pipe is made of an alloy of molten pig iron alloyed with various elements such as Carbon, Manganese, Phos-

### TABLE XXVIII
### Classes of Pipe Designations for Pressure

| Class of Pipe | Head in Feet | Pounds Per Square Inch |
|---|---|---|
| A | 100 | 43 |
| B | 200 | 86 |
| C | 300 | 130 |
| D | 400 | 173 |
| E | 500 | 217 |
| F | 600 | 260 |
| G | 700 | 304 |
| H | 800 | 347 |
| 50 | 115 | 50 |
| 100 | 231 | 100 |
| 150 | 346 | 150 |
| 200 | 462 | 200 |
| 250 | 577 | 250 |
| 300 | 693 | 300 |
| 350 | 808 | 350 |

—From Permission of Cast Iron Pipe Research Association.

phorus, Silicon, Sulphur, and other materials to give a material which has strength and properties to withstand handling, construction shock or vibration, and to allow for flexibility in physical characteristics such as elongation, contraction, pressures, etc. Cast iron pipe is made by two processes, either by sand or metal mold casting or by centrifugal casting. The tensile strength of cast iron pipe varies from 20,000 pounds per square inch upwards and is determined by the method of pipe construction and diameter of pipe.

Cast iron pipe is commercially available in diameters of three inches to 48 inches. However, special orders may be fulfilled to diameters to 84 inches. Commercial lengths as manufactured are 12-foot, 16-foot, 16½-foot, 18-foot, and 20-foot lengths. The common length is 12 feet. Cast iron pipe is readily tapped for service lines of all sizes.

Cast iron pipe is easily subject to corrosion by waters of low pH where the Carbon Dioxide content is high. Such corrosion may be in the form of creation of tubercles within the pipe thus greatly reducing the carrying capacity of the pipe. Many different type of coatings are available for cast iron pipes where corrosion may be a problem. Common types of coatings are cement, bitumastic or tar-enameled which are usually applied in the manufacture of the pipe. It is also possible to clean old cast iron pipes of tubercles and to add certain protective coatings with the pipe remaining in place.

3. Concrete Pressure Pipe[10]. Concrete pressure pipe is made of high density concrete and reinforcing steel. The strength of concrete pressure pipe can be made to meet spe-

cific conditions by altering the thickness and the amount of reinforcing placed within the pipe. This pipe is commercially available in diameters ranging from 16 inches to 84 inches, but may be designed for even larger diameters to meet specific conditions. The standard manufactured length is 16 feet, but may be obtained in lengths to 32 feet if desired. Concrete pressure pipe is easily tapped under pressure for all size of service lines. It is resistant to ordinary corrosion and electrolysis as described for cement-asbestos pipe. It also retains a high carrying capacity or coefficient as the flow is not reduced by tuberculation or corrosion effects.

4. Copper Pipe, Type K[11]. Copper pipe, type K*, is made of a hard or soft tempered alloy of copper to give durable and flexible properties as necessary for water pipe. Copper pipe, type K, is available in diameters from ¼ inch to 12 inches. The diameters from ¼ inch to 1½ inches are available in 60-foot coils whereas the diameters larger than 1½ inches, are commercially available in lengths of 12 feet and 20 feet. Copper pipe, type K, provides high resistance to corrosion by natural waters, however, it is somewhat more corrosive to the reaction of waters of low pH which have a high carbon dioxide content. Such corrosion will result in blue stains on plumbing fixtures. Care should be taken also to prevent electrolysis by the use of dissimilar metals. Copper pipe, type K, is widely used for service lines because of its length and flexibility in

---

*Type refers to primary use of certain kinds of copper pipe. For example, Type K pipe is use dprimarily for domestic water supply lines because of its durability and economical use. Type L pipe is primarily used for refrigeration piping. Type M pipe is primarily used for industrial and general piping work.

handling and its durability.

5. Plastic Pipe[9] [12]. Plastic pipe, satisfactory for use in the transmission of portable water, must be made of virgin plastic material such as virgin polyethylene or polyvinyl chloride. It is important that such plastic pipe for water bear the stamp of approval of the National Sanitation Foundation. The reason for the above statements is to assure the pipe composition to be free of toxic materials and to be free of taste and odor producing materials. Many times, plastic pipe is made of remelted plastic, therefore, the virgin material should only be accepted for pipe composition. Plastic pipe is commercially available in diameters ranging from $\frac{1}{2}$ inch to six inches. The diameters up to and including three inches, are commercially available in lengths up to 100 feet. The four-inch and six-inch pipe are available to lengths of 20 feet. Plastic pipe is entirely resistant to corrosion by natural waters and waters of low pH and high carbon dioxide. The carrying capacity of the pipe will remain high because of its smoothness and lack of tuberculation. This type of pipe is widely used for service lines because of its lengths, flexibility, durability, and corrosion resistant properties.

6. Steel Pipe[11]. Steel pipe used in water systems is made of high grade steel. Steel pipe of standard wall thickness is usually available in black pipe. It is commercially available in small diameters ranging $\frac{1}{2}$ inch to large diameters to 96 inches. Available lengths are 16 feet and 22 feet with lengths of 40 feet available for specific conditions. Steel pipe as cast iron pipe, is readily protected against corrosion by the application of protective coatings. Such coatings give excellent protection so that the pipe will retain in a high carrying capacity.

7. Wrought Iron Pipe[9]. Wrought iron pipe is made of a composition of high grade iron and a glass-like slag of iron silicate. In this composition, wrought iron pipe differs from the other types of iron pipe because of the presence of the glass-like slag. Wrought iron pipe is commercially available in diameters from $\frac{1}{4}$ inch to 24 inches and in lengths of 16 feet to 22 feet. Greater lengths to 44 feet may be obtained for specific circumstances. Wrought iron pipe is somewhat resistant to corrosion to natural waters. Protective coatings are available for use where aggressive waters must be transmitted. Such coatings may be as galvanizing, tar-enameled, etc. In view of its ability to withstand high pressures, its light weight, and its ease of installation, wrought iron pipe is widely used for water supply service lines, distribution lines, etc.

Table XXIX summarizes typical pipe characteristics for the various types of pipe.

# TABLE XXIX
## Typical Pipe Characteristics

| Type of Pipe Composition | Diameters Available Inches | Lengths Available Feet | Remarks |
|---|---|---|---|
| Asbestos-Cement Pressure Pipe | 4, 6, 8, 10, 12, 14, 16, 18, 20, 24, 30, 36 | 13 | Gasket-type joints. |
| Cast Iron | 3, 4, 6, 8, 10, 12, 12, 16, 18, 20, 24, 30, 36, 42, 48, 54, 60, 66, 72, 84 | 12, 16, 16½, 18, 20, Common-12 | Coupled, gasket, leaded, and mechanical joints. Coatings for corrosion such as cement, bitumastic. |
| Concrete-Pressure | 16, 20, 24, 30, 36, 42, 48, 54, 60, 66, 72, 84 | 16 | Gasket-type joints. Larger diameters and lengths available. |
| Copper, Type K | ½, ¾, 1, 1¼, 1½, 2, 2½, 3, 4, 6 | Small size in 60-foot coils. Larger pipe in lengths to 20 feet. | Primarily used for service lines and industrial piping. |
| Galvanized Iron | ½, ¾, 1, 1¼, 1½, 2, 2½, 3 | 12, 16 | Threaded and mechanical-type joints. Primarily used for small feeder mains and service lines. |
| Plastic | ½, ¾, 1, 1¼, 1½, 2, 3, 4, 6 | Small size in 100-foot coils. Larger pipe in lengths to 20 feet. | Primary use is for small feeder mains and service lines. Should be of virgin material and bear the stamp of approval of the National Sanitation Foundation. |
| Steel | ½, ¾, 1, 1¼, 1½, 2, 2½, 3, 3½, 4, 5, 6, 8, 10, 12, 14, 16, 18, 20, 24 | 16, 20, 40 | Gasket and mechanical-type joints. |
| Wrought Iron | ½, ¾, 1 1¼, 1½, 2, 2½, 3, 4, 5, 6, 8, 10, 12, 14, 16, 18, 20, 24 | 16, 20, 22, 44 | Threaded and coupled joints. Coatings for corrosion such as cement, galvanizing, bitumastic, etc. |

# TABLE XXX
## Weights of Mechanical Joint Pipe for Water

STANDARD THICKNESSES AND WEIGHTS OF CAST IRON MECHANICAL JOINT PIPE
CENTRIFUGALLY CAST IN METAL AND SAND LINED MOLDS FOR WATER AND OTHER LIQUIDS

Note: Thicknesses in accordance with A.S.A. Specifications, 18,000 psi full length bursting tensile, 40,000 psi ring modulus of rupture. For pipe laid without blocks on flat bottom trench with tamped backfill under 5 feet of cover. For other conditions consult the manufacturer.

| Size ins. | Thick-ness ins. | Out-side Diam. ins. | 12 ft. Lgth. * | | 16 ft. Lgth. * | | 16½ ft. Lgth. * | | 18 ft. Lgth. * | | 20 ft. Lgth. * | |
|---|---|---|---|---|---|---|---|---|---|---|---|---|
| | | | Avg. per ft. | per Lgth. | Avg. per ft. | per Lgth. | Avg. per ft. | per Lgth. | Avg. per ft. | per Lgth. | Avg. per ft. | per Lgth. |
| Class 50—50 Lb. Pressure—115 Foot Head | | | | | | | | | | | | |
| 3 | .32 | 3.96 | 12.3 | 150 | 12.2 | 195 | 12.1 | 200 | 12.0 | 215 | | |
| 4 | .35 | 4.80 | 16.6 | 200 | 16.4 | 260 | 16.3 | 270 | 16.2 | 290 | | |
| 6 | .38 | 6.90 | 26.1 | 315 | 25.7 | 410 | 25.6 | 420 | 25.5 | 460 | | |
| 8 | .41 | 9.05 | 37.2 | 445 | 36.7 | 585 | 36.6 | 605 | 36.4 | 655 | | |
| 10 | .44 | 11.10 | 49.3 | 590 | 48.5 | 775 | 48.4 | 800 | 48.2 | 870 | | |
| 12 | .48 | 13.20 | 64.0 | 770 | 62.9 | 1005 | 62.8 | 1035 | 62.6 | 1125 | 62.3 | 1245 |
| 14 | .48 | 15.30 | 76.2 | 915 | 74.6 | 1195 | 74.4 | 1230 | 74.1 | 1335 | 73.6 | 1470 |
| 16 | .54 | 17.40 | 97.1 | 1165 | 95.0 | 1520 | 94.9 | 1565 | 94.5 | 1700 | 94.0 | 1880 |
| 18 | .54 | 19.50 | 109.8 | 1320 | 107.5 | 1720 | 107.2 | 1770 | 106.7 | 1920 | 106.0 | 2120 |
| 20 | .57 | 21.60 | 128.7 | 1545 | 125.9 | 2015 | 125.7 | 2075 | 124.9 | 2250 | 124.2 | 2485 |
| 24 | .63 | 25.80 | 170.2 | 2040 | 166.5 | 2665 | 166.1 | 2740 | 165.2 | 2975 | 164.2 | 3285 |
| 30 | .79 | 32.00 | | | 259.5 | 4150 | 259.0 | 4275 | | | 256.0 | 5120 |
| 36 | .87 | 38.30 | | | 343.9 | 5500 | | | | | | |
| 42 | .97 | 44.50 | | | 445.7 | 7130 | | | | | | |
| 48 | 1.06 | 50.80 | | | 557.1 | 8915 | | | | | | |
| Class 100—100 Lb. Pressure—231 Foot Head | | | | | | | | | | | | |
| 3 | .32 | 3.96 | 12.3 | 150 | 12.2 | 195 | 12.1 | 200 | 12.0 | 215 | | |
| 4 | .35 | 4.80 | 16.6 | 200 | 16.4 | 260 | 16.3 | 270 | 16.2 | 290 | | |
| 6 | .38 | 6.90 | 26.1 | 315 | 25.7 | 410 | 25.6 | 420 | 25.5 | 460 | | |
| 8 | .41 | 9.05 | 37.2 | 445 | 36.7 | 585 | 36.6 | 605 | 36.4 | 655 | | |
| 10 | .44 | 11.10 | 49.3 | 590 | 48.5 | 775 | 48.4 | 800 | 48.2 | 870 | | |
| 12 | .48 | 13.20 | 64.0 | 770 | 62.9 | 1005 | 62.8 | 1035 | 62.6 | 1125 | 62.3 | 1245 |
| 14 | .51 | 15.30 | 80.4 | 965 | 78.8 | 1260 | 78.6 | 1295 | 78.2 | 1410 | 77.8 | 1555 |
| 16 | .54 | 17.40 | 97.1 | 1165 | 95.0 | 1520 | 94.9 | 1565 | 94.5 | 1700 | 94.0 | 1880 |
| 18 | .58 | 19.50 | 117.0 | 1405 | 114.7 | 1835 | 114.4 | 1890 | 113.9 | 2050 | 113.2 | 2265 |
| 20 | .62 | 21.60 | 138.7 | 1665 | 135.9 | 2175 | 135.7 | 2240 | 134.9 | 2430 | 134.2 | 2685 |
| 24 | .68 | 25.80 | 182.2 | 2185 | 178.5 | 2855 | 178.1 | 2940 | 177.2 | 3190 | 176.2 | 3525 |
| 30 | .79 | 32.00 | | | 259.5 | 4150 | 259.0 | 4275 | | | 256.0 | 5120 |
| 36 | .87 | 38.30 | | | 343.9 | 5500 | | | | | | |
| 42 | .97 | 44.50 | | | 445.7 | 7130 | | | | | | |
| 48 | 1.06 | 50.80 | | | 557.1 | 8915 | | | | | | |
| Class 150—150 Lb. Pressure—346 Foot Head | | | | | | | | | | | | |
| 3 | .32 | 3.96 | 12.3 | 150 | 12.2 | 195 | 12.1 | 200 | 12.0 | 215 | | |
| 4 | .35 | 4.80 | 16.6 | 200 | 16.4 | 260 | 16.3 | 270 | 16.2 | 290 | | |
| 6 | .38 | 6.90 | 26.1 | 315 | 25.7 | 410 | 25.6 | 420 | 25.5 | 460 | | |
| 8 | .41 | 9.05 | 37.2 | 445 | 36.7 | 585 | 36.6 | 605 | 36.4 | 655 | | |
| 10 | .44 | 11.10 | 49.3 | 590 | 48.5 | 775 | 48.4 | 800 | 48.2 | 870 | | |
| 12 | .48 | 13.20 | 64.0 | 770 | 62.9 | 1005 | 62.8 | 1035 | 62.6 | 1125 | 62.3 | 1245 |
| 14 | .51 | 15.30 | 80.4 | 965 | 78.8 | 1260 | 78.6 | 1295 | 78.2 | 1410 | 77.8 | 1555 |
| 16 | .54 | 17.40 | 97.1 | 1165 | 95.0 | 1520 | 94.9 | 1565 | 94.5 | 1700 | 94.0 | 1880 |
| 18 | .58 | 19.50 | 117.0 | 1405 | 114.7 | 1835 | 114.4 | 1890 | 113.9 | 2050 | 113.2 | 2265 |
| 20 | .62 | 21.60 | 138.7 | 1665 | 135.9 | 2175 | 135.7 | 2240 | 134.9 | 2430 | 134.2 | 2685 |
| 24 | .73 | 25.80 | 194.2 | 2330 | 190.4 | 3045 | 190.1 | 3135 | 189.2 | 3405 | 188.2 | 3765 |
| 30 | .85 | 32.00 | | | 277.3 | 4435 | 276.8 | 4565 | | | 273.8 | 5475 |
| 36 | .94 | 38.30 | | | 368.9 | 5900 | | | | | | |
| 42 | 1.05 | 44.50 | | | 479.1 | 7665 | | | | | | |
| 48 | 1.14 | 50.80 | | | 595.2 | 9525 | | | | | | |

* Including Bell. Calculated weight of pipe rounded off to nearest 5 pounds.
References: A.S.A.—A-21.6—pipes cast in metal molds. A.S.A.—A-21.8—pipe cast in sand lined molds. A.S.A.—21.11—mechanical joints.

## TABLE XXX (Continued)

# Weights of Mechanical Joint Pipe for Water

| Size ins. | Thick-ness ins. | Out side Diam. ins. | 12 ft. Lgth.* Avg. per ft. | per Lgth. | 16 ft. Lgth.* Avg. per ft. | per Lgth. | 16½ ft. Lgth.* Avg. per ft. | per Lgth. | 18 ft. Lgth.* Avg. per ft. | per Lgth. | 20 ft. Lgth.* Avg. per ft. | per Lgth. |
|---|---|---|---|---|---|---|---|---|---|---|---|---|
| | | | | Class 200—200 Lb. Pressure—462 Foot Head | | | | | | | | |
| 3 | .32 | 3.96 | 12.3 | 150 | 12.2 | 195 | 12.1 | 200 | 12.0 | 215 | | |
| 4 | .35 | 4.80 | 16.6 | 200 | 16.4 | 260 | 16.3 | 270 | 16.2 | 290 | | |
| 6 | .38 | 6.90 | 26.1 | 315 | 25.7 | 410 | 25.6 | 420 | 25.5 | 460 | | |
| 8 | .41 | 9.05 | 37.2 | 445 | 36.7 | 585 | 36.6 | 605 | 36.4 | 655 | | |
| 10 | .44 | 11.10 | 49.3 | 590 | 48.5 | 775 | 48.4 | 800 | 48.2 | 870 | | |
| 12 | .48 | 13.20 | 64.0 | 770 | 62.9 | 1005 | 62.8 | 1035 | 62.6 | 1125 | 62.3 | 1245 |
| 14 | .55 | 15.30 | 86.0 | 1030 | 84.4 | 1350 | 84.2 | 1390 | 83.8 | 1510 | 83.4 | 1670 |
| 16 | .58 | 17.40 | 103.5 | 1240 | 101.5 | 1625 | 101.3 | 1670 | 100.9 | 1815 | 100.3 | 2005 |
| 18 | .63 | 19.50 | 125.9 | 1510 | 123.5 | 1975 | 123.3 | 2035 | 122.8 | 2210 | 122.2 | 2445 |
| 20 | .67 | 21.60 | 148.7 | 1785 | 145.9 | 2335 | 145.7 | 2405 | 144.9 | 2610 | 144.2 | 2885 |
| 24 | .79 | 25.80 | 208.4 | 2500 | 204.8 | 3275 | 204.4 | 3375 | 203.5 | 3665 | 202.6 | 4050 |
| 30 | .92 | 32.00 | | | 298.1 | 4770 | 297.6 | 4910 | | | 294.6 | 5890 |
| 36 | 1.02 | 38.30 | | | 397.4 | 6360 | | | | | | |
| 42 | 1.13 | 44.50 | | | 512.3 | 8195 | | | | | | |
| 48 | 1.23 | 50.80 | | | 637.9 | 10205 | | | | | | |
| | | | | Class 250—250 Lb. Pressure—577 Foot Head | | | | | | | | |
| 3 | .32 | 3.96 | 12.3 | 150 | 12.2 | 195 | 12.1 | 200 | 12.0 | 215 | | |
| 4 | .35 | 4.80 | 16.6 | 200 | 16.4 | 260 | 16.3 | 270 | 16.2 | 290 | | |
| 6 | .38 | 6.90 | 26.1 | 315 | 25.7 | 410 | 25.6 | 420 | 25.5 | 460 | | |
| 8 | .41 | 9.05 | 37.2 | 445 | 36.7 | 585 | 36.6 | 605 | 36.4 | 655 | | |
| 10 | .44 | 11.10 | 49.3 | 590 | 48.5 | 775 | 48.4 | 800 | 48.2 | 870 | | |
| 12 | .52 | 13.20 | 68.8 | 825 | 67.7 | 1085 | 67.6 | 1115 | 67.4 | 1215 | 67.1 | 1340 |
| 14 | .59 | 15.30 | 91.6 | 1100 | 90.0 | 1440 | 89.8 | 1480 | 89.4 | 1610 | 89.0 | 1780 |
| 16 | .63 | 17.40 | 111.5 | 1340 | 109.6 | 1755 | 109.4 | 1805 | 108.9 | 1960 | 108.3 | 2165 |
| 18 | .68 | 19.50 | 134.8 | 1620 | 132.5 | 2120 | 132.2 | 2180 | 131.7 | 2370 | 131.0 | 2620 |
| 20 | .72 | 21.60 | 158.6 | 1905 | 155.7 | 2490 | 155.5 | 2565 | 154.8 | 2785 | 154.1 | 3080 |
| 24 | .79 | 25.80 | 208.4 | 2500 | 204.8 | 3275 | 204.4 | 3375 | 203.5 | 3665 | 202.6 | 4050 |
| 30 | .92 | 32.00 | | | 318.7 | 5100 | 318.2 | 5250 | | | 315.2 | 6305 |
| 36 | 1.10 | 38.30 | | | 425.8 | 6815 | | | | | | |
| 42 | 1.22 | 44.50 | | | 549.5 | 8790 | | | | | | |
| 48 | 1.33 | 50.80 | | | 685.2 | 10965 | | | | | | |
| | | | | Class 300—300 Lb. Pressure—693 Foot Head | | | | | | | | |
| 3 | .32 | 3.96 | 12.3 | 150 | 12.2 | 195 | 12.1 | 200 | 12.0 | 215 | | |
| 4 | .35 | 4.80 | 16.6 | 200 | 16.4 | 260 | 16.3 | 270 | 16.2 | 290 | | |
| 6 | .38 | 6.90 | 26.1 | 315 | 25.7 | 410 | 25.6 | 420 | 25.5 | 460 | | |
| 8 | .41 | 9.05 | 37.2 | 445 | 36.7 | 585 | 36.6 | 605 | 36.4 | 655 | | |
| 10 | .48 | 11.10 | 53.3 | 640 | 52.5 | 840 | 52.4 | 865 | 52.2 | 940 | | |
| 12 | .52 | 13.20 | 68.8 | 825 | 67.7 | 1085 | 67.6 | 1115 | 67.4 | 1215 | 67.1 | 1340 |
| 14 | .59 | 15.30 | 91.6 | 1100 | 90.0 | 1440 | 89.8 | 1480 | 89.4 | 1610 | 89.0 | 1780 |
| 16 | .68 | 17.40 | 119.3 | 1430 | 117.3 | 1875 | 117.2 | 1935 | 116.7 | 2100 | 116.2 | 2325 |
| 18 | .73 | 19.50 | 143.7 | 1725 | 141.4 | 2260 | 141.1 | 2330 | 140.6 | 2530 | 140.0 | 2800 |
| 20 | .78 | 21.60 | 170.4 | 2045 | 167.6 | 2680 | 167.3 | 2760 | 166.6 | 3000 | 165.9 | 3320 |
| 24 | .85 | 25.80 | 222.6 | 2670 | 219.0 | 3505 | 218.6 | 3605 | 217.7 | 3920 | 216.8 | 4335 |
| | | | | Class 350—350 Lb. Pressure—808 Foot Head | | | | | | | | |
| 3 | .32 | 3.96 | 12.3 | 150 | 12.2 | 195 | 12.1 | 200 | 12.0 | 215 | | |
| 4 | .35 | 4.80 | 16.6 | 200 | 16.4 | 260 | 16.3 | 270 | 16.2 | 290 | | |
| 6 | .38 | 6.90 | 26.1 | 315 | 25.7 | 410 | 25.6 | 420 | 25.5 | 460 | | |
| 8 | .41 | 9.05 | 37.2 | 445 | 36.7 | 585 | 36.6 | 605 | 36.4 | 655 | | |
| 10 | .52 | 11.10 | 57.2 | 685 | 56.4 | 900 | 56.3 | 930 | 56.1 | 1010 | | |
| 12 | .56 | 13.20 | 73.6 | 885 | 72.5 | 1160 | 72.4 | 1195 | 72.2 | 1300 | 71.9 | 1440 |
| 14 | .64 | 15.30 | 98.5 | 1180 | 96.9 | 1550 | 96.7 | 1595 | 96.3 | 1735 | 95.9 | 1920 |
| 16 | .68 | 17.40 | 119.3 | 1430 | 117.3 | 1875 | 117.2 | 1935 | 116.7 | 2100 | 116.2 | 2325 |
| 18 | .79 | 19.50 | 154.3 | 1850 | 152.0 | 2430 | 151.7 | 2505 | 151.2 | 2720 | 150.6 | 3010 |
| 20 | .84 | 21.60 | 182.1 | 2185 | 179.3 | 2870 | 179.0 | 2955 | 178.3 | 3210 | 177.6 | 3550 |
| 24 | .92 | 25.80 | 239.2 | 2870 | 235.4 | 3765 | 235.1 | 3880 | 234.2 | 4215 | 233.2 | 4665 |

—From Permission of Cast Iron Pipe Research Association.

## TABLE XXXI
## Standard Thicknesses and Weights of Asbestos-Cement Pipe

| Pipe Size Inches | Weight, Pounds | | |
|---|---|---|---|
| | Pipe Per Foot | Couplings Each | Rings Each |
| **Class 100—100-Pound Pressure—231-Foot Head** | | | |
| 4 | 6.2 | 6.5 | .19 |
| 6 | 10.6 | 9.8 | .26 |
| 8 | 15.7 | 13.3 | .34 |
| 10 | 21.7 | 17.9 | .39 |
| 12 | 28.9 | 27.2 | .45 |
| 14 | 30.6 | 42.0 | .52 |
| 16 | 36.8 | 52.5 | .61 |
| **Class 150—150-Pound Pressure—346-Foot Head** | | | |
| 4 | 7.1 | 7.5 | .20 |
| 6 | 12.2 | 12.3 | .28 |
| 8 | 18.9 | 19.1 | .36 |
| 10 | 30.4 | 29.8 | .42 |
| 12 | 41.2 | 45.2 | .48 |
| 14 | 54.5 | 70.0 | .84 |
| 16 | 67.5 | 88.3 | .93 |
| **Class 200—200-Pound Pressure—462 Feet Head** | | | |
| 4 | 9.4 | 9.3 | .20 |
| 6 | 15.3 | 17.2 | .28 |
| 8 | 23.6 | 26.0 | .36 |
| 10 | 25.1 | 39.8 | .42 |
| 12 | 48.5 | 62.5 | .48 |
| 14 | 66.0 | 96.5 | .84 |
| 16 | 85.3 | 121.3 | .93 |

—From Permission of Johns-Manville Corp.

## TABLE XXXII
## Standard Thicknesses and Weights of Concrete Pressure Pipe

| Pipe Size Inches | Outside Diameter Inches | Weight Per Linear Foot Pounds | Approximate Weight Per Standard Length of 16.03 Feet Pounds | Normal Maximum Operating Pressure Heads* Pounds Per Square Inch |
|---|---|---|---|---|
| **Prestressed Concrete Cylinder Pipe** | | | | |
| 16 | 19.5 | 138 | 2,215 | 250 |
| 20 | 24 | 187 | 3,005 | 250 |
| 24 | 28.5 | 238 | 3,820 | 200 |
| 30 | 35.25 | 349 | 6,000 | 200 |
| 36 | 42 | 476 | 7,630 | 170 |
| 42 | 48.75 | 593 | 8,506 | 150 |
| 48 | 55.5 | 759 | 12,170 | 125 |
| **Prestressed Concrete Embedded Cylinder Pipe, Regular Wall** | | | | |
| 36 | 42 | 476 | 7,630 | 200 |
| 42 | 49 | 593 | 8,506 | 180 |
| 48 | 56 | 759 | 12,170 | 170 |
| 54 | 64 | 995 | 15,950 | 200 |
| 60 | 72 | 1,250 | 20,040 | 200 |
| 66 | 79 | 1,480 | 23,725 | 200 |
| 72 | 86 | 1,745 | 28,000 | 200 |
| **Prestressed Concrete Embedded Cylinder Pipe, Heavy Wall** | | | | |
| 36 | 46 | 692 | 11,095 | 300 |
| 42 | 53 | 895 | 14,350 | 275 |
| 48 | 60 | 1,105 | 17,710 | 275 |
| 54 | 67 | 1,340 | 21,500 | 250 |
| 60 | 74 | 1,530 | 24,525 | 250 |
| 66 | 81 | 1,875 | 30,060 | 250 |
| 72 | 88 | 2,160 | 34,625 | 250 |

—From Permission of Price Brothers Co.

*Higher pressure heads are available with design modifications which include the use of heavier cylinders, greater wall thicknesses, increased reinforcing and special concrete mixes.

## TABLE XXXIII
### Standard Thicknesses and Weights of Plastic Pipe

| Normal Pipe Size Inches | Outside Diameter Inches | Inside Diameter Inches | Wall Thickness* Inches | Weight, Pounds | | |
|---|---|---|---|---|---|---|
| | | | | Per Foot | Per 10 Feet | Per 20 Feet |
| Class 100—100-Pound Pressure—231-Foot Head | | | | | | |
| 2 | 2.25 | 2.100 | 0.075 | 0.239 | 2.39 | 4.78 |
| 2½ | 2.570 | 2.400 | 0.085 | 0.310 | 3.10 | 6.20 |
| 3 | 3.250 | 3.070 | 0.090 | 0.417 | 4.17 | 8.34 |
| 4 | 4.100 | 3.880 | 0.110 | 0.644 | 6.44 | 12.88 |
| 6 | 6.220 | 5.990 | 0.160 | 1.422 | 14.22 | 28.44 |
| Class 150—150-Pound Pressure—346-Foot Head | | | | | | |
| ½ | 0.600 | 0.500 | 0.050 | 0.040 | 0.40 | 0.80 |
| ¾ | 0.855 | 0.755 | 0.050 | 0.059 | 0.59 | 1.18 |
| 1 | 1.140 | 1.020 | 0.060 | 0.095 | 0.95 | 1.90 |
| 1¼ | 1.420 | 1.300 | 0.060 | 0.120 | 1.20 | 2.40 |
| 1½ | 1.730 | 1.600 | 0.065 | 0.159 | 1.59 | 3.18 |
| 2 | 2.250 | 2.080 | 0.085 | 0.270 | 2.70 | 5.40 |
| 2½ | 2.570 | 2.370 | 0.100 | 0.362 | 3.62 | 7.24 |
| 3 | 3.250 | 3.000 | 0.125 | 0.573 | 5.73 | 11.46 |
| 4 | 4.100 | 3.790 | 0.155 | 0.897 | 8.97 | 17.94 |
| 6 | 6.220 | 5.750 | 0.235 | 2.063 | 20.63 | 41.26 |

—From Permission of Naugatuck Chemical Division of U.S. Rubber Company.

*Wall Thickness—Calculated via Barlow Formula: $S = \dfrac{P\ Do}{Z\ T}$ where

S** = Effective Tensile (2,000 psi 10-year figure)
P  = Working Pressure (psi)
Do = Outside Diameter (inches)
T  = Wall Thickness (inches)

**Based on a long-term failure strength of 3,200 psi. These values are a measure of bursting strength and are the primary basis of wall thickness.

## TABLE XXXIV

## Standard Thicknesses and Weights of Wrought Iron Pipe

### Byers Genuine Wrought Iron Standard Weight Pipe (Schedule 40)

| Nom. Size | Ext. Diam. | Int. Diam. | Thickness | Wt. per Ft. Plain Ends | Wt. per Ft. Nom. Thrds. and Cplgs. | Thrds. per Inch | Couplings Nom. O.D. | Couplings Nom. Lgth. | Mill Test Butt | Mill Test Lap | Trans. Area Ext. | Trans. Area Int. | Trans. Area NetMetal | Circ. Ext. | Circ. Int. | Ext. Area per Lin. Ft. (Sq. Ft.) | Lgth. per 1 Sq. Ft. Sur. Ext. | Lgth. per 1 Sq. Ft. Sur. Int. | Lgth. in Ft. Vol. 1 Cu. Ft. | U.S. Gal. per 1 Lin. Ft. | Wt. of Water per 1 Lin. Ft. |
|---|---|---|---|---|---|---|---|---|---|---|---|---|---|---|---|---|---|---|---|---|---|
| ¼ | .540 | .360 | .090 | .42 | .42 | 18 | .719 | 1 3/16 | 700 | | .229 | .1018 | .1272 | 1.696 | 1.131 | .141 | 7.073 | 10.608 | 1414.233 | .005 | .044 |
| ⅜ | .675 | .489 | .093 | .57 | .57 | 18 | .875 | 1 3/16 | 700 | | .358 | .1879 | .1710 | 2.121 | 1.536 | .177 | 5.658 | 7.812 | 766.990 | .010 | .081 |
| ½ | .840 | .617 | .111 | .85 | .85 | 14 | 1.063 | 1 9/16 | 700 | | .554 | .2990 | .2550 | 2.639 | 1.939 | .220 | 4.547 | 6.189 | 481.320 | .016 | .130 |
| ¾ | 1.050 | .819 | .115 | 1.13 | 1.13 | 14 | 1.313 | 1 5/8 | 700 | | .866 | .5270 | .3390 | 3.299 | 2.573 | .275 | 3.637 | 4.664 | 273.296 | .027 | .228 |
| 1 | 1.315 | 1.049 | .136 | 1.68 | 1.68 | 11½ | 1.576 | 2 | 700 | 1000 | 1.358 | .8546 | .5034 | 4.131 | 3.277 | .344 | 2.904 | 3.662 | 168.474 | .044 | .371 |
| *1¼ | 1.660 | 1.380 | .143 | 2.27 | 2.28 | 11½ | 1.900 | 2 1/16 | 800 | 1000 | 2.164 | 1.4824 | .6816 | 5.215 | 4.316 | .435 | 2.301 | 2.780 | 97.125 | .077 | .643 |
| *1½ | 1.900 | 1.610 | .148 | 2.72 | 2.73 | 11½ | 2.200 | 2 1/16 | 800 | 1000 | 2.835 | 2.0199 | .8151 | 5.969 | 5.039 | .498 | 2.010 | 2.382 | 71.281 | .105 | .876 |
| 2 | 2.375 | 2.067 | .158 | 3.65 | 3.68 | 11½ | 2.750 | 2 1/8 | 800 | 1000 | 4.430 | 3.3444 | 1.0956 | 7.461 | 6.473 | .622 | 1.608 | 1.854 | 43.184 | .173 | 1.446 |
| 2½ | 2.875 | 2.469 | .208 | 5.79 | 5.82 | 8 | 3.250 | 2 5/8 | | 1200 | 6.492 | 4.7529 | 1.7389 | 9.032 | 7.728 | .753 | 1.328 | 1.552 | 30.297 | .247 | 2.060 |
| 3 | 3.500 | 3.068 | .221 | 7.58 | 7.62 | 8 | 4.000 | 3 | | 1200 | 9.621 | 7.3889 | 2.2725 | 10.996 | 9.610 | .917 | 1.091 | 1.249 | 19.596 | .382 | 3.186 |
| 3½ | 4.000 | 3.548 | .231 | 9.11 | 9.20 | 8 | 4.625 | 3 1/8 | | 1200 | 12.566 | 9.8885 | 2.7370 | 12.566 | 11.116 | 1.047 | .954 | 1.079 | 14.644 | .511 | 4.263 |
| 4 | 4.500 | 4.026 | .242 | 10.79 | 10.89 | 8 | 5.000 | 3 1/4 | | 1200 | 15.904 | 12.6670 | 3.2370 | 14.137 | 12.617 | 1.178 | .848 | .951 | 11.368 | .658 | 5.492 |
| 5 | 5.563 | 5.047 | .263 | 14.62 | 14.81 | 8 | 6.296 | 3 3/4 | | 1200 | 24.306 | 19.9209 | 4.3851 | 17.477 | 15.827 | 1.456 | .686 | .758 | 7.229 | 1.035 | 8.636 |
| 6 | 6.625 | 6.065 | .286 | 18.97 | 19.18 | 8 | 7.390 | 3 3/4 | | 1200 | 34.472 | 28.7798 | 5.6922 | 20.813 | 19.017 | 1.734 | .577 | .631 | 5.004 | 1.495 | 12.477 |
| 8 | 8.625 | 8.071 | .283 | 24.70 | 25.00 | 8 | 9.625 | 5 1/4 | | 1000 | 58.426 | 51.0172 | 7.4088 | 27.096 | 25.320 | 2.257 | .443 | .474 | 2.823 | 2.650 | 22.177 |
| 8 | 8.625 | 7.981 | .329 | 28.55 | 28.80 | 8 | 9.625 | 5 1/4 | | 1000 | 58.426 | 49.8598 | 8.5662 | 27.096 | 25.031 | 2.257 | .443 | .479 | 2.889 | 2.590 | 21.616 |
| 10 | 10.750 | 10.192 | .284 | 31.20 | 32.00 | 8 | 11.750 | 5 3/4 | | 1000 | 90.763 | 81.0172 | 9.3603 | 33.772 | 31.983 | 2.817 | .355 | .375 | 1.789 | 4.229 | 35.290 |
| 10 | 10.750 | 10.136 | .313 | 34.24 | 35.00 | 8 | 11.750 | 5 3/4 | | 1000 | 90.763 | 80.4910 | 10.2720 | 33.772 | 31.804 | 2.817 | .355 | .377 | 1.789 | 4.181 | 34.875 |
| 10 | 10.750 | 10.020 | .372 | 40.48 | 41.13 | 8 | 11.750 | 5 3/4 | | 1000 | 90.763 | 78.6181 | 12.1449 | 33.772 | 31.432 | 2.817 | .355 | .382 | 1.832 | 4.084 | 34.083 |
| 12 | 12.750 | 12.090 | .336 | 43.77 | 45.00 | 8 | 14.000 | 6 1/8 | | 1000 | 127.676 | 114.5441 | 13.1319 | 40.055 | 37.940 | 3.338 | .299 | .316 | 1.257 | 5.950 | 49.658 |
| 12 | 12.750 | 11.985 | .382 | 49.56 | 50.70 | 8 | 14.000 | 6 1/8 | | 1000 | 127.676 | 112.8074 | 14.8686 | 40.055 | 37.651 | 3.338 | .299 | .319 | 1.277 | 5.860 | 48.905 |

*Can be furnished in both butt-weld and lap-weld, and unless otherwise specified butt-weld will be furnished.

Standard weight pipe is regularly furnished with threads and couplings; and in random lengths of 16 feet and over with not more than 5% of the total number of lengths as joints, unless otherwise ordered. Threads are cut to American Modified Pipe Thread Standard with ¾ inch taper per foot.
When ordering 8", 10" or 12" sizes, please specify weight of pipe desired.

—From Permission of A. M. Byers Company.

# Byers Genuine Wrought Iron Standard Weight Pipe (Schedule 80)

| Nom. Size | Ext. Diam. | Int. Diam. | Thick-ness | Weight Per Foot | | Thrds. Per Inch | Mill Test Pressure | | Couplings | | Transverse Areas in Sq. In. | | | Circum. In. | | Ext. Area Per Lin. Ft. Pipe (Sq. Ft.) | Lgth. of Pipe in Ft. Per 1 Sq. Ft. Sur. | | Lgth. of Pipe in Feet Having Vol. of 1 Cu. Ft. | U. S. Gal. Per 1 Lin. Ft. Pipe | Weight of Water Per 1 Lin. Ft. Pipe |
|---|---|---|---|---|---|---|---|---|---|---|---|---|---|---|---|---|---|---|---|---|---|
| | | | | Plain Ends | Nom. Thrds. and Cplgs. | | Butt | Lap | Nom. O.D. In. | Nom. Lgth. In. | Ext. | Int. | Net Metal | Ext. | Int. | | Ext. | Int. | | | |
| 1/4 | .540 | .295 | .122 | .54 | .... | .... | 850 | .... | .719 | 1 5/8 | .229 | .0685 | .1605 | 1.696 | .928 | 0.141 | 7.073 | 12.932 | 2101.515 | .004 | .030 |
| 3/8 | .675 | .417 | .129 | .74 | .... | .... | 850 | .... | .875 | 1 5/8 | .358 | .1366 | .2214 | 2.121 | 1.309 | 0.177 | 5.658 | 9.164 | 1055.355 | .007 | .059 |
| 1/2 | .840 | .539 | .151 | 1.09 | .... | .... | 850 | .... | 1.063 | 2 1/8 | .554 | .2279 | .3261 | 2.639 | 1.693 | 0.220 | 4.547 | 7.088 | 631.366 | .012 | .099 |
| 3/4 | 1.050 | .735 | .157 | 1.47 | .... | .... | 850 | .... | 1.313 | 2 1/8 | .886 | .4241 | .4419 | 3.299 | 2.308 | 0.275 | 3.637 | 5.199 | 339.622 | .022 | .183 |
| 1 | 1.315 | .949 | .183 | 2.17 | .... | .... | 850 | .... | 1.576 | 2 5/8 | 1.358 | .7067 | .6513 | 4.131 | 2.973 | 0.344 | 2.904 | 4.037 | 204.247 | .037 | .306 |
| *1 1/4 | 1.660 | 1.269 | .195 | 3.00 | .... | .... | 1100 | 1500 | 2.054 | 2 3/4 | 2.164 | 1.2652 | .8988 | 5.215 | 3.988 | 0.435 | 2.301 | 3.009 | 113.796 | .066 | .549 |
| *1 1/2 | 1.900 | 1.491 | .204 | 3.63 | .... | .... | 1100 | 1500 | 2.200 | 2 3/4 | 2.835 | 1.7457 | 1.0893 | 5.969 | 4.684 | 0.498 | 2.010 | 2.562 | 82.475 | .091 | .757 |
| 2 | 2.375 | 1.929 | .223 | 5.02 | .... | .... | 1100 | 1500 | 2.875 | 3 1/4 | 4.430 | 2.9234 | 1.5066 | 7.461 | 6.061 | 0.622 | 1.608 | 1.980 | 49.255 | .152 | 1.267 |
| 2 1/2 | 2.875 | 2.311 | .282 | 7.66 | .... | .... | .... | 1500 | 3.375 | 4 1/8 | 6.492 | 4.1937 | 2.2983 | 9.032 | 7.259 | 0.753 | 1.328 | 1.653 | 34.339 | .218 | 1.818 |
| 3 | 3.500 | 2.887 | .306 | 10.25 | .... | .... | .... | 1500 | 4.000 | 4 1/4 | 9.621 | 6.5454 | 3.0756 | 10.996 | 9.069 | 0.917 | 1.091 | 1.323 | 22.000 | .340 | 2.838 |
| 3 1/2 | 4.000 | 3.350 | .325 | 12.51 | .... | .... | .... | 1700 | 4.625 | 4 3/8 | 12.566 | 8.8145 | 3.7515 | 12.566 | 10.525 | 1.047 | .954 | 1.140 | 16.336 | .458 | 3.822 |
| 4 | 4.500 | 3.811 | .344 | 14.98 | .... | .... | .... | 1700 | 5.200 | 4 1/2 | 15.904 | 11.4091 | 4.4949 | 14.137 | 11.974 | 1.178 | .848 | 1.002 | 12.621 | .593 | 4.946 |
| 5 | 5.563 | 4.797 | .383 | 20.78 | .... | .... | .... | 1700 | 6.296 | 4 5/8 | 24.306 | 18.0726 | 6.2334 | 17.477 | 15.070 | 1.456 | .686 | .796 | 7.968 | .939 | 7.835 |
| 6 | 6.625 | 5.743 | .441 | 28.57 | .... | .... | .... | 1700 | 7.390 | 4 7/8 | 34.472 | 25.90C1 | 8.5719 | 20.813 | 18.041 | 1.734 | .576 | .665 | 5.560 | 1.345 | 11.228 |
| 8 | 8.625 | 7.604 | .510 | 43.39 | .... | .... | .... | 1700 | 9.625 | 5 1/4 | 58.426 | 45.4096 | 13.0164 | 27.096 | 23.888 | 2.257 | .442 | .502 | 3.171 | 2.359 | 19.687 |
| 10 | 10.750 | 9.729 | .510 | 54.74 | .... | .... | .... | 1600 | 11.750 | 5 3/4 | 90.763 | 73.3425 | 16.4205 | 33.772 | 30.565 | 2.817 | .355 | .393 | 1.937 | 3.862 | 32.229 |
| 12 | 12.750 | 11.729 | .510 | 65.41 | .... | .... | .... | 1600 | 14.000 | 6 1/8 | 127.676 | 108.0515 | 19.6245 | 40.055 | 36.849 | 3.338 | .299 | .326 | 1.333 | 5.613 | 46.844 |

*Can be furnished in both butt-weld and lap-weld, and unless otherwise specified butt-weld will be furnished.
Byers Extra Strong Pipe is regularly furnished in Plain Ends, and in random lengths of 12 feet and over.
Byers Extra Strong Pipe with threads only, or threaded and with couplings, is subject to an extra charge.
Threads are cut to American Modified Pipe Thread Standard with 3/4 inch taper per foot.
Threaded and coupled weight per foot and threads per inch will be furnished upon request.

—From Permission of A. M. Byers Company.

## B. Pipe Joints[7]

In the consideration of pipe composition and construction, the type of joints are of great importance because the several types of joints available, make certain types more desirable for specific instances than others. The relationship between pipe composition and type of joints must be considered from the standpoint that pipe is manufactured with special type ends suitable for certain type of joints. In the consideration of joints for use are such factors as resistance against failure by blowing out, ease of construction, weather conditions to be encountered, economics, flexibility of the joint, stresses and strains which must be endured, handling, and the service life of the particular type of joint. The following is a discussion of common type of joints used for water pipe.

*(1) Calked and Leaded Joint.* The most common of all joints is the calked and leaded joint using bell and spigot end pipe. The bell-end of the pipe is tapered and grooved so that the spigot-end may be centered and seated, then leaded with hot molted lead to give a tight joint. The joint is calked using a yarn so as to give a seat for the lead. Care must be taken in the selection of yarn to assure it to be free of oils and grease, and to be of such composition as not to impart taste or odor to the water or if the water contains a slight residual of chlorine ,that a reaction will not occur with the chlorine to cause related taste or odors.

In this type of joint, the yarn is driven into the joint, then a lead runner is placed around the pipe with a small amount of clay built up around the pourin gmouth. Molten lead is then poured between the runner and the pipe thus filling the joint. The

lead, when cooled, is driven in to give a smooth joint.

Bell and spigot leaded joints give a tight, leakproof joint with great resistance to blowing out. This type of joint is primarily used for cast iron pipe.

*(2) Couplings.* In many cases, it is necessary to use joints on plain-ends of pipe which are without special grooving, threads or provisions for jointing. In such cases, a special type of fitting known as the coupling is used for jointing of such type pipe. Couplings consist of a rubber-type gasket, which is placed under compression by means of a mechanical cast integral so as to form a watertight joint between the coupling body and the pipe.

Couplings are manufactured for ready field use requiring little skill for their installation. They are constructed to allow for great flexibility in final installation as to absorb stresses and strains within the pipeline. Couplings may be used for joints on cast iron pipe, concrete pressure pipe, cement-asbestos pipe, copper pipe, galvanized iron pipe, plastic pipe, steel pipe, and wrought iron pipe.

The coupling is especially important as a repair unit in case of pipe failure. In such cases, the coupling is slipped into position over the point of failure and is tightened to give a water tight repair without taking the pipe out of service for long periods of time.

*(3) Flanged Joint.* The flanged-type joint is used for pipe in which both ends of the pipe are manufactured with bells which are flanged so that the pipes may be jointed by bolting together. A special rubber-type gasket is used within the joint for water tightness and flexibility. This type of joint may be used for cast iron pipe

and plastic pipe which are provided with flanged ends, or other metallic pipe which may be threaded or non-metallic pipes which may be provided with special fittings. Advantages of flanged joints include minimum of skill for their installation, all-weather installation, and water-tight joints.

*(4) Gasket Joint.* Many pipes are provided with special grooving which are designed to utilize a simple type of joint. This type of joint consists of a rubber-type gasket which is inserted within the grooving and the second pipe is forced into an interlocked position to give a watertight and flexible joint. Each type of pipe utilizing this type of joint will have special gaskets for that specific type

of pipe and will require certain techniques for making such joints.

Gasket-type joints may be used for cast iron pipe, cement-asbestos pipe, and concrete pressure pipe. The advantages of this type of joint may be summarized as a simple type of joint requiring little skill for its installation, all-weather installation, watertight, flexibility, and ability to absorb shock, vibration, and stresses or strains.

*(5) Mechanical Joint.* The mechanical type of joint is used for joining pipe which contain a bell-end which is flanged and a plain-end which is not flanged. The joint consists of a ring and gasket which are placed around the plain-end of one pipe, and

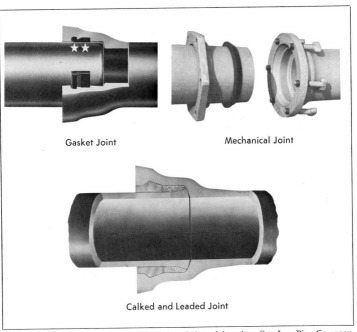

Gasket Joint

Mechanical Joint

Calked and Leaded Joint

—From Permission of American Cast Iron Pipe Company.

**Figure 31. Typical Cast Iron Pipe Joints.**

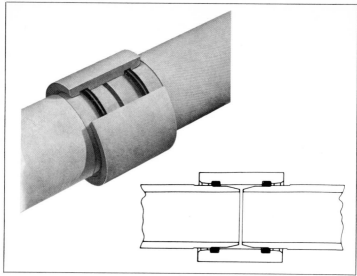

—From Permission of Johns-Manville Company.

**Figure 32. Typical Asbestos-Cement Pipe Joint.**

then are bolted to the bell flanged end of the other pipe. The gasket is compressed, thus giving a water-tight joint. This joint provides flexibility in absorbing stresses and strains and allows for some expansion and contraction. This type joint requires little skill in its installation and may be used in all types of weather. Mechanical joints are used for cast iron pipe joints.

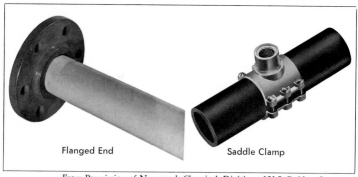

Flanged End                    Saddle Clamp

—From Permission of Naugatuck Chemical, Division of U.S. Rubber Company.

**Figure 33. Typical Fittings for Plastic Pipe.**

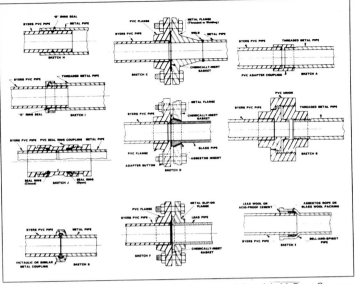

—From Permission of A. M. Byers Company.

**Figure 34. Typical Sections and Joints for Plastic Pipe.**

### 5. Distribution System Appurtenances

In the design and construction of distribution systems, certain basic criteria should be followed regarding the location of valves, hydrants, air relief valves, and blow-offs.

### A. Gate Valves

An adequate number of gate valves must be located throughout the distribution system. The purpose of strategically locating an adequate number of such valves is that in the event of a break or if it is necessary to take the line out of service for some purpose, only a small section of the line may be cut out of service by closing the gate valves. In the event of an unexpected break as mentioned above, the broken section may be cut off so that the storage will not be entirely lost and that repairs may be rapidly made in a trench not subject to continuous flooding.

Table XXXV gives the recommended location and number of gate valves within the distribution system[2].

## TABLE XXXV
## Location and Number of Gate Valves Required

| Type of Pipe and Connection | Location of Gate Valves |
|---|---|
| Long Single Lines with no Laterals. | Valve desired each 1,000 feet for small lines up to three inches. For larger mains, from 1,500 to 2,500 feet. |
| Tee, Single Branch Line from Main Line. Cross, Two Branch or Laterals from Main Line. | Two valves, one on main line and on on lateral. Three valves, one on main line and one cn each lateral. |

Gate valves are available in both rising and non-rising stems. Within the non-rising stem, the gate rises by being lifted on the stem threads, while the rising stem, commonly referred to as Outside Screw and Yoke (OS and Y), the gate is lifted as the stem rises.

Gate valves are also available in many types of ends for ready installation within the pipeline. Types of ends are hub, mechanical joint, flanged, and screwed ends. Arrangements of all of these ends are available to meet the specific needs as required for the pipeline conditions.

Illustrations of typical gate valves and valve ends are given in Figure 35.

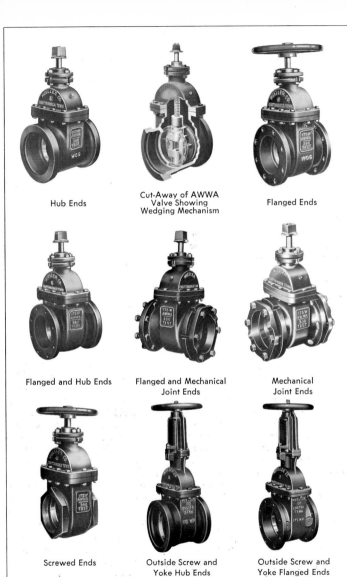

Hub Ends

Cut-Away of AWWA
Valve Showing
Wedging Mechanism

Flanged Ends

Flanged and Hub Ends

Flanged and Mechanical
Joint Ends

Mechanical
Joint Ends

Screwed Ends

Outside Screw and
Yoke Hub Ends

Outside Screw and
Yoke Flanged Ends

—©1953, Mueller Company, By Permission.

**Figure 35.  Typical Gate Valves and Valve Ends.**

## TABLE XXXVI
## Location of Fire Hydrants

| Type of Area Served | Location of Hydrant |
|---|---|
| Residential. | Within 400 feet of each residence. |
| Commercial, Industrial High-value District. | Located so that an adequate number of fire streams may be utilized. Should be conveniently located for fire engine access. |

### B. Hydrants

Within large systems and some smaller systems, fire protection is desired by the water consumers in addition to domestic water. Therefore, the pipelines will be sized as discussed within the paragraphs on Fire Flows. The location of fire hydrants should be as indicated in Table XXXVI above[2].

It is recommended that a gate valve be located on the lead-out to the hydrant so that in the event the hydrant is damaged or becomes out of order to need replacement, it may be easily accomplished by closing the gate valve thereby not interferring with water service. To prevent the water surge or water hammer from breaking the lead-out and hydrant connections, a block of concrete should be poured to the outside of the hydrant and the hydrant should be strapped with at least two one-half-inch round steel rods, some distance back on the lead-out pipe, to act as an anchor for the hydrant.

Hydrants are available in four, four and one-half, five, and six-inch sizes with one, two, and three outlets including streamer connection. The service main serving the hydrant should be of at least four inches in diameter with preferable six inches being the minimum. Inlet ends of hydrants are available in hub, flanged, and mechanical joint ends.

Typical illustrations for fire hydrants, hydrant ends, cross-section, and nomenclature are given in Figures 36 and 37.

### C. Air Valves

Air entrained in water, tends to accumulate at the high points within long single feed lines where there are no services. Therefore, air relief valves should be located at these high points to release the air as it accumulates within the system. This is usually accomplished by a float arrangement within the air valve which is actuated by the air pressure within the valve thus allowing the air to escape through a small orifice. The water displacing the air will cause the float to rise and close the orifice.

Air valves should be located in either metal or concrete vaults which are easily accessible for inspection and maintenance. Vaults should be provided with adequate sized drains to keep the vault dry.

(Continued on Page 108)

Two Way       Three Way       With Auxiliary
Gate Valve

Hub End Inlet     Flanged      Universal      Mechanical
             End Inlet     End Inlet     Joint End Inlet

Size of Inlet End: 4″ or 6″ on 4¼″, 4½″ and 5¼″ hydrants; 6″ or 8″ on 6¼″ hydrants.

**Figure 37. Cross-Section of Fire Hydrant.**

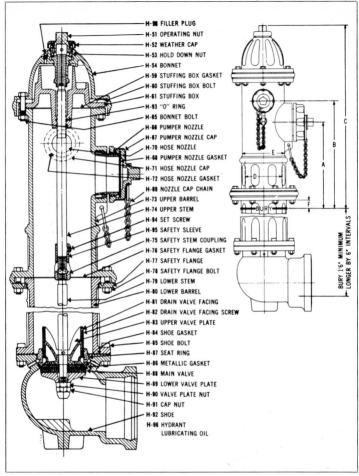

H-50 FILLER PLUG
H-51 OPERATING NUT
H-52 WEATHER CAP
H-53 HOLD DOWN NUT
H-54 BONNET
H-59 STUFFING BOX GASKET
H-60 STUFFING BOX BOLT
H-61 STUFFING BOX
H-63 "O" RING
H-65 BONNET BOLT
H-66 PUMPER NOZZLE
H-67 PUMPER NOZZLE CAP
H-70 HOSE NOZZLE
H-68 PUMPER NOZZLE GASKET
H-71 HOSE NOZZLE CAP
H-72 HOSE NOZZLE GASKET
H-69 NOZZLE CAP CHAIN
H-73 UPPER BARREL
H-74 UPPER STEM
H-94 SET SCREW
H-95 SAFETY SLEEVE
H-75 SAFETY STEM COUPLING
H-76 SAFETY FLANGE GASKET
H-77 SAFETY FLANGE
H-78 SAFETY FLANGE BOLT
H-79 LOWER STEM
H-80 LOWER BARREL
H-81 DRAIN VALVE FACING
H-82 DRAIN VALVE FACING SCREW
H-83 UPPER VALVE PLATE
H-84 SHOE GASKET
H-85 SHOE BOLT
H-87 SEAT RING
H-86 METALLIC GASKET
H-88 MAIN VALVE
H-89 LOWER VALVE PLATE
H-90 VALVE PLATE NUT
H-91 CAP NUT
H-92 SHOE
H-96 HYDRANT LUBRICATING OIL

Figure 36. Typical Fire Hydrants and Hydrant Inlets.

Air valves should be sized in accordance with the size of the pipeline. It is suggested that such sizes be one inch diameter for each one foot of pipe diameter.

## D. Blow-Off Valves

Undersirable products of corrosion may accumulate within the distribution system and especially in locations such as dead end lines, depressions such as dead end lines, depression or low places on long distribution lines, and in areas where large pipelines are located but the usage is extremely low. Therefore, it is desirable to have valves on waste lines so that large volumes of water at high velocities may be discharged at certain points. Fire hydrants are usually used for blowing this inferior water out of the system. In the use of fire hydrants for this use, care must be taken to open and close the hydrant slowly to reduce surge and water hammer.

However, in some cases, long feed lines are used to carry low flows without the location of fire hydrants on such lines. In such cases, blow-off valves should be used in low areas so that the line may be cleaned by creating high velocities by use of these blow-off valves. The sizing of blow-off valves are given in Table XXXVII.

Care should be taken in anchoring the blow-off valve and line to the water main in the same manner as recommended for the fire hydrant.

In location of blow-off valves, consideration should be given to the possibility of flooding adjacent property because of the high discharge and the large total volume of water which must be drawn off at times to completely clean the line of sediment.

## TABLE XXXVII
## Recommended Sizing of Blow-Off Valves and Lines

| Size of Water Main | Size of Blow-Off Valve |
|---|---|
| Up to Four Inches. | Same size as main. |
| Six Inches. | Four-inch line and valve. |
| Eight Inches and Over. | Six-inch line and valve. |

### E. Service Connections, Lines, and Meters

The proper selection of service lines and meter sizes are extremely important in providing an adequate supply of water to each user. In many cases, hte water at the street supply will provide ample supply and pressure, but small service lines and inadequate sized meters increase the friction to such an extent that low flows and pressures are encountered and the user does not receive the benefit of the street supply.

The selection of the size of service line should be based on the maximum instantaneous flow calculated for the particular user as obtained from Tables XXI, XXII, and XXIII as a guide, *and* upon the size of meter necessary to supply this flow as determined from Table XXXVIII. In other words, if the user is some distance from the street feeder main, it is necessary to get the larger quantity of water to the meter and the size of the meter should be adequate to provide the designated quantity without a significant increase in friction or head loss. The service line serving the meter should *always* be equal in size or greater than the meter size in

## TABLE XXXVIII
## Selection of Water Meter Size from Flow Demand

| Meter Size Inch | Required Flow By User GPM |
|---|---|
| 5/8 | 15 |
| 3/4 | 25 |
| 1 | 37 |
| 1 1/2 | 75 |
| 2 | 120 |
| 3 | 225 |
| 4 | 350 |
| 6 | 750 |
| 8 | 1,200 |
| 10 | 2,000 |

cases where the meter is near the user. In the event that the meter is placed at the street and a long service line is necessary to serve the user from the meter location, then the meter should be equal to that size line and should not be smaller so as to form a bottleneck within the system by causing reduced pressure and flow.

Therefore, the following steps should be used in sizing both the service line and meter service:

1. Determine the maximum instantaneous water demand from Tables XXI, XXII, and XXIII. This is the same calculation that is made to determine sizing of the distribution system as discussed on Page 62. As in the case of institutions, commercial areas, etc., the future water flows should be estimated so that the meter and service lines will be adequate for usage as that time.

2. Determine the size of the meter. The following table may be used for the selection of meter size. This table provides for a friction loss equivalent to 50% or less of the distribution system pressure. It also provides for a flow equivalent to 75% or less of the maximum flow through the meter.

In cases where the meter is at the distribution or street main and a long service line extends between the user and the meter, the meter should be sized equal to or greater than the service line.

3. The service line should meet the criteria that it should be of adequate size to supply the maximum demand of the user from the average distribution system pressure and it should not be less in size than the selected meter size. Therefore, in the case where the service line is short, one should select the meter size from a knowledge of flow demand, then compare with Table XXIV through XXVI to determine if an equivalent size line is adequate to carry the required flow of water. In the case where the feed line is extremely long and the meter is near the user, the size of the service line should be determined from Table XXXVIII and should be equal in size or greater in size than the meter. If the meter were at the beginning of a long service line, the size of the service line would be determined from Table XXIV through XXVI and a meter of equivalent size would be installed.

For expedience in determining the size of service lines and meters to supply certain quantities of water for varying lengths of service lines, Table XXXIX may be used to give size of service line and size of meter.

## TABLE XXXIX
## Sizing of Service Lines and Meters for Various Flows and Various Lengths of Service Lines When the Meter is Located at the Distribution System Under an Average Pressure of 40 Pounds per Square Inch*

| Flow Required by User in GPM | Meter Size Inches | Length of Service Line from Meter to User, Feet | | | | | | | | | | |
|---|---|---|---|---|---|---|---|---|---|---|---|---|
| | | 50 | 100 | 200 | 300 | 400 | 500 | 600 | 700 | 800 | 900 | 1,000 |
| | | Size of Service Line, Inches | | | | | | | | | | |
| 10 | 5/8 | 3/4 | 3/4 | | | | | | | | | |
| 10 | 3/4 | 3/4 | 3/4 | 3/4 | | | | | | | | |
| 10 | 1 | 1 | 1 | 1 | 1 | 1 | | | | | | |
| 10 | 1½ | 1½ | 1½ | 1½ | 1½ | 1½ | 1½ | 1½ | 1½ | 1½ | 1½ | 1½ |
| 20 | 3/4 | 3/4 | 3/4 | | | | | | | | | |
| 20 | 1 | 1 | 1 | 1 | | | | | | | | |
| 20 | 1½ | 1½ | 1½ | 1½ | 1½ | 1½ | 1½ | 1½ | 1½ | 1½ | 1½ | 1½ |
| 30 | 1 | 1 | | | | | | | | | | |
| 30 | 1½ | 1½ | 1½ | 1½ | 1½ | 1½ | 1½ | 1½ | 1½ | 1½ | 1½ | 1½ |
| 40 | 1½ | 1½ | 1½ | 1½ | 1½ | 1½ | 1½ | | | | | |
| 40 | 2 | 2 | 2 | 2 | 2 | 2 | 2 | 2 | 2 | 2 | 2 | 2 |
| 50 | 1½ | 1½ | 1½ | 1½ | 1½ | | | | | | | |
| 50 | 2 | 2 | 2 | 2 | 2 | 2 | 2 | 2 | 2 | 2 | 2 | 2 |
| 60 | 1½ | 1½ | 1½ | 1½ | | | | | | | | |
| 60 | 2 | 2 | 2 | 2 | 2 | 2 | 2 | 2 | 2 | 2 | 2 | |
| 60 | 3 | 3 | 3 | 3 | 3 | 3 | 3 | 3 | 3 | 3 | 3 | 3 |
| 70 | 2 | 2 | 2 | 2 | 2 | 2 | 2 | 2 | | | | |
| 70 | 3 | 3 | 3 | 3 | 3 | 3 | 3 | 3 | 3 | 3 | 3 | 3 |
| 80 | 2 | 2 | 2 | 2 | 2 | 2 | 2 | | | | | |
| 80 | 3 | 3 | 3 | 3 | 3 | 3 | 3 | 3 | 3 | 3 | 3 | 3 |
| 90 | 2 | 2 | 2 | 2 | 2 | 2 | | | | | | |
| 90 | 3 | 3 | 3 | 3 | 3 | 3 | 3 | 3 | 3 | 3 | 3 | 3 |
| 100 | 2 | 2 | 2 | 2 | 2 | | | | | | | |
| 100 | 3 | 3 | 3 | 3 | 3 | 3 | 3 | 3 | 3 | 3 | 3 | 3 |
| 125 | 3 | 3 | 3 | 3 | 3 | 3 | 3 | 3 | 3 | 3 | 3 | 3 |
| 150 | 3 | 3 | 3 | 3 | 3 | 3 | 3 | 3 | 3 | 3 | 3 | 3 |
| 175 | 3 | 3 | 3 | 3 | 3 | 3 | 3 | 3 | 3 | 3 | 3 | 3 |
| 200 | 3 | 3 | 3 | 3 | 3 | 3 | 3 | 3 | 3 | 3 | | |
| 200 | 4 | 4 | 4 | 4 | 4 | 4 | 4 | 4 | 4 | 4 | 4 | 4 |
| 300 | 4 | 4 | 4 | 4 | 4 | 4 | 4 | 4 | 4 | 4 | 4 | 4 |
| 400 | 6 | 6 | 6 | 6 | 6 | 6 | 6 | 6 | 6 | 6 | 6 | 6 |
| 500 | 6 | 6 | 6 | 6 | 6 | 6 | 6 | 6 | 6 | 6 | 6 | 6 |

*Note: For flows less than 300 gpm, the length of service lines must be decreased by approximately 50% when the average operating pressure of the distribution system is 20 pounds per square inch rather than 40 pounds per square inch.

A further method of sizing the service main to a building is by the calculation of flow from the number of fixture units[15]. Fixture units are determined by the number and type of plumbing fixtures within a building on the basis that:

A water closet equals to six fixture units.

A residential-type lavatory, urinal, kitchen sink, and shower equals to two fixture units each.

A drinking fountain equals to one fixture unit.

Combination fixtures equal to two fixture units.

Other type fixtures equal to three fixture units each.

The total number of fixtures times their respective fixture units will give the total number of fixture units within a building. The required flow is then based on one gallon per minute flow per fixture unit:

$$\text{Required Flow, gpm} = 1 \text{ gpm/fixture unit} \times \text{Total Number of Fixture Units}$$

From known distribution system pressure, the size of the service line may be obtained by trial and error selection by trying the different size of pipes and computing the overall differential pressure so that the residual main pressure will be greater than the total pressure loss within the service line and building plumbing. This may be formulated as follows:

Differential Pressure, psi = Distribution — Desired Pressure at — Meter Friction —
(This must be a positive number) Main Pressure in psi Highest Fixture in Building, psi (Select 20 psi) Loss, psi (Table XLI)

$$\left[\frac{\text{Height of Building Plumbing in Feet} + \text{Total Friction Loss in Pipe in Feet per 100 feet} + \text{Length of Pipe in 100 Feet Units}}{2.31}\right]$$

The desired pressure on the highest plumbing fixture within the building should not be less than 20 pounds per square inch for proper operation of fixtures and prevention of back-siphonage.

In many instances, the distribution system is unmetered. Therefore, the service lines may be selected from Tables XXIV through XXVI. Table XL is a compilation of various flows and lengths of service lines for rapid selection of pipe size for the service line.

## TABLE XL
### Selection of Sizes of Service Lines for Various Flows and Lengths of Such Lines for Unmetered Systems Where the Operating Pressure is 40 Pounds per Square Inch

| Flow Required by Consumer in GPM | \multicolumn{11}{c}{Length of Service Line from Distribution System to Meter in Feet} | | | | | | | | | | |
|---|---|---|---|---|---|---|---|---|---|---|---|
| | 50 | 100 | 200 | 300 | 400 | 500 | 600 | 700 | 800 | 900 | 1,000 |
| 10 | | | 3/4 | 1 | | | | | | 1¼ | 1½ |
| 20 | 3/4 | 1 | | | | | 1¼ | | | | 1½ |
| 30 | | 1 | | | 1¼ | | | | | | 1½ |
| 40 | 1 | | | 1¼ | | 1½ | | | | | 2 |
| 50 | | | 1¼ | 1½ | | | | | | | 2 |
| 60 | | | 1½ | | | | | | | 2 | 3 |
| 70 | 1¼ | 1½ | | | | | 2 | | | | 2½ |
| 80 | | | | | 2 | | | | | | 2½ |
| 90 | | | | 2 | | | | | | 2½ | 3 |
| 100 | | | | 2 | | | | | 2½ | | 3 |
| 125 | | | 2 | | 2½ | | | | | | 3 |
| 150 | | 2 | | 2½ | | | | | | | 3 |
| 175 | | 2 | 2½ | | | | | | | | 3 |
| 200 | | 2 | 2½ | | | | | | 3 | | 4 |
| 300 | | 2½ | | 3 | | | | | | | 4 |
| 400 | | | 3 | | | 4 | | | | | 6 |
| 500 | | 3 | | 4 | | | | | | | 6 |

Note: The length of service lines must be decreased by approximately 50% when the average operating pressure of the distribution system is 20 pounds per square inch rather than 40 pounds per square inch.

Typical Meter Data relating to disc-type meters is given in Table XLI[13].

## TABLE XLI
### Typical Meter Data-Disc Type Meters

| Mete Size Inches | Meter Dimensions, Inches | | Weight in Pounds | Maximum Safe Flow GPM | Head Loss in Pounds at Maximum Discharge |
|---|---|---|---|---|---|
| | Length | Height | | | |
| 5/8 | 7½ | 7¾ | 11 | 26 | 15 |
| 3/4 | 9 | 8 | 13 | 40 | 11 |
| 1 | 10¾ | 9 | 20 | 65 | 12 |
| 1½ | 12⅝ | 9¾ | 31 | 130 | 8½ |
| 2 | 15½ | 11 | 53 | 160 | 4 |
| 3 | 14 | 16 | 135 | 350 | 10 |

—Courtesy of Badger Meter Mfg. Company.

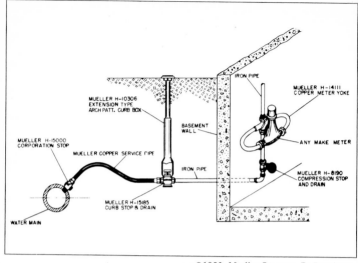

**Figure 38. Typical Distribution Connection for Large Mains.**

### 6. Distribution System Pipe Testing

After the completion of installation of a pipeline, a test of tightness or leakage of the joints should be made by applying pressure on the line by means of a test pump. The leakage test may be conducted using either water or air. It is usual procedure to use a water test and apply a pressure of 150 pounds per square inch on the pipe for a teest period of not less than three hours. The desired leakage should be less than 65 gallons per day per mile based on an eight-inch diameter pipe. Or in other words, the leakage in gallons should be less than the pipe diameter in inches x 0.00154 x the length of pipe of feet[2].

### 7. Depth of Cover Over Pipeline

The depth of cover for a pipeline is governed by the climatical and the structural conditions which exist within the area where the pipe is to be constructed. To meet these conditions, it is desirable to have the depth great enough so that the pipe will be below the frost line. This depth in the moderate temperature zones will range from two to three feet, while in the extreme zones will range from four to six feet. Structural conditions such as roads, railways, weight of backfill, etc., greatly influence the depth of the pipeline. No definite rule may be established concerning these obstacles for the depth of pipeline location. However, it is suggested that a minimum depth of from two to three feet be established, thus reducing such effects as freezing, expansion due to temperature, vibration, shock, etc., to a very minimum[2].

# Economics of Water Systems

**General**

The economics of a community water system should be given careful consideration before one proceeds with the construction and operation of such a system. The economics of a water system depends upon the initial cost of the installation, depreciation, and the estimated life of the component parts of the system, revenue produced, easements and rights-of-way, and finally the cost of maintenance and operation of the system. Due to the larger cost of certain components of a water system, the economics is greatly dependent upon the size of the system or number of connections to be served because operation and maintenance of the system will call for full-time personnel in large systems whereas part-time personnel may be utilized for smaller systems.

**1. Sources of Water Supply**
**A. Ground Water Supplies**

Profitable time is warranted in the early planning stage of a water system in appraising every cost in order that an estimate may be obtained prior to the actual construction of the system. Within this chapter, cost estimates are given for the many components of the water system. As these vary greatly from locality to locality, local dealers, well drillers, pipe companies, pump manufacturers, etc., should be contacted in order that reliable current prices may be obtained for planning purposes. The cost data within these many tables may however, be used to give rough estimations of cost.

From reliable local sources, it is possible to obtain general information as to the depth and possible yields of wells within the local area. Therefore, whatever values are obtained should be used in the estimation of the supply to be used. To be included in the total cost of the well is the price of the land which can only be estimated from prevailing land prices. The amount of land to be purchased should be approximately one acre. If this amount of land is not available, then a 100-foot by 100-foot lot should be purchased as the minimum in order to prevent sources of pollution from being located nearer to the well installation. Table XLII gives estimated costs for construction of the well.

## TABLE XLII
### Estimated Drilling Costs for Wells

| Diameter of Well | Cost Per Foot |
|---|---|
| 4 inches | $5.00 - $6.00 |
| 6 inches | 6.00 - 8.00 |
| 8 inches | 8.00 - 10.00 |
| 10 inches | 10.00 - 12.00 |

The depths of community water supply wells are usually about 175 to 225 feet. In some cases, shallow wells of 75 to 100 feet are found to yield adequate amounts while in other areas, 300 to 350 feet are necessary to meet adequate yields. For protection of the well, a four-foot square slab of six inches in thickness should be used around the well. This will require approximately a yard of concrete. The wellhouse design is optional, depending upon the type of pump used and the desired space within that is needed. It is important that the design and construction of the wellhouse be in conformity with the existing or proposed architecture of the community, otherwise it will stand out as an undesirable structure to injure the community. Of course, if any type of chemical treatment is to be used at the well such as disinfection or corrosion control, then it will be necessary to provide a much larger house to properly house and operate these units. A wellhouse above ground level is certainly desirable from the standpoint of operation and weatherproofing of electrical controls and other equipment. In most cases, the total cost of the wellhouse of an adequate size to properly house controls and equipment, six feet by eight feet, will be in the order of $650.00. For estimating purposes only, one may estimate the following:

Lot for Well, 100 feet by 100 feet at $3,000.00 per acre ...... $  750.00
Concrete Slab around well, six-inch thickness for
  six feet by eight feet .............................. 100.00
Wellhouse, brick construction, six feet by eight feet ........ 650.00

Total cost of wellhouse ........................... $1,500.00

The cost of development of a surface water supply greatly exceeds that of a ground supply because of the complexity of treatment involved. Within the realm of surface supplies are the many factors such as location and adequacy of source, size of the treatment works, duplicate pumping such as raw and finished water, filtration, chemical treatment, and clearwater storage.

It is most difficult to establish within reason, cost estimates for treatment facilities because of the many variables which enter into the problem. However, as a rough guide, the following is given:

Reservoir .......... $3,000 - $4,500 - $6,000 per million gallons stored
Raw Water Pumping Station $30,000 - $50,000 per million gallons treated
Treatment Works
            $200,000 - $300,000 - $450,000 per million gallons treated
Influencing the cost of each will be construction obstacles, length of transmission lines, mechanical equipment and valves.

A breakdown of the investment of a water system, the following distribution is usually found:

|  | Per Cent Distribution of Investment Avg. |
| --- | --- |
| Raw Water Storage, Pumping, Transmission .......... | 25 - 32 - 40 |
| Filtration Plant, Finished Water Pumping ............ | 20 - 24 - 30 |
| Distribution System ............................. | 30 - 33 - 40 |
| Elevated Storage ................................ | 8 - 11 - 15 |

### 2. Pumping and Wiring

In the selection of the pump for each specific use, it will be necessary to design the pump for each installation to give the most efficient performance for the head and capacity of the installation. Therefore, each pump must be selected on the basis of the job it is to do. A reliable pump manufacturer should be contacted so that the details of the design may be worked out.

The cost of operation of a pump installation is the power cost and the amount required for maintenance, amortization of investment with interest, and insurance. The latter may be reasonably estimated to be 10 to 15 per cent of the total investment. Power cost will vary with pumpage time and power rates as follows[3]:

$$
\begin{array}{c}
\text{Cost of} \\
\text{Power} \\
\text{for Pump} \\
\text{Operation} \\
\text{per year}
\end{array}
=
365 \text{ days} \times
\begin{array}{c}
\text{Hours} \\
\text{Pump} \\
\text{Operated} \\
\text{per Day}
\end{array}
\times 0.746 \times \text{Pump Horsepower} \times
\begin{array}{c}
\text{Power} \\
\text{Cost} \\
\text{in Cents} \\
\text{Per KW-} \\
\text{Hour}
\end{array}
=
\begin{array}{c}
\$ \\
\text{per} \\
\text{Year}
\end{array}
$$

Table XLIII will be of value in estimating the cost of the pump installation from the horsepower required obtained from Page 31.

## TABLE XLIII
### Estimated Cost of Pump Installation*

| Horsepower of Pump | Cost of Installation |
|---|---|
| 1/2 | $ 265.00 |
| 3/4 | 336.00 |
| 1 | 420.00 |
| 1 1/2 | 570.00 |
| 2 | 720.00 |
| 3 | 1,020.00 |
| 4 | 1,200.00 |
| 5 | 1,420.00 |
| 7 1/2 | 1,620.00 |
| 10 | 1,920.00 |
| 15 | 2,200.00 |
| 20 | 2,620.00 |
| 25 | 3,000.00 |
| 30 | 3,600.00 |
| 40 | 4,500.00 |
| 50 | 5,040.00 |

* Includes Motor, Pump, Controls, etc.

## 3. Storage

The economics of storage facilities of the water system is affected by the capacity of such facilities and the type of storage to be utilized as discussed in Chapter III. These types are low pressure with high pressure, pneumatic storage, and elevated storage. First of all, it should be decided from information available, what type of storage is desirable and the quantity of storage which must be available to have an adequate system. Utilizing Tables XLIV and XLV, it is possible to determine, after comparison, just what type of storage will be most economical.

Table XLIV states "Storage in Place." This means that the facility is ready for use in that valves, footing pipe inlets and outlets, and drains are completely installed.

In all storage installations, the drain and overflow pipes should discharge into storm drains which are properly trenched. Care should be taken not to discharge the overflow or drain into a sanitary sewer because of back-siphonage or the flooding of the sewer.

## TABLE XLIV
### Estimated Cost of Storage Facilities in Place

| Amount of Storage (in gallons) | Low Pressure | Pneumatic | Elevated |
|---|---|---|---|
| 500 | $    120.00 | $    450.00 | |
| 750 | 160.00 | 630.00 | |
| 1,000 | 190.00 | 750.00 | |
| 1,500 | 280.00 | 900.00 | |
| 2,500 | 475.00 | 1,440.00 | |
| 5,000 | 1,050.00 | 2,540.00 | 3,600.00 |
| 7,500 | 1,450.00 | 3,600.00 | 5,050.00 |
| 10,000 | 1,920.00 | 4,800.00 | 6,040.00 |
| 15,000 | 2,340.00 | 5,750.00 | 12,000.00 |
| 20,000 | 3,360.00 | 7,200.00 | 14,400.00 |
| 25,000 | 4,675.00 | 9,000.00 | 16,200.00 |
| 30,000 | 5,600.00 | | 21,500.00 |
| 40,000 | 8,640.00 | | 25,200.00 |
| 50,000 | 12,000.00 | | 31,500.00 |
| 60,000 | 15,800.00 | | 42,000.00 |
| 75,000 | 23,500.00 | | 50,400.00 |
| 100,000 | 35,000.00 | | 57,600.00 |

Recommended size for inlets, outlets, drains, and overflows for storage tanks are given in Table XLV.

## TABLE XLV
## Minimum Size Piping for Storage Facilities (Inches)

| Amount of Storage (in gallons) | Low Pressure Inlet-Outlet | High Pressure Inlet-Outlet | Overflow | Drain |
|---|---|---|---|---|
| 500 | 2 | 2 | 2 | 2 |
| 750 | 2 | 2 | 2 | 2 |
| 1,000 | 2 | 2 | 2 | 2 |
| 1,500 | 2 | 3 | 2 | 3 |
| 2,500 | 2 | 3 | 2 | 3 |
| 5,000 | 2 | 4 | 3 | 4 |
| 7,500 | 3 | 4 | 3 | 4 |
| 10,000 | 3 | 4 | 3 | 4 |
| 15,000 | 3 | 4 | 3 | 4 |
| 20,000 | 4 | 6 | 4 | 6 |
| 25,000 | 4 | 6 | 4 | 6 |
| 30,000 | 4 | 6 | 4 | 6 |
| 40,000 | 6 | 8 | 6 | 8 |
| 50,000 | 6 | 8 | 6 | 8 |
| 60,000 | 6 | 8 | 6 | 8 |
| 75,000 | 8 | 10 | 6 | 10 |
| 100,000 | 8 | 10 | 8 | 12 |

### 4. Distribution System

The distribution system consists of the feeder lines, valves, service lines, meters, and fire hydrants.

In order to estimate the cost of the distribution system, it is necessary to scale from the layout to get the approximate footage of each size of pipe within the system. Table XLVI sets forth estimated cost per foot for varied sized pipes.

Service lines from the main to the

## TABLE XLVI
## Distribution System Pipe Cost

| Pipe Size (Inches) | Cost Per Foot Installed |
|---|---|
| 1 (Galvanized) | $1.30 |
| 1½ | 1.90 |
| 2 | 2.60 |
| 3 | 3.00 |
| 4 (Cast Iron) | 3.60 |
| 6 | 4.40 |
| 8 | 5.20 |
| 10 | 6.60 |
| 12 | 9.00 |
| 16 | 12.60 |
| 18 | 15.00 |
| 20 | 19.20 |

meter should be ¾ or one inch with the one inch being preferable.

Valves within a distribution system provide adequate operational control of the system. Table XXXV sets forth the recommended location of valves within the system. By knowing the location of the valves within a proposed system, the total number and sizes of valves can be obtained. Table XLVII gives the estimated cost of valves including valve boxes and installation cost.

All valve boxes should be brought to the surface of the street and care should be taken during repavement of any street that this is done.

Used within water systems are check valves at such locations as pump installations in which the flow is prevented from flowing in both directions. Check valve and installation costs are given in Table XLVIII.

## TABLE XLVII
### Gate Valve and Installation Cost

| Valve Size (Inches) | Cost of Valve Installation |
|---|---|
| ¾ | $    4.55 |
| 1 | 6.50 |
| 1½ | 13.00 |
| 2 | 39.00 |
| 3 | 65.00 |
| 4 | 110.00 |
| 6 | 135.00 |
| 8 | 175.00 |
| 10 | 286.00 |
| 12 | 350.00 |
| 16 | 915.00 |
| 18 | 1,170.00 |
| 20 | 1,430.00 |
| 24 | 2,175.00 |

## TABLE XLVIII
### Check Valve and Installation Cost

| Valve Size (Inches) | Cost of Installation of Class 300 Valve | |
|---|---|---|
| | Threaded Joint | Butt or Flanged End |
| 2 | $35.00 | $ 38.00 |
| 2½ | 42.00 | 45.00 |
| 3 | 50.00 | 54.00 |
| 4 | 69.00 | 74.00 |
| 6 | | 128.00 |
| 8 | | 215.00 |
| 10 | | 325.00 |
| 12 | | 425.00 |

## TABLE XLIX
## Meter and Installation Cost

| Meter Size | Meter and Installation Cost |
| --- | --- |
| 5/8 | $ 72.00 |
| 3/4 | 76.00 |
| 1 | 130.00 |
| 1½ | 275.00 |
| 2 | 357.00 |
| 3 | 445.00 |
| 4 | 720.00 |
| 6 | 1,080.00 |
| 8 | 1,420.00 |
| 10 | 1,800.00 |

* ¾″ to 1″ Service Lines, estimate $3.00 per foot.

The meter installation includes the cost of the goose neck where the service line ties to the main feeder in the street, the curb stop, the meter yoke, meter box, and box cover. Figure 38 illustrates a typical distribution system connection for large mains and indicates integral parts for such a connection.

The service line from the distribution system to the consumer should be of adequate size to supply the needs of the consumer at all times. Typical meter data for disc-type meters is given on Page 113. Cost of meter and installation of same is given in Table XLIX.

For large distribution systems, it is desirable to install fire hydrants as the transmission and storage systems will usually be large enough to furnish an ample supply for fire fighting purposes. Fire hydrants should be of ample size and should be installed so that each residence is within 400 feet of a hydrant. In the high value districts, commercial, institutional, etc., it is desirable to locate the hydrants closer together so that several fire streams may be had in small confined areas. A gate valve should be located between the system and the hydrant leadout, so that in the event of accident or necessary replacement of the hydrant, such may be done without interfering with the water service on the system. Cost of installation including cost of hydrant, gate valve, leadout, etc., are given in Table L.

## TABLE L
## Cost of Fire Hydrant Installation

| Size of Hydrant (Inches) | Cost of Installation |
| --- | --- |
| 4—One-way | $156.00 |
| 4½—Two-way | 175.00 |
| 5—Three-way | 225.00 |
| 6—Three-way | 330.00 |

## 5. Life of Component Parts of Water System, Depreciation

Each integral component of the water system has an expected life of its own. Therefore, it is impossible to establish one life expectancy to serve for the life of the entire system. All water systems should be established with a life expectancy equal to that of the community, or in most cases for 40 or 50 years. In many cases, it is desirable to establish systems which will remain in service for a definite period of years at which time it will be replaced by a municipal or water district water service. In that case it may be desirable to use the design criteria of the municipality so that at that time, the system may be purchased by the municipality or water district as a part of their system. Such requirements as this should be looked into so that the system will meet all of the requirements of the municipal system so that at the time of purchase, no changes will be necessary.

Life expectancy of the many components of a water system is recommended in Table LI in which a depreciation schedule is set forth.

## 6. Operational Costs, Rates, Revenue
## A. Small Ground Water Systems

Every water system should be operated on revenue received from water sales. In many cases the systems are not metered and charges are made on a flat monthly rate. Flat rates are not as desirable as metered rates because there is little or no control as to the amount of water which an individual consumer may use in a given period where the revenue is based on flat rates. In the case of metered rates, the consumer pays for actual water used above a pre-set minimum quantity and charge. The consumer in such cases, will be more conscientious about his water usage. The difference between the actual water used in the flat rate system and the metered rate system will be of a variation of some 100 to 300 per cent greater for the flat rate system than for the metered system. Therefore, for the water company involved, a greater revenue per 1,000 gallons of water pumped will be realized where the water is metered and sold on a sliding scale. Where metering is in effect, the amount of water sold will be from 85 to 98 per cent of that actually

## TABLE LI
## Expected Life of Integral Components of a Water System

| Component of System | Life Expectancy (Years) |
|---|---|
| Wellhouse | 20 - 25 - 40 |
| Well Installation | 15 - 25 - 35 |
| Pump, Motors, Controls | 5 - 10 - 15 |
| Concrete Structures | 30 - 40 - 50 |
| Storage Tanks | 20 - 25 - 40 |
| Machinery, Equipment | 5 - 10 - 15 |
| Distribution Mains | 20 - 35 - 50 |
| Meters | 10 - 15 - 20 |
| Valves, Gate, Check | 10 - 15 - 25 |

pumped, because of loss in leakage, meter efficiency, etc., or in other words, the water company should count on an actual water loss from 10 to 15 per cent of the total produced.

When a system is completely metered, there comes the question of the frequency of meter reading. Should the meters be read on a monthly, bimonthly, or quarterly basis? This will depend upon the rates which are being charged versus bookkeeping and billing, and the size of the system being served. Usually the difference in revenues by monthly readings and billing exceeds the bimonthly and quarterly readings and billings by 10 to 25 per cent per meter month. Table LII sets forth from the economics standpoint the suggested frequency of meter reading, based upon the number of services within the system.

Monthly billing will of course provide a greater control for the water company over the system in that the bills, being smaller in amount, will be more readily paid by the consumer. Thus loss in bad debts will be less. Furthermore, it gives opportunity for closer check on the meter operation so that inoperative meters may be replaced when discovered during the reading cycle.

Water rates for any water system should be set up so that the minimum revenue received each month or collection period, will be adequate to meet expenses of operation, maintenance and amortization of the investment in addition to rendering a reasonable profit. Many items are included in the economics of an investment in a water system. These items may be listed as follows:

1. Depreciation on System.
2. Operation:
   a. Administration.
   b. Operational Factors, Repairs, Power, etc.
3. Profit or Return on Investment.

In establishing water rates for a new water system, it is most difficult to predict operating costs for the standpoint of upkeep, repairs, and administrative costs. Therefore, the above may be calculated using the following information.

1. Depreciation of system. Refer to Table LI, Page 122, for schedule of expected or replacement life for components of the water system. Considered within this table is the need of repair of the many components to the stage of being beyond repair.

2. Operation:

a. Administration. Included within administration is the maintaining of office facilities, bookkeeping, billing, meter reading, and supervision. This cost will vary from $ .10 to $ .50 per month per service for large system to $ .50 to $1.25 per month per service for smaller systems.

## TABLE LII
### Frequency of Water Meter Reading and Billing

| Number of Services | Frequency of Meter Reading |
|---|---|
| 0 - 25 | Quarterly |
| 26 - 100 | Bi-monthly |
| Over 100 | Monthly |

b. Operational factors. Power cost is one of the larger costs of operation of a water system. It can be closely approximated from knowing power rates, total head, and the related pump and motor efficiency and daily hours of operation.

Cost of Power Per Month = 22.75 x Hours Per Day Operated x Motor Horsepower x Cost of Power in Cents/KW-Hour

Cost of Power Per Year = 272 x Hours Per Day Operated x Motor Horsepower x Cost of Power in Cents/KW-Hour

Table LIII may be used as a quick method of obtaining power cost by using unit costs of operation for pump operation, then correcting for head and hours per day of pump operation. From this table, the power cost may be obtained as follows:

Cost of Power Per Month = Cost from Table LIII x Head in Hundreds x Hours Per Day Operated x Cost of Power in Cents/KW-Hour

## TABLE LIII
### Monthly Power Costs*

| Gallons Per Day at Total Head of 100 Ft. | Cost Per Month at One Cent Per KW-Hour |
|---|---|
| 10,000 | $ 6.15 |
| 20,000 | 12.30 |
| 40,000 | 24.60 |
| 60,000 | 36.90 |
| 80,000 | 49.20 |
| 100,000 | 61.50 |
| 125,000 | 76.88 |
| 150,000 | 92.25 |
| 175,000 | 107.50 |
| 200,000 | 123.00 |
| 300,000 | 184.50 |
| 400,000 | 246.00 |
| 500,000 | 307.50 |

*Based on efficiency of 64%.

The prediction of maintenance costs is a most difficult problem, therefore it is recommended that a figure of three to five per cent of the total investment be used for this estimate. This figure will not be unreasonable as the system increases in age, the maintenance problems become more acute.

3. Profit or Return on Investment. A fair return should be made by the owner of a community water system on the large sum which he has invested. Many water systems are so inefficiently operated, that the owner's return is far less than five per cent of his investment. Every effort should be made so that a return of five to 10 per cent is made on the investment at the receipt of the minimum monthly rates from the consumers.

In establishing monthly water rates, the total cost of the system, together with operational and supervisional costs, should be estimated and totaled, then broken down to a monthly per consumer rate. This will establish the minimum monthly charge for each consumer based on a certain volume of water.

An example is given for a community which serves 39 services. The system is served by one well, six inches in diameter, 187 feet in depth, utilizes a three-horsepower pump with a drawdown of 140 feet and a yield of 25 gallons per minute. The cost of power is 1½ cents per KW-Hour. Storage facilities consist of a 2,500-gallon pneumatic tank. This system is metered with ¾-inch meters and the distribution system consists of 400 feet of three-inch pipe, 2,300 feet of two-inch pipe. A connection fee of $65.00 is charged to each consumer. What will the monthly service charges be?

a. Cost of the System:
1. Lot and Wellhouse, Page 116 ......................... $ 1,500.00
2. Well Installation, Table XLII ......................... 1,122.00
3. Pump Installation, Table XLIII ...................... 1,020.00
4. Storage, Pneumatic, Table XLIV ..................... 1,440.00
5. Pipelines, 400 feet of three-inch, Table XLVI ......... 1,200.00
   2,300 feet of two-inch ............................ 5,980.00
6. Valves, five, two-inch valves, Table XLVII ........... 195.00
   One, three-inch valve ............................. 65.00
7. Meter Installations, 39, Table XLIX ................. 2,964.00

Total Cost of Water System ....................... $15,486.00
Less Receipts from Connection Fees, 39 connections
   @ $65.00 each .................................. $ 2,535.00

Actual Investment ............................... $12,951.00
b. Cost of Operation Per Month:
1. Power Cost.
   22.75 x Hours Operation x Pump Horsepower x Cost
   per KW-Hour = 22.75 x 12 x 3 x 0.015 ........... $ 12.29
2. Maintenance. Estimate at 3% of investment per annum.
   0.03 x Investment ÷ 12 = 0.03 x $12,951.00/12 ..... 32.38
3. Administration. Estimate at $ .50 per service.
   $ .50 x Number of Services = 0.50 x 39 ............. 19.50

Total Monthly Cost of Operation ..................... $ 64.17

c. Depreciation (Straight-line).
   1. Well Installation, 25 years . . . . . . . . . . . . $2,622.00/25 . . . . $104.88
   2. Pump Installation, 10 years . . . . . . . . . . . .  1,020.00/10 . . . . 102.00
   3. Storage Facilities, 25 years . . . . . . . . . . . . .  1,440.00/25 . . . .  57.60
   4. Distribution System, 50 years . . . . . . . . . .  7,180.00/50 . . . . 143.60
   5. Valves, Meters, 15 years . . . . . . . . . . . . . .  3,224.00/15 . . . . 214.80

   Total Cost of Depreciation (yearly) . . . . . . . . . . . . . . . . . . .$622.88
   Total Cost of Depreciating (monthly) . . . . . . . . . . . . . . . . .  51.90

As the actual investment is $12,951.00 rather than $15,486.00, then the
portion of the above depreciation as applied to this system would be
$\frac{\$12,951.00}{\$15,486.00}$ x $51.90 = $43.49 per month.

d. Return or profit on investment. Select 5% return.
   0.05 x Investment = 0.05 x $12,951.00 = $647.55 per year
                                         = $  53.96 per month
   Actual revenue received per month should be at least equal to that calculated above:
   Total Monthly Cost of Operation plus Depreciation plus Return or
   profit = $64.17 + $43.49 + $53.96 = $161.62 per month or per
   service, $161.62/39 = $4.14 per month. This will approximate a
   monthly minimum service charge of $4.00 for a particular quantity
   of water.

It can be calculated that the above costs are determined on the basis of 25 gallons per minute for a period of 12 hours per day to give 18,000 gallons per day or 525,000 gallons per month. On the basis of the total cost, the water will cost 21.2 cents per 1,000 gallons. Unaccounted water which includes breaks, leaks, blow-offs, etc., is extremely high for small systems and will range from 25 to 100 per cent. Therefore, the cost will vary from 26.5 to 42.4 cents per 1,000 gallons. One must balance between the monthly minimum charge of $4.00 per service and the maximum expected cost of water production which in this case will be 42.4

**TABLE LIV**
**Suggested Minimum Charges and Quantities**
**for Small Water Systems**

| Number of Services* | Monthly Minimum Charges | Monthly Quantity for Minimum Charge (Gallons) |
|---|---|---|
| 0 - 50 | $3.00 to $4.00 | 6,000 to 7,500 |
| 51 - 75 | 2.50 to 3.50 | 4,500 to 6,000 |
| 76 - 100 | 2.00 to 3.00 | 3,500 to 4,500 |
| 101 - 150 | 1.75 to 2.50 | 3,000 to 3,500 |
| 150 - 200 | 1.50 to 2.25 | 2,500 to 3,000 |
| Over 200 | 1.25 to 2.00 | 2,000 to 2,500 |

*Residential services only.

cents per 1,000 gallons. In this case the quantity for the minimum charge would be 6,000 to 7,500 gallons. This rate would then drop rapidly to the 21.2 cents per 1,000 gallons.

Table LIV suggests minimum rates and quantities in relation to the number of services for small water systems.

The sliding scale to be used in conjunction with Table LIV on the basis of $1\frac{1}{2}$ cents per KW-Hour is given in Table LV.

## TABLE LV
### Suggested Charges for Quantities Above Minimum

| Quantity of Water Above Monthly Minimum Given in Table LIV | Minimum Charge Per 1,000 Gallons Above Minimum Quantity |
|---|---|
| Next 10,000 _____ | $ .45 |
| Next 25,000 _____ | .40 |
| Next 50,000 _____ | .35 |
| Next 100,000 _____ | .30 |
| Over Above _____ | .25 |

With varying power cost, the values in Table LV should be altered by the factor of $1 - \dfrac{\text{Cost in Cents per KW-Hour}}{1.5\ \text{Cents}}$ . For example, if the cost of power in a community is $1\frac{1}{4}$ cents per KW-Hour, then the charges per 1,000 gallons given in Table LV should be reduced by a factor of

$$1 - \frac{1.25}{1.50} = 1 - 0.834 = 16.6\%.$$

It should be remembered that the smaller the water system, the more difficult the problems of operation and economics involved.

In billing, it is usually customary to indicate water rates, meter readings, gallons used, charge, and total amount due on the bill to customers. This provides the customer with adequate information and will tend to clarify any misunderstanding. An example of a typical form used in billing water customers is given in Figure 39.

#### Connection Fees

In many communities, it is desirable to charge a tap or connection fee

which will pay for the initial investment of the water system. This of course would be the most desirable method for a supplier to have the system installed. When the comparison is made of this charge with the cost of the individual privately owned well, the consumer will see that he greatly profits from connecting to the community water system.

Connection fees will vary widely from community to community. The range is from $45.00 to $200.00. The higher fee is more satisfactory from several standpoints. First of all, the water system will be more stable concerning revenue and cost of operation.

| WATER RATES | | |
|---|---|---|

Minimum Charge __$3.00

First 6M _____ .50 per M

Next 10M _____ .45 per M

Next 25M _____ .40 per M

Next 50M _____ .35 per M

Next 100M _____ .30 per M

Over _____ .25 per M

_____Water Company

Month of_____19_____

Meter Number_____

Consumer_____

Address_____

**Meter Readings:**

| Present | Previous | Gallons | Charge | Total Due |
|---|---|---|---|---|
| | | | | |

Received Payment:

This Bill Payable On or
Before 10th of Month.

_____
Collector

**Figure 39. Typical Water Billing Form.**

Second, the water rates may be lowered considerably. Third, the water company, being in better financial position, will be able to provide better service to the consumer.

For small water systems, where the revenue is limited each month, a higher connection fee is recommended. This will alleviate much of the economic strain placed on the system. The connection fee should be from $150.00 to $200.00. For larger systems, the fee should be from $75.00 to $125.00. In no case should the fee be such that it is less than the price of the meter to be installed.

**B. Surface Water Supplies**

The economics of a surface water system is one of the most complex problems of the water works industry because of the many variables which must be dealt with. The organization of a department of water supply may be subdivided into several categories as follows:

| | Per Cent of Budget Avg. |
|---|---|
| Administration | 5 - 7 - 10 |
| Business Office | |
| Engineering | |
| Billing Department | 8 - 13 - 15 |
| Meter Reading | |
| Water Billing and Collection | |
| Debt Service | 12 - 15 - 20 |
| Bonds and Interest | |
| Miscellaneous | 1 - 2 - 3 |
| Retirement, Pensions | |
| Reserve for Contingencies | 3 - 8 - 10 |
| Water Construction | 20 - 33 - 35 |
| Maintenance | |
| Water Production | 18 - 22 - 30 |

For very large systems, the above subdivisions are further subdivided, whereas in many smaller systems the above subdivisions are consolidated into fewer departments. Therefore, the above breakdown should be viewed in light of the size of the operation, the amount of debt service, and extreme difficulties pertinent to the particular operation.

The administration and engineering staff account for from five to 10 per cent of the total budget of the water operation. The responsibilities for proper supervision of operation such as purchasing, the planning and layout of new extensions, budget planning, and personnel records lie within this staff. The size of the staff is based upon the magnitude of the operation.

The billing or accounting department provides for the reading of the water meters, bookkeeping, and billing of water accounts. The ease of which this operation is done depends upon the type of office equipment available. The use of automatic accounting equipment, addressing machines, etc., will greatly reduce the per account cost.

Construction and maintenance of a water system will have many variables so that it is extremely difficult to obtain an accurate method of comparing one system with another. Such factors as size and age of the system, water quality, type of construction methods used in installation, major improvement programs, and methods of assessment enter into the problem so that it is difficult to obtain accurate data. It may be reasonable to assume that not over one-third of the total budget is used for water construction and maintenance.

In the study of the economics of water treatment, the size and age of the plant, the condition of plant equipment, the qualifications of the operators, and the quality of the water to be treated must be taken into consideration.

A study of many plants which use alum and lime coagulation in the treating of a water which is not ad-

verse to such treatment, shows that the cost of water production will vary from around $40.00 to $100.00 per million gallons of water, dependent upon the water quality and the size of the plant. A one million gallon-per-day plant will have operational costs of $80.00 to $100.00 per million gallons, while a two million gallon-per-day plant will average around $70.00 per million gallons. Factors influencing this cost are power costs, length of water transmission lines, and the efficiency of the operation. For comparison, a ten million gallon-per-day plant will have water costs varying from $40.00 to $50.00 per million gallons. A breakdown of individual costs is given as follows:

|  | Per Cent of Total Cost Avg. |
|---|---|
| Chemicals | 12 - 20 - 30 |
| Labor | 20 - 33 - 40 |
| Power | 20 - 35 - 40 |
| Repairs, Heat | 7 - 12 - 15 |

Provided within the water economics picture is the debt service, miscellaneous items such as retirement, etc., and contingencies. Provisions should be made to see that these obligations are included within the economics structure.

*(1) Water Rates* [14 26 27 28]. The water rates for a large water system should be so established that the revenue from water sales will be sufficient for debt service, system operation, and system maintenance. In too many cases water rates have remained unchanged for years and act as a hindrance in community growth. Inadequate operating funds reflect in poor operation and maintenance of the treatment works and inadequate care of the distribution system.

Water rates should be reviewed at least each five years to provide a balance for revenue and expenditure. The water revenue should equal to or slightly exceed the total of debt service, operating expenses, contingencies, and equipment replacement costs. Too frequent changes in rate structure tend to be a disadvantage because it interferes with public relations and the consumers attitude. Any changes in rate structures should be consistent with existing rates so that no significant changes are made for any special group of consumers unless the existing rate schedule is entirely unrealistic. The establishment of rates is not a simple matter of mathematical accounting, but a problem involving operation and future planning of the system.

Rates should be established on an equalized basis that will be fair to all consumers, both small and large, rich and poor. Water rates greatly influence the usage of water within a community. High base rates tend to work a hardship on those persons who have limited plumbing facilities and who will not use a quantity near the minimum charge. It will also interfere with the economy of the medium water consumers. Therefore, rates should be established with this in mind.

Rates are established on the basis of consumption breakdown, size of meters, proportional payments for integral parts of system, fire protection, future expansion of basic components of the system, and consumers located outside of the district limits. Consumers are subdivided on the basis of domestic, medium or intermediate, and large consumers. This breakdown may be on the basis of water consumption or meter sizing as follows:

The base water rate is calculated by totaling the debt service which includes the cost of all supply and treatment works, distribution system, and elevated storage facilities, and the system operational and maintenance costs. Many water works committees studying rates suggest that in the debt service a breakdown be had of feeder mains and storage so that proper allocation may be made to the different classes of users. This allocation requires that all users share in the cost of all feeder mains 12 inches and larger, that domestic users share in the cost of all water mains, and that the intermediate users share in the eight- and 10-inch mains. Elevated storage for fire protection should be allocated on the basis of percentage of consumers in each class and the water consumption of each class. This portion of storage is 50 to 66 per cent of the total storage. Fire hydrants should be shared by all consumers.

Further charges should be made to outsider consumers (50 to 100 per cent over inside) and for private fire hydrants and fire sprinkler systems.

It should be noted that in the proportioning of facility costs, that actual cost of facilities is not required, but a percentage of the total system costs because it is to be used only as a means of allocation of each component of the system. In many cases, permanent records are not available, therefore estimates must be made for this proportioning.

A study of many municipalities revealed that the base rate of water is within the range of 35 to 60 cents per 1,000 gallons with the minimum

Domestic
($\frac{5}{8}$", $\frac{3}{4}$", 1" Meters) .... 0 to 10,000 - 20,000 - 30,000 gallons/month
Intermediate ($1\frac{1}{4}$", $1\frac{1}{2}$", 2" Meters)
        Domestic to 100,000 - 200,000 - 300,000 gallons/month
Lare (3", 4", 6", 8" Meters) .......... In excess of the Intermediate User

quantity being from 1,500 to 3,500 gallons. Minimum monthly charges are within the range of $1.00 to $1.45 per month for the base quantity. A comparison of users, rates, and quantities are as follows:

existing rate structure or schedule so that there may be a comparison with the proposed. A base line should be drawn on this graph to indicate the production cost of water per thousand gallons so that at the high usages,

| User | Base Rate | Base Quantity |
|---|---|---|
| Domestic for 5/8" Meter | Base Rate/1,000 gallons | 1,500 - 2,000 - 3,500 gallons |
| Intermediate | 85 to 95% Base Rate | Computed as shown below |
| Large | 60 to 75% Base Rate | Computed as shown below |

The base quantities for the numerous sized meters should be as calculated on the following basis:

| Base Quantity for Meter of Diameter, D" | = 2.65 x | Base Quantity for Domestic, 5/8" Meter in Gallons or Cubic Feet | x | (Diameter of Meter, D)$^2$ (in Inches) |
|---|---|---|---|---|

Data for the above should be plotted on two-cycle Logarithmic Graph paper with the abscissa stated in terms of cost per 1,000 gallons and the ordinate in terms of monthly consumption of units of 1,000 gallons. On this graph should also be plotted the

the curves may converge. This is illustrated in Figure 40.

Concerning the breakdown of distribution system costs, approximate values of cost distribution within a water system are found in Table LVI.

## TABLE LVI
### Distribution of Cost for Pipe Sizes in Per Cent of Total Cost of Distribution System

| Population Served | 6" or Less | 8" and 10" | 12" | Over 12" |
|---|---|---|---|---|
| Less than 1,500 | 95 | 5 | 0 | 0 |
| 3,500 | 91 | 8 | 1 | 0 |
| 5,000 | 85 | 12 | 2 | 1 |
| 10,000 | 75 | 18 | 5 | 2 |
| 25,000 | 68 | 21 | 8 | 3 |
| 50,000 | 60 | 23 | 12 | 5 |

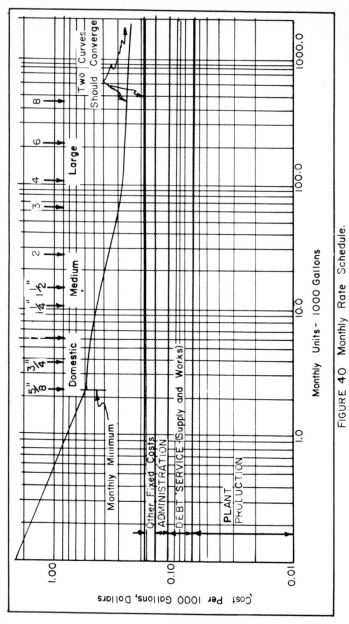

FIGURE 40 Monthly Rate Schedule.

A simple breakdown of allocation of cost to the different classes of water users may be stated as follows:

1. Debt Service:

| Domestic | Medium or Intermediate | Large |
|---|---|---|
| Share Cost of All Mains | Share Cost of 8" Mains and Larger | Share Cost of 10" and Larger Mains |
| Bear Total Cost of 6" Mains and Smaller | Share Cost of Fire Storage | Share Cost of Fire Storage |
| Bear Total Cost of Equalizing Storage | Share Cost of Fire Appurtenances | Share Cost of Fire Appurtenances |
| Share Cost of Fire Storage | Share Cost of Works and Supply | Share Cost of Works and Supply |
| Share Cost of Fire Appurtenances | | |
| Share Cost of Works and Supply | | |

2. Administration, Operation, and Maintenance:

All classes to share this cost.

3. Special Service:

Medium or Intermediate Class and Large Users to pay specific charges for Sprinkler Service and for special fire hydrants.

Out of city or district customers should pay a proportionate higher cost.

All water costs should be so allocated that users are justly charged for service received. For example, the user with an eight-inch meter will receive no benefit from water mains of less than the meter size, while the user with a two-inch service line will benefit from all sized mains.

# CHAPTER VI

# Maintenance and Operation

## General

Every water system regardless of its size, should have a definite planned program to ascertain proper maintenance and efficient operation for the production and supply of a constant high quality of water to the consumers. The lack of such a planned program will result in not only financial distress, but poor and unsatisfactory service to consumers. Such dissatisfaction among consumers from unsatisfactory service will result in the construction of private wells throughout the community, upsetting public relations and economic stability of the water company. Therefore, it is a must that the water company have such a planned organization to give the customer prompt emergency service. In the case of very small water systems that do not warrant full time personnel, a local plumbing company may be contracted with to supervise and furnish such maintenance. For larger water companies, adequate and trained personnel should be employed and equipped with best equipment to save time and money by being able to make rapid repairs with a minimum time of interrupted service.

## 1. Ground Water Supplies
## A. Source of Supply, Pumps, and Control

Where mechanical equipment is involved, the manufacturers recommendations concerning operation and maintenance should be strictly adhered to. One should be careful to follow such recommendations very closely, because only by following such can the warranty, best of care, of such equipment in addition to best of operation be obtained. Care should be taken to use the recommended lubricants in amounts suggested at specific intervals. Records should be made so that one could refer to previous repairs, lubrication and other maintenance. The pump and fittings should always be kept clean and free of rust. If rusting occurs, it should be immediately cleaned and a protective coatnig applied.

Pump discharges as known pressures should be checked at regular intervals so that the pump efficiency may be known. It is suggested that such tests be made at least semiannually. When pump efficiency decreases to such an extent that power costs exceeds five or six cents per 1,000 gallons pumped, one should consider the replacement of the pump.

To check the discharge of a pump, it is either necessary to have a meter on the well installation so that records of pump discharge and rate may be kept. Or it is necessary to provide a blow-off valve along with a pressure gauge so that pumping conditions may be duplicated. The procedure to check the discharge when a meter is not on the installation is as follows:

1. Open the blow-off line control valve until the pressure gauge reads average line pressure meanwhile closing the system discharge valve until it is completely closed. Average system pressures will vary from about 40 to 80 pounds. For larger systems, the average pressure should be used.

2. Collect the water for a known period of time in a closed container

if the discharge is small. The flow is equal to the volume divided by the time in minutes to give gallons per minute. For larger yield wells it is more practical to use a large container with orifice or small holes at varied elevations around the container. With the pump discharge going into this container, a certain elevation will be reached. When this occurs, catch the flow from each orifice for a known period of time, then total these individual flows to obtain the total discharge from the pump.

Controls used on water systems provide a means for controlled operation without the problem of constant manual supervision. Controls may be of the float type or electrodes within an elevated or low pressure tank or a pressure operated or mercury-type switch for the operation of a pump. One should be careful in the selection of controls. Selection of controls should be on the basis of service and durability. The controls should be on the basis of service and durability. The control should be weatherproof for operation in dampness or high humidity. It should be such that lightning will not interfere with its operation. Also the control should be purchased from a reputable firm so that warranty and service will be valid and available.

A draw-down gage is a necessity to evaluate the operation of a well supply. The draw-down gage is an air line placed within the well to record the depth of water within the well. The depth of the turbine, jet, or submersible pump is indicated by a fixed pointer on this gage. Before the pump is placed in operation, the depth recorded on the gage is the static level depth. When the pump is in operation, the depth indicated is the pumping level, pumping depth, or draw-down. When the pump is stopped, the water will return to the static level. The time for this to occur is known as the recovery period. Of importance in the operation of a system is the static level, pumping level, and the recovery time. By keeping records of these three values, one can determine if the well is beginning to fail, or is being over-pumped. These values will vary greatly for each well in every locality. Therefore, it is necessary that a draw-down gage be placed on each installation.

Many times, the yield of a well decreases with usage over the years. The reason for this may be that the ground water table is lowering, or that the under ground water channels are clogged by either calcium or iron deposits. Treatment of these sources to increase yield has been accomplished in two ways. Where calcium deposits are the cause for decreased yield, a dry ice treatment is used. The dry ice is placed within the well and the well casing is capped. The pressure created from the disintegration of the dry ice forces its way into these channels thus opening them again. If the decrease comes from iron deposits, the use of hexametaphosphate and chlorine to dissolve the iron deposit so that it may be removed is used. The dosage rates used are on the basis of one-tenth to one-half pound of hexametaphosphate to 10 gallons of water. The solution as such is allowed to stand in the well for a 24-hour period. Chlorine to a dosage of 50 parts per million is then added for an additional 24 hours. This solution is then pumped out of the well and continuous treatment of both hexametaphosphate and chlorine is then applied to the well.

## 2. Surface Water Supplies
### A. Sources of Supply

Particular supervision should be given to surface sources of supply to prevent pollution of the supply. In many cases this is regulated under state or local laws.

*(1) Unfiltered Surface Supplies.* Unfiltered surface water supplies should be patrolled at regular intervals to prevent the trespassing of unauthorized persons in view of pollution which may take place. Since this type of supply has little degree of treatment, it is necessary to take as much precaution as is possible in the protection of water quality.

Since these sources are heavily forested, care should be taken to see that the forest is well cared for by well-planned operations such as thinning and replanting. Fire lanes should be provided and maintained. Definite rules governing sanitation of workers on the watershed must be provided and enforced. The forestry program is a vital part of water quality protection, therefore must be well planned and carried out.

Intake structures should be adequate in capacity and should be maintained on a daily basis. This involves cleaning of coarse and fine screens to remove the accumulation of leaves, brush, other floating debris, etc. Since chemical treatment in the form of chlorination and possibly corrosion control is provided at the intake structure, daily maintenance should be given to this equipment.

Blow-offs on the main feed line should be operated at regular intervals to clean the line of sediment. Air relief valves along this line should be inspected at regular intervals for necessary repair.

*(2) Filtered Surface Supplies.* Along streams used for a water supply, care must be taken to control inlets of pollution to prevent gross pollution of water supplies.

When a stream is impounded for use as a water supply, many problems arise relating to the effect of storage on water quality. Storage facilities aid in many ways the quality of the water. Yet in other ways, it may degrade or lower the water quality. The enhancement of water quality by storage may be by the following ways:

a. Sedimentation of silt of incoming water during storage period.

b. Provides a constant quality of water to the plant during periods of stratification.

c. Provides a water of higher quality by selection of water depth to draft from.

d. Provides a period for stabilization of organic matter for satisfying of oxygen demand.

Yet during certain periods of the year, the quality of the water by storage creates problems as follows:

a. Provides a medium for algae growths which may cause taste and odor.

b. Provides a habitat for insects to breed to create a nuisance problem within the community.

c. During periods of turn-over, will produce a water of low dissolved oxygen, high iron and manganese concentration, and high in organic matter to cause taste, odor, and undesirable chemical characteristics.

The proper operation of an impounded stream will involve the following considerations:

a. Reservoir Turnover. In the operation of an impounded water supply, one should become familiar with the storage phenomenon which includes stratification and homogeneity of the body of water. When a water flows into a reservoir, the silt will build up along the inlet and former stream channels which are located in the deeper sections of the reservoir areas. As the water flows into the reservoir during the warmer months or during the season when the air and water temperature is above four degrees centigrade (density of water at this temperature is 1.0000), the water will form in layers according to its density. In other words, it will stratify in layers and will remain in these defined layers. When the weather temperature drops below four degrees centigrade (39.2 degrees Fahrenheit), the water on surface will begin to drop in temperature and will increase in density until it reaches 1.0000 at which time it is heaviest. This heavy water begins to settle and the reservoir will "turn-over." The reservoir will then be homogeneous in its entirety. The turn-over brings undesirable organic matter, iron, manganese, hydrogen sulphide, etc., into suspension, thus creating a taste and odor problem as well as manganese trouble.

b. Algae Control. Other reservoir problems are due to algae which grow during the warm seasons of the year. Regular counts should be made to determine the concentration and identification of algae. After a period of counting, a certain count will be derived at which point taste and odor problems will become prevalent or trouble will be encountered in filter clogging by certain species of algae. At this specified concentration of algae, the reservoir should be treated. If counting facilities are not available, a regular program may be adopted to treat the reservoir at intervals of three to four weeks.

Experience indicates that a dosage of approximately one to $1\frac{1}{4}$ ppm of Copper Sulphate will kill algae without effect upon fish life. Therefore, on this basis, eight to 10 pounds of Copper Sulphate per million gallons of water stored should be used to treat the reservoir. The method of application is to mark off the reservoir in sections so that the boat may be driven along a pre-set pattern for the application of the Copper Sulphate. The pattern should be set so that the boat will pass in lanes of 10 feet center to center and at speeds of from eight to 12 miles per hour. The path of the boat should not parallel the shoreline in the first application because the fish will try to cross this path to get the cooler waters of the tributary streams and will be killed by the dosage of Copper Sulphate. The chemical may be applied by either pulling in bags behind the boat or by mechanical spreading across the water surface.

c. Insect Control. To control insect breeding, the shoreline should be kept reasonably clean. All waters should be maintained at a depth of at least two feet. Water vegetation should be removed from the shallow waters. Shallow areas may be eliminated by dredging and the construction of islands within the reservoir, or by the construction of a small reservoir above the large reservoir so that the water level may be fluctuated in the small reservoir to prevent insect breeding. In the use of small reservoirs, it is necessary that the toe of the dam of the small reservoir be located within the large reservoir so that the small reservoir will include the shallow water area. Since most chemicals used in weed or insect control are toxic or will create other problems in water treatment, it is best to control such growths and insects by fluctuation of water level.

d. Reservoir Operation. The reservoir operation involves not only a program for algae and mosquitoe control, but constant survellience of water quality to determine the best depth from which to draw the supply of water. Experience indicates that best depths range from the surface to around 15 feet for deep reservoirs during periods of stratification and from the surface to around eight feet during periods of homogeneity. During periods of high flow, the flood gates and bottom drains of the reservoir should be opened to remove sediment.

## B. Pressure Filtration

Types of pressure filtration units are sand and gravel, diatomaceous filters, and zeolite filters. The types specify the type of filtration media used.

Sand, gravel, and diatomaceous filters should be operated on the loss of head cycle. When the loss of head reaches seven feet, the filters should be backwashed at a rate of eight to 12 gallons per minute per square feet of filter area. For the diatomaceous filter, a pressure head of 50 to 60 pounds per square inch is required before the filter is washed. This pressure is required so that the filter cake may be broken away from the filter cylinders. These filters should be opened at frequent intervals and the surface of the filters cleaned.

Zeolite filters should be backwashed daily. The regeneration cycle is once per week using as a regenerant, a sodium compound at a dosage of 10 pounds per million gallons.

## C. Gravity Filtration Plants[16]

Gravity water filtration plants involve coagulation, sedimentation, filtration, and water disinfection and stabilization.

*(1) Pumping Equipment.* The maintenance of pump and control equipment should be as discussed under Ground Water Supplies on Page 135.

*(2) Chemical Feed Equipment.* Mechanical feed equipment should be kept clean and in good repair. All feed lines should be at least two inches in diameter with lengths as short as possible. Where lengths exceed 20 feet, rigid pipe should not exceed 20-foot sections so that it may be easily disassmbled and cleaned. Flexible pipe such as plastic or rubber is preferred to aid in the ease of removing and cleaning process. Clogging is a frequent problem. Therefore, the pipes should be regularly cleaned with water under pressure.

*(3) Basins, Mixing and Sedimentation.* Mixing of treatment chemicals with the source of water is one of the most important processes within the plant because this treatment removes the suspended matter and a majority of the bacteria load. If mechanical mixers as flash mix, flocculators, or air mix are used, this mechanical equipment should be inspected for wear and lubricated at regular intervals. Necessary adjustments should be made when needed.

All basins should be drained at quarterly or such intervals to remove the accumulation of sludge. Floating materials should be removed daily. The draining and cleaning of basins should be arranged so that it will not be necessary to do this in the extreme dry period of the year when draft upon the plant is maximum.

*(4) Filters.* The water if properly treated, should be of such quality, that when it is received at the filters, the turbidity should be less than 10.0 parts per million. Since this water is usually of low pH from the coagulation process, the wash water trough, if of metal, and the surface wash mechanism should be provided with a protective coating to prevent corrosion. Filters are operated at a rate of two gallons per minute per square foot or 125 million gallons per acre per day of filter area. This filtration rate should be calculated at regular intervals as a check of the rate controller and gauges. This rate is calculated by closing the filter influent

valve and measuring the length of time that it takes the filter to drop exactly one foot. The calculation is as follows:

$$\text{Rate of Filtration, gpm/square foot} = \frac{7.5}{\text{Time in minutes to drop one foot}}$$

$$\text{Rate of Filtration, gpm/Filter Area} = \text{gpm/square foot} \times \text{Filter Area}$$

$$\text{Rate of Filtration, mgd/Filter} = 1,400 \times \text{gpm/Filter Area}$$

This rate in mgd should be the same as indicated on rate controller and rate of flow gauge.

Filters should be frequently inspected for the formation of mud balls. This procedure should be carried out during the washing procedure. Backwashing of the filter should be done when the loss of head reaches seven to 10 feet. The filter should be washed until clean. The washing time usually averages from five to seven to 10 minutes. The rate of backwash should be 24 inches rise per minute (15 gallons per minute per square foot) for sand filters and 18 inches rise per minute (11¼ gallons per minute per square foot) for anthrafilt coal filter media. The rate of wash water should be checked at frequent intervals by closing the waste valve and timing the rise of the wash water for a rise of 24 inches. The rate of wash water rise is calculated as:

When this figure falls below 60 hours, filter clogging organisms may be suspected or poor plant operation is the cause. After washing, the filter should be rewashed (filtering to waste) for several minutes before placing the filter back into operation.

Surface filter washes are desirable for filter surface agitation during the washing cycle. Surface washes should be operated during the entire filter wash cycle.

Regular maintenance should be provided for rate controllers, rate of flow gauges, loss of head gauges, sand expansion gauges, surface wash mechanisms, and all filter operating valves. Maintenance should include adjustment of pulleys, cords, wires, valve packing, levers, etc. Controller diaphrams should be checked at frequent intervals for leakage.

*(5) Chlorination Practice.* Disinfection of water is obtained by the use of chlorine gas, adjusted in feed through the plant by the use of the chlorinator. Chlorine may be applied at many points throughout the plant, but is commonly added at two loca-

$$\text{Rate of Wash Water Rise, Inches Per Minute} = \frac{24 \times \text{Area of Filter in Sq. Feet}}{\text{Time in Minutes for 24-inch rise}}$$

The percentage of wash water should be less than 3.0 per cent of the total water treated. For a well-operated plant, this percentage will average about 1.0 per cent. In other words, this is an expression of filter run or filter hours of operation between washes. Filter runs should average from 90 to 140 hours between washes.

tions, the plant influent (application at this point is known as Pre-Chlorination), and at the filter effluent (application at this point is known as Post-Chlorination). Other points of application may be the top of filter and at the finished water pumping station. Pre-chlorination is sometimes applied at the raw water pumping station providing additional benefits in that it prevents algae growths in small intermediate reservoirs and slime growths in the raw water lines.

Chlorine serves two main purposes in water treatment. First, it is an aid in the treatment process by providing disinfection, control of algae and slime growths, taste and odor control, and control of iron and manganese. Second, it is an aid in providing to the distribution system, disinfection, control of slime and iron bacteria growth, and added protection against back-siphonage from plumbing defects.

The effectiveness of chlorine or chlorination to water is related to the dosage of chlorine applied. Chlorination practice involves the application of chlorine in many ways:

a. Chloramines. When chlorine is applied to a water which contains high nitrogeneous material or added ammonia, the chemical reaction between the chlorine and ammonia will result in the formation of Chloramines. Chloramines are noted for their prolonged periods of effectiveness because they are more stable than low dosages of chlorine. Their potential killing effect is not as great as that of chlorine. As the ratio of Chlorine to Ammonia increases to 10 to one, the ammonia is oxidized and the chlorine appears as free residual chlorine. At this point, the break-point has been reached which signifies that all of the nitrogeneous material has been oxidized.

b. Break-Point Chlorination. Upon the oxidation of all nitrogeneous material in water, the break-point is reached, above which all chlorine appears as free residual chlorine. Chlorine appearing above this concentration has large oxidizing power and is used widely in the control of taste and odors. The break-point is the point of least taste and odors in a water.

c. Super-Chlorination. Same as break-point chlorination in that the free residual chlorination is used as disinfecting agent.

d. Chlorine Dioxide. The reaction of chlorine and sodium chlorite produces a powerful oxidizing compound of chlorine. This ratio of chlorine to sodium chlorite is one to four. This is used extensively in controlling taste and odors, especially those involving industrial wastes and algae.

e. Desired Chlorine Residuals. The desired residuals of chlorine are as follows: Dosage to raw water should be ample to provide 0.75 to 1.0 on filters, dosage in finished water to provide at least 0.3 parts per million in distribution system. For manganese control, it is necessary to maintain at least 0.50 parts per million on the filter at all times.

*(6) Taste and Odor Control.* The control of taste and odors in a water supply is one of the most repeated problems facing plant operation. Most taste and odors are created by microorganisms within the source of raw water. Used for controlling taste and odors are Activated Carbon, Chlorine, or a combination of Carbon and Chlorine. In consideration of the method of applicaton of Carbon and Chlorine to a water, the type of causitive agent must be considered. It should be remembered that Carbon will absorb a portion of the chlorine, therefore, adjustments in feeding rate must be made. There are two methods for use of these compounds in the control of taste and odors. First, the pre-chlorine is added to the plant influent and carbon is added at the mid-point of the mixing chamber. The theory here is that some oxidation or conversion of the aromatic oils, etc., is obtained so that it is more easily removed by the carbon.

The second method is the reverse of the first in that the carbon is added first. Here it is theorized that the carbon is more effective in removing the taste and odor producing compound and will have less effect upon the chlorine. Threshold taste and odors are difficult to determine. Therefore, chemical dosages, economics, and most of all, the effectiveness of the treatment, should govern which method to use because the removal of the problem is in many cases a trial and error practice. In addition to the above, when the taste and odor problem first becomes apparent at the plant, carbon should be placed on top of the filter in the amount of 10 to 15 pounds per 100 square feet.

*(7) Plant Housekeeping.* In plant operation and maintenance, the problem of plant housekeeping should not be overlooked. Plant housekeeping should include care of the grounds, building, and other structures relating to water treatment. The plant should be kept clean and orderly. The interior of the plant should be painted in attractive colors. Color coding of all piping is not essential, but will aid in plant maintenance and attractiveness.

The chemical feed equipment should be kept clean and free of corrosion. The storage of chemicals should be on wooden platforms raised off the floor.

### 3. Storage Facilities

Storage facilities require less maintenance than any part of the water system. In their construction, care should be taken to assure that all elevated or low pressure storage is provided with an adequate sized drain, screened overflow which is elbowed down to prevent entrance of insects, and locked down manhole covers. In low pressure or ground storage, the manhole covers should be

provided with a rubber gasket or constructed to give a shoe-box lid effect to prevent surface contamination from seepage.

The maintenance required for storage facilities is the periodic flushing or draining and the washing of the tank interior to rid the tank of solids, slime, etc. At the time of tank cleaning, the interior surface of the tank should be inspected for cracks, corrosion, and the condition of the protective coating. The frequency of this inspection to provide greatest control must be done at intervals not to exceed two years. Protective coatings for metal tanks are of several types: plastic such as vinyl, organic zinc, metallic, and a wax-type grease coating. Most of these coatings may be applied whether hot or cold. Another type of protection is the use of cathodic protection units which involves the use of a magnesium rod within the tank. By setting up a current flow between the magnesium anode and the tank wall, the magnesium rod will corrode rather than the tank surface. The prime consideration in the selection of a protective coating for a tank is that it not impart taste and odor to the water.

For high service storage in the form of pneumatic storage tanks, it is necessary to add air to the tank to prevent the tank from becoming water-logged. Pneumatic tanks should be provided with indicating pressure gauges for pressure checks of the system and with an air valve so that air may be added to the tank without interfering with the operation.

### 4. Distribution System

A detail layout map should be kept of the entire water system. This layout map should be kept up-to-date of the location and depth of all the water lines, valves, service lines, etc., so that in case of needed repairs, little time would be required in locating the system. Valve stems and boxes should be located at street or paving elevation to allow for rapid use and testing at regular intervals.

Prior to installation of gate valves, the number of turns required to fully open and close should be recorded and filed so that the valve will be fully opened during operation. This is especially important where large valves are concerned. Every valve within the system should be operated at least annually and should be properly maintained if needed at that time.

Water will become "stale" in the extremities or dead ends, therefore, it is necessary to flush dead end lines at frequent intervals. If the source is adequate, dead ends should be flushed on a monthly basis. If the supply is limited, the frequency may be set up for quarterly flushings on the lines which have little trouble and on an every other month basis for dead ends where complaints are received. The installation of loops to give recirculation within the system will eliminate this stale water.

It is desirable to test or flush all hydrants twice a year or at a minimum of at least annually. All hydrants should be numbered and checked by number so that all will be tested and no "dead" hydrant will be overlooked. During the winter season, no water should be allowed to remain in the hydrant stems and become frozen.

One of the most common troubles encountered with well supplies within the distribution system, is the development of taste and odors from the "iron-forming bacteria" known as Chrenothrix or Gallionella. This growth is more prevalent in systems which have high concentarations of iron. Taste and odors developed from

this condition are characteristic of hydrogen sulphide or "rotten egg" and the water will appear red or muddy in most cases as this growth sloughs off the pipe. This condition is only remedied by the introduction of a high concentration of chlorine within the system (50 parts per million of chlorine) and allowed to remain within the system for a period of 24 hours before draining. During the period of treatment, all consumers should be advised not to use the water. Continuous chlorination of the water after the above treatment is desirable in order to maintain a chlorine residual within the system at all times.

For repair of broken mains, an adequate number of sleeves or couplings for all sized pipes within the system should be kept on hand at all times.

For the protection of the distribution system against plumbing defects, certain precautions should be made for the use of protective devices upon certain type of fixtures, thus preventing back-siphonage. For back-siphonage to occur, several occurrances must happen within a distribution system. Such occurrances may be low main pressure, small service lines, sluggish building sewers, and submerged water inlets to plumbing fixtures. With large service lines and adequate sewers, the problem in many cases may prevail because of submerged inlets. If it is impossible to have an air gap of at least one inch or twice the pipe diameter, a backflow preventer or vacuum breaker should be installed on such plumbing lines. In particular, backflow preventers should be provided on all flushometer valves. This type of valve should be supplied with at least a two-inch supply line and a minimum pressure of at least 20 pounds per square inch. The vacuum breaker should be installed on the discharge side of the valve so that it will not remain under pressure.

The water in the distribution system should be sampled at regular intervals to determine the bacterial as well as chemical quality. The frequency of such samples is dependent upon the size of the system and should vary from daily to weekly for bacterial samples and from weekly to monthly for chemical samples.

### 5. Meters

The water meter is the most important control appurtenance of the water system. With continued wear or the entrance of trash into the meter, the meter will record slower, thereby letting more water through than is actually recorded. Therefore, it is desirable to replace the meters at periodic intervals and recalibrate so that accurate readings of water usage may be had. The frequency of checking meters is an arbitrary time selection. Within Table LVII is given the accepted frequency for checking of water meters.

### 6. Chemical Treatment
#### A. Ground Water Supplies

Water quality of ground water supplies within certain areas are usually typical in characteristics of chemical quality. The majority of ground waters which are not located within the saline coastal region, are usually slightly on the acid side of neutral, slightly corrosive, and contain trace quantities of iron. Therefore, in most cases, it is desirable to treat the water to some degree to prevent iron stains, reduce the corrosiveness, and provide a small amount of chlorine for disinfection and the prevention of slime growths within the system.

For corrosion treatment, it is usually customary to add a hexametaphosphate solution in the concentration of two to five parts per million. The solution is best added by a solution pump directly into the wall. The adding of this solution directly into the well has two distinct advantages. One is to provide protection to the pump suction line or turbine. The second is to provide contact time before the reaction of chlorine so as to

## TABLE LVII
## Frequency of Meter Testing

| Meter Size, Inches | Frequency of Testing, Years |
|---|---|
| 8 | 1 |
| 6 | 2 |
| 4 | 4 |
| 3 | 6 |
| 2 | 8 |
| less than 2 | 10 to 12 |

In fairness to all concerned, both water company and consumer, the frequency of meter testing should be on a basis that water charges will be as accurate as possible regarding meter efficiency.

eliminate the interference between the polyphosphate and the chlorine. In the prevention of corrosion within the system, the polyphosphate will provide a microscopical coating on the metal surfaces thereby reducing the action of water on these surfaces. For the protection of such surfaces, a recommended minimum dosage of two parts per million is recommended.

Small concentrations of iron may be controlled by additional amounts of polyphosphates. The reaction of the phosphates is to sequester the iron or in other words, hold the iron in solution to prevent its precipitation thus causing "red" water, stains, etc. The concentrations of polyphosphates recommended for iron control is two parts per million phosphate per one part per million of iron. Iron may be controlled by this process upwards to two parts per million. Furthermore, the polyphosphates should not be added in amounts exceeding 10 parts per million for any purpose in potable water.

Chlorination is desirable for ground water supplies from not only the standpoint of disinfection, but prevents the formation of slime growths within the system. Chlorine should be applied to the pump discharge. Since most well waters are slightly acid, it is desirable to carry a chlorine residual of approximately one part per million at this point. Satisfying the demand for chlorine

within the water at the well, the chlorine will be carried to a greater distance within the distribution system. A good criteria for chlorine dosage application is to test the chlorine residual at the ends of the distribution lines. At that point a trace or 0.15 parts per million is desirable. If the chlorine residual exceeds this, the application rate at the well may be reduced accordingly. It is not desirable to increase the dosage at the well above two parts per million as a slight chlorinous taste and odor may develop.

Table LVIII may be used in determining feeding rates for polyphosphates and chlorine when fed in solution form. Chlorine is available in either the liquid form or in the calcium or sodium hypochlorite powdered form. In the powdered or granular form, chlorine is obtainable in 15, 30, 50 or 70 per cent of available chlorine. In the preparation of the chlorine solution to be fed by a solution type feeder, the solubility of the compound should be considered. Therefore, the chlorine solution should be prepared in maximum strength of about four per cent. The preparation of this solution may be calculated by the following formulas:

| Ounces of 15% Chlorine Compound Required | = 8.90 x | % Chlorine Solution Strength Desired for Feeding | x | Capacity of Container in Gallons |
|---|---|---|---|---|

| Ounces of 30% Chlorine Compound Required | = 4.45 x | % Chlorine Solution Strength Desired for Feeding | x | Capacity of Container in Gallons |
|---|---|---|---|---|

| Ounces of 50% Chlorine Compound Required | = 2.67 x | % Chlorine Solution Strength Desired for Feeding | x | Capacity of Container in Gallons |
|---|---|---|---|---|

$$\begin{array}{l}\text{Ounces of } 70\% \\ \text{Chlorine Compound} \\ \text{Required} \end{array} = 1.91 \times \begin{array}{c}\% \text{ Chlorine} \\ \text{Solution} \\ \text{Strength Desired} \\ \text{for Feeding} \end{array} \times \begin{array}{c}\text{Capacity} \\ \text{of Container} \\ \text{in Gallons} \end{array}$$

In the preparation of the chlorine solution, it is necessary for the solution to be prepared in an earthware crock or similar type material which will not be reacted upon by the active chlorine solution. Table LVIII is prepared in order to give the number of milliliters per minute feed rate for different strength of solutions. This table also gives the feed rate for sodium hexametaphosphate or polyphosphate to be used in a feeding dosage rate of two parts per million for different strength solutions. Other dosage rates may be calculated from this table by taking the feed rate from this table and multiplying by the factor of $\dfrac{\text{desired dosage rate}}{\text{dosage rate of two ppm}}$ thus obtaining the desired dosage rate for the desired dose. The preparation of the hexameta-or polyphosphate solution is as follows:

$$\begin{array}{l}\text{Ounces of Hexameta—} \\ \text{or Polyphosphate Compound} \\ \text{Required} \end{array} = 1.33 \times \begin{array}{c}\text{Per Cent} \\ \text{Solution Strength} \\ \text{Desired} \end{array} \times \begin{array}{c}\text{Capacity of} \\ \text{Container in} \\ \text{Gallons} \end{array}$$

## TABLE LVIII
## Chlorine and Phosphate Feeding Rates*

| Pumping Rate GPM | Chlorine Dosage of One Part Per Million | | | | | | Polyphosphate Dosage of Two Parts Per Million | | | | |
|---|---|---|---|---|---|---|---|---|---|---|---|
| | Solution Strength (Per Cent) | | | | | | Solution Strength (Per Cent) | | | | |
| | 0.5 | 1.0 | 1.5 | 2.0 | 3.0 | 4.0 | 1.0 | 2.0 | 3.0 | 4.0 | 5.0 |
| | milliliters per minute | | | | | | milliliters per minute | | | | |
| 10 | 8 | 4 | 3 | 2 | 1 | 1 | 8 | 4 | 3 | 2 | 1 |
| 20 | 15 | 7 | 5 | 4 | 3 | 2 | 14 | 7 | 5 | 4 | 3 |
| 30 | 22 | 11 | 8 | 6 | 4 | 3 | 22 | 11 | 8 | 6 | 4 |
| 40 | 30 | 15 | 10 | 7 | 5 | 4 | 30 | 15 | 10 | 7 | 6 |
| 50 | 37 | 19 | 13 | 9 | 6 | 5 | 37 | 19 | 13 | 9 | 7 |
| 60 | 44 | 22 | 15 | 11 | 8 | 6 | 44 | 22 | 15 | 11 | 9 |
| 70 | 52 | 26 | 18 | 13 | 9 | 6 | 52 | 26 | 18 | 13 | 10 |
| 80 | 59 | 30 | 20 | 15 | 10 | 7 | 59 | 30 | 20 | 15 | 12 |
| 90 | 67 | 33 | 23 | 17 | 11 | 8 | 67 | 33 | 23 | 17 | 13 |
| 100 | 74 | 37 | 25 | 19 | 13 | 9 | 74 | 37 | 25 | 19 | 15 |
| 125 | 93 | 46 | 31 | 23 | 16 | 12 | 93 | 46 | 31 | 23 | 19 |
| 150 | 111 | 56 | 38 | 28 | 18 | 14 | 111 | 56 | 38 | 28 | 22 |
| 200 | 148 | 74 | 50 | 37 | 25 | 19 | 148 | 74 | 50 | 37 | 30 |

*Note: Milliters per minute may be converted to gallons of solution per day by:
$$\begin{array}{c}\text{Gallons Per Day} \\ \text{of Solution Fed} \end{array} = 0.38 \times \begin{array}{c}\text{Feed Rate of} \\ \text{Milliliters Per Minute} \end{array}$$

This solution in any strength will tend to be corrosive, therefore an earthenware or plastic container should be used. This solution may be made less corrosive by the addition of 10 per cent by weight of soda ash

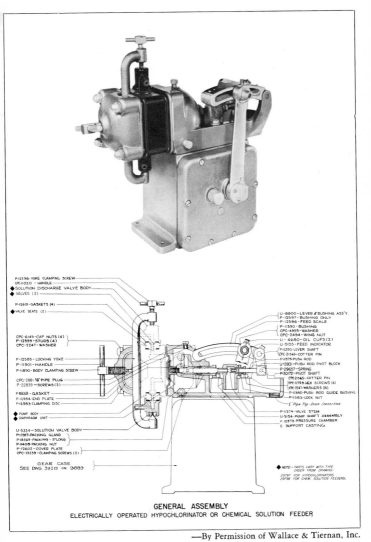

P-12598-YOKE CLAMPING SCREW
CPC-1102.0 - HANDLE
◆ SOLUTION DISCHARGE VALVE BODY
◆ VALVES (2)

◆ VALVE SEATS (2)

CPC-6145-CAP NUTS (4)
P-12599-STUDS (4)
CPC-2247-WASHER

P-12585-LOCKING YOKE
P-11901-HANDLE
P-11850-BODY CLAMPING SCREW

CPC-288-⅛" PIPE PLUG
P-22839-SCREWS (2)

P-8358-GASKET
P-1386-END PLATE
P-12583-CLAMPING DISC

◆ PUMP BODY
◆ DIAPHRAGM UNIT

U-5334-SOLUTION VALVE BODY
P-11587-PACKING GLAND
P-11369-PACKING - 5"LONG
P-11408-PACKING NUT
P-12602-COVER PLATE
CPC-13239-CLAMPING SCREWS (2)

GEAR CASE
SEE DWG. 39219 OR 9889

U-8800-LEVER & BUSHING ASS'Y.
P-12597-BUSHING ONLY
P-12598-FEED SCALE
P-11390-BUSHING
CPC-4955-WASHER
CPC-2494-WING NUT
U-5155-FEED INDICATOR
P-12590-LEVER SHAFT
CPC-21365-COTTER PIN
P-11375-PUSH ROD
U-13931-PUSH ROD PIVOT BLOCK
P-29657-SPRING
P30172-PIVOT SHAFT
CPC-21365-COTTER PIN
CPC-2759-HEX SCREWS (4)
CPC-2747-WASHERS (4)
P-11360-PUSH ROD GUIDE BUSHING
P-11383-LOCK NUT
¼" Pipe Tap. Drain Connection

P-11374-VALVE STEM
U-5154-PUMP SHAFT ASSEMBLY
P-12573-PRESSURE CHAMBER
6 SUPPORT CASTING

◆ NOTE - PARTS VARY WITH TYPE
ORDER FROM DRAWING.
29797 FOR HYPOCHLORINATORS
29798 FOR CHEM. SOLUTION FEEDERS.

GENERAL ASSEMBLY
ELECTRICALLY OPERATED HYPOCHLORINATOR OR CHEMICAL SOLUTION FEEDER

—By Permission of Wallace & Tiernan, Inc.

**Figure 41. Typical Chemical Solution Feeder.**

to the solution container. It is best to have two containers so that the solution may be made up ahead of time to allow for complete dissolution of the chemical into the water solution. The containers should be large enough to allow several days of operation at the strength solution selected.

The polyphosphate should be added into the well to allow for protection of the pump fittings and piping. This also allows for contact time prior to the introduction of the chlorine which interferes with the phosphate reaction. If it is necessary to add the phosphate into the pump discharge, then the chlorine feed line should be located some 20 feet away from the point of entry of phosphate into the water. This will allow for adequate contact for the phosphate to be effective.

Typical solution type feeders for feeding chemicals to a water system are illustrated in Figure 41. Installation of such feeders are shown in Figure 42.

Recent developments in the field of phosphate chemicals for corrosion control have resulted in the development of a phosphate with a zinc carrier which has advantages both in ease of application and its immediate reaction to form a coating within the pipe to give immediate protection. The application dosage rate is the same as the other phosphates but the feeding is greatly simplified in that a positive type proportional feeder is not required. The method of application requires an earthenware or plastic container with an inlet pressure pipe adjusted to a flow of five to 10 gallons per minute. The outlet pipe discharges by gravity flow this same flow. The amount of phosphate used is the required amount to treat the water at the proper dosage rate for a period of eight hours as this is the dissolution rate of the phosphate compound.

The feeding of fluorides by means of a solution feeder is more complicated than the feeding of chlorine or phosphates. This added complication is brought about by the fact that the dosage of fluoride must be closely controlled. Public health authorities have established the optimum dosage of fluoride compound as flouride ion at 1.0 parts per million, this concentration including the natural fluoride content of the water, even though the maximum concentration is established at 2.0 parts per million.

The compound used in solution feeders for that application of fluorides is the Sodium Fluoride. The use of Sodium Fluoride is based upon its constant solubility rate of 4.0 per cent even with change in temperature. Sodium Fluoride varies in purity from 95 to 98 per cent and the fluoride ion varies from 43 to 44 per cent $(F/NaF = 19.00/41.997 = 45.3\%)$. Sodium Fluoride is a crystaline compound, soluble to approximately 4.0 per cent in water, and is non-corrosive in solution.

Equipment needed for feeding fluoride solution is an earthenware or plastic container, a special shaped porous cone on which is located a layer of from four to six inches of fine sand, a small sized inlet water line with meter and float control, and a solution feeder. A schematic of this layout is as follows:

| Inlet Water Line | Water Meter | Float | Container of | Solution | Water |
|---|---|---|---|---|---|
| | ⅝ to ¾″ | Control | 4% Fluoride Solution | Feeder | Service Main |

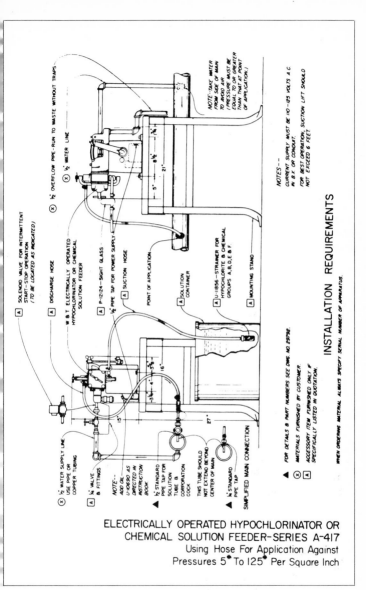

**INSTALLATION REQUIREMENTS**

WHEN ORDERING MATERIAL ALWAYS SPECIFY SERIAL NUMBER OF APPARATUS.

ELECTRICALLY OPERATED HYPOCHLORINATOR OR
CHEMICAL SOLUTION FEEDER–SERIES A-417
Using Hose For Application Against
Pressures 5" To 125" Per Square Inch

—By Permission of Wallace & Tiernan, Inc.

**Figure 42. Typical Chemical Solution Feeder Installation.**

— 149 —

The fluoride compound is placed on the sand and dissolves to form a four per cent solution. The solution is adjusted to feed at the rate so that the fluorides pumped in addition to the natural fluorides in the water will give a concentration of one parts per million. Calculation of feeding rate of the solution feeder is as follows:

$$\text{Feeding Rate of Solution Feeder, ml/min} = \frac{20.8 \times \text{Parts Per Million Dosage Desired} \times \text{Flow of Water to be Treated in GPM}}{\text{Purity of Sodium Fluoride Compound in Per Cent}}$$

The total quantity of fluoride fed per day is obtained from the water flow meter reading and is calculated as follows:

$$\text{Total Pounds of Sodium Fluoride Fed Per Day} = 0.00336 \times \text{Number of Gallons Shown on Meter Reading that Day} \times \text{Purity of Compound in Per Cent}$$

The amount of Fluoride ion fed per day will be:

$$\text{Total Pounds of Fluoride Ion Fed Per Day} = 0.00152 \times \text{Number of Gallons Shown on Meter Reading that Day} \times \text{Purity of Compound in Per Cent}$$

Examples of using these formulas in determining rates and amounts, is illustrated as follows: Sodium Fluoride is to be added to a water system whose natural fluoride content is 0.2 parts per million. It is desired to increase the dosage to 1.0 parts per million. The rate of water to be treated is 300 gallons per minute. At what dosage rate should the solution feeder be set? Per cent purity of the compound is 95%.

$$
\begin{aligned}
\text{Feeding Rate of Feeder, ml/min} &= \frac{20.8 \times \text{PPM Desired} \times \text{Flow of Water Treated, GPM}}{\text{Per Cent Purity}} \\
&= \frac{20.8 \times (1.0 - 0.2) \times 300}{95} = 52.6 \text{ ml/min}
\end{aligned}
$$

At the end of a 24-hour period, the water meter indicates that 20 gallons of solution has been pumped in the treating of 432,000 gallons of water. How much sodium fluoride compound has been used?

$$
\begin{aligned}
\text{Total Pounds of Sodium Fluoride Used Per Day} &= 0.00336 \times \text{Number of Gallons Shown on Water Meter Per Day} \times \text{Purity of Compound in Per Cent} \\
&= 0.00336 \times 20 \times 95 \\
&= 6.33 \text{ pounds}
\end{aligned}
$$

$$
\begin{aligned}
\text{Total Pounds of Fluoride Ion Used Per Day} &= 0.00152 \times \text{Number of Gallons Shown on Water Meter Per Day} \times \text{Purity of Compound in Per Cent} \\
&= 0.00152 \times 20 \times 95 \\
&= 2.88 \text{ pounds}
\end{aligned}
$$

## B. Surface Water Supplies

Water treatment in gravity-type treatment facilities involve the use of dry chemical feed machines because of the large amount of chemicals fed per day. The use of chemicals are involved in the coagulation process, taste and odor control, corrosion, disinfection and fluoridation.

*(1) Coagulation.* Coagulation is the process of using chemicals to precipitate the suspended matter ,some dissolved matter, foreign matter, microorganisms, and bacteria into a "floc" or a conglomerate of a chemical and suspended combination to create a settleable material. The use of the coagulation process provides a method of water treatment which reduces within the water, the amount of turbidity, bacteria, etc. The coagulation process utilizes certain chemicals which are known to produce this phenomenon by the tie up of alkalinity, either natural or added, with the coagulant.

The required amount of chemicals for optimum coagulation effect can best be determined by the jar test method which is given on page 177. It can be best controlled by the pH and alkalinity measurements in relation to the dosage rates as found by the jar test. Primary coagulants used in water treatment with trade names are as follows:

(a) Coagulants.
1. Aluminum Sulfate (Alum) — $Al_2(SO_4)_3.18H_2O$
2. Ferric Sulfate ("Ferrisul" or Ferri-floc) — $Fe_2(SO_4)_3. 9 H_2O$
3. Ferrous Sulfate (Copperas) — $FeSO_4.7H_2O$
4. Ferric Chloride — $FeCl_3.6H_2O$
5. Sodium Aluminate — $Na_2Al_2O_4$

(b) Alkalies.
1. Calcium Hydroxide (Lime, hydrated or slaked) — $Ca(OH)_2$
2. Sodium Carbonate (Soda Ash) — $Na_2CO_3$

(c) Coagulation Reactions.
1. Alum and Natural Alkalinity
$$Al_2(SO_4)_3.18H_2O + 3Ca(HCO_3)_2 = 2Al(OH)_3 + 3CaSO_4 + 18H_2O + 6CO_2$$

Alum and Lime
$$Al_2(SO_4)_3.18H_2O + 3Ca(OH)_2 = 2Al(OH)_3 + 3CaSO_4 + 18H_2O$$
Alum and Soda Ash
$$Al_2(SO_4)_3.18H_2O + 3Na_2CO_3 = 2Al(OH)_3 + 3Na_2SO_4 + 3CO_2 + 18H_2O$$

2. Ferric Sulfate and Natural Alkalinity
$$Fe_2(SO)_4 + 3Ca(HCO_3)_2 = 3CaSO_4 + 2Fe(OH)_3 + 6CO_2$$
Ferric Sulfate and Lime
$$Fe(SO_4)_3 + 3Ca(OH)_2 = 3CaSO_4 + 2Fe(OH)_3$$

3. Ferrous Sulfate (Copperas) and Lime (necessary)
$$FeSO_4.7H_2O + Ca(OH)_2 = Fe(OH)_2 + CaSO_4 + 7H_2O$$
$$4Fe(OH)_2 + O_2 = 2H_2O + 4Fe(OH)_3$$
Ferrous Sulfate (Copperas) and Chlorine
$$6FeSO_4.7H_2O + 3Cl_2 = Fe_2(SO_4)_3 + 4FeCl_3 + 7H_2O$$

4. Ferric Chloride and Lime
$$2FeCl_3 + 3Ca(OH)_2 = 2Fe(OH)_3 + 3CaCl_2 + 6CO_2$$

5. Sodium Aluminate and Natural Alkalinity
$$Na_2Al_2O_4 + Ca(HCO_3)_2 = CaAl_2O_4 + Na_2CO_3 + 2CO_2 + H_2O$$
Sodium Aluminate and Lime
$$Na_2Al_2O_4 + CaOH_2 = CaAl_2O_4 + 2NaOH$$

The alkalinity required on the basis of one part per million of coagulant added is as follows:

1. Alum
    Natural as $CaCO_3$ . . . . . . 0.4505
    Added, lime as $Ca(OH)_2$ 0.3336
    Added, soda ash . . . . . . . 0.4773

2. Ferric Chloride
    Natural as $CaCO_3$ . . . . . . 0.9255
    Added, lime as $Ca(OH)_2$ 0.6852

3. Ferrous Sulfate (Copperas)
    Natural as $CaCO_3$ . . . . . . 0.7500
    Added, lime as $Ca(OH)_2$ 0.2665

Dosages of chemicals should be determined by the jar test with the dosage rates indicated by the jar test being placed upon the feed machines. These rates should be further checked by collection of the machine output for a period of two minutes and then the dosage calculated as follows:

$$\text{Chemical Dosage in Parts Per Million} = 131.16 \times \frac{\text{Output of Machine for Two Minutes}}{\text{Flow of Water Treated in GPM}}$$

$$= 0.189 \times \frac{\text{Output of Machine for Two Minutes}}{\text{Flow of Water Treated in Million Gallon}}$$

$$\text{Machine Setting in Grams Per Minute} = 0.00381 \times \text{Dosage Rate in Parts Per Million} \times \text{Rate of Flow of Water Treated, GPM}$$

$$\text{Machine Setting in Grams Per Minute} = 2.625 \times \text{Chemical Dosage in Parts Per Million} \times \text{Rate of Flow of Water Treated, MGD}$$

From the actual poundage of chemicals added per day to the treated water, the dosage rate may be obtained as follows:

$$\text{Chemical Dosage in Parts Per Million} = \frac{\text{Pounds of Chemical Used Per Day}}{8.34 \times \text{Total Treated Water, MGD}}$$

A tabulated scale of machine setting in grams per minute versus parts per million for plant flows should be made and attached to the side of the chemical feed machine so that this may be readily referred to for proper machine settings from the jar test results. Typical dry feed machines are shown in Figures 43 and 44.

For taste and odor control, activated carbon and chlorine are widely used as they are effective agents in the control of taste and odors. Dosages for taste and odor control are in many cases, difficult to determine. In order to determine the taste and odor dosages, a series of jars with various dosages of carbon and/or chlorine applied to the water are used. Dependent upon the problem, dosages may

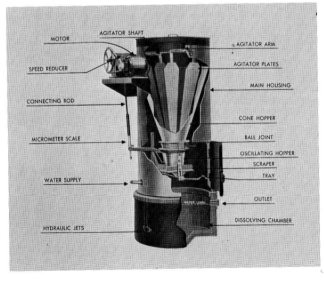

MOTOR

AGITATOR SHAFT

SPEED REDUCER

CONNECTING ROD

MICROMETER SCALE

WATER SUPPLY

HYDRAULIC JETS

AGITATOR ARM

AGITATOR PLATES

MAIN HOUSING

CONE HOPPER

BALL JOINT

OSCILLATING HOPPER

SCRAPER

TRAY

OUTLET

DISSOLVING CHAMBER

WATER LEVEL

—By Permission of Omega Machine Co., BIF Industries.

**Figure 43. Typical Volumetric Dry Chemical Feeder.**

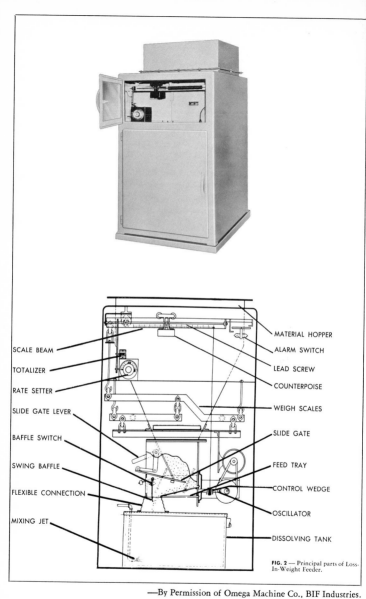

SCALE BEAM

TOTALIZER

RATE SETTER

SLIDE GATE LEVER

BAFFLE SWITCH

SWING BAFFLE

FLEXIBLE CONNECTION

MIXING JET

MATERIAL HOPPER

ALARM SWITCH

LEAD SCREW

COUNTERPOISE

WEIGH SCALES

SLIDE GATE

FEED TRAY

CONTROL WEDGE

OSCILLATOR

DISSOLVING TANK

**FIG. 2** — Principal parts of Loss-In-Weight Feeder.

—By Permission of Omega Machine Co., BIF Industries.

**Figure 44. Typical Loss-In-Weight Gravimetric Chemical Feeder.**

— 154 —

vary from 0.5 to 25.0 parts per million. Dosage rates are calculated as above from carbon, chlorine, and a combination of the two reagents. Chlorine Dioxide is an effective agent in controlling many taste and odors, especially where phenols and industrial wastes are concerned.

The feeding of fluorides to a surface water supply takes much more consideration than the application of other chemicals because of the close control of desired dosages. This desired dosage is 1.0 parts per million (Natural Fluorides plus added Fluorides), appearing as the fluoride ion. In many localities, the application of fluorides to a water supply is varied in concentration with the seasons of the year on the basis of water consumption by children. This basis is that a child drinks more water during the summer than in the winter. Therefore, in these localities, the fluoride concentration is varied from 0.7 parts per million in the summer to 1.2 parts per million within the winter. The concentrations are increased and decreased at concentrations of about 0.1 parts per million per week until the maximum and minimum concentrations are reached rather than make abrupt changes.

Several fluorides are used in the application of fluorides to a water. These compounds are:

Sodium Fluorides (95 to 98% Purity) (NaF).

Sodium Silicofluoride (98% Purity) ($Na_2Si_6F$)

Hydrofluosilicic Acid (30% Purity) ($H_2SiF_6$)

Hydrofluoric Acid (Commercial Grade) (HF).

In the feeding of these compounds, several important factors which must be considered are: dust control, handling methods, corrosiveness, effect upon water pH, and the dissolution rate of the compound used. The compounds most commonly used in the field of water treatment is the Sodium Fluoride and the Sodium Silicofluoride. Calculations of dosage for dry feeding of these compounds are as follows:

a. Sodium Fluoride:

$$\text{Feeding Rate of Sodium Fluoride in Pounds Per Day} = 1847.0 \times \frac{\text{Dosage Desired, PPM (Total Desired—Natural)} \times \text{Rate of Flow, MGD}}{\text{Purity of Sodium Fluoride in Per Cent}}$$

$$= 2.657 \times \frac{\text{Dosage Desired, PPM (Total Desired—Natural)} \times \text{Rate of Flow, GPM}}{\text{Purity of Sodium Fluoride in Per Cent}}$$

$$\text{Feeding Rate of Sodium Fluoride in Pounds Per Hour} = 76.96 \times \frac{\text{Dosage Desired, PPM (Total Desired—Natural)} \times \text{Rate of Flow, MGD}}{\text{Purity of Sodium Fluoride in Per Cent}}$$

$$= 0.1107 \times \frac{\text{Dosage Desired, PPM (Total Desired—Natural)} \times \text{Rate of Flow, GPM}}{\text{Purity of Sodium Fluoride in Per Cent}}$$

Expressed as the Fluoride ion, the total dosage will be:

Pounds of Fluoride Added as the Fluoride Ion = 45.2 x (Pounds of Sodium Fluoride Fed) x (Purity of Sodium Fluoride in Per Cent)

b. Sodium Silicofluoride:

$$\text{Feeding Rate of Sodium Silicofluoride in Pounds Per Day} = 1375.0 \times \frac{\text{Desired Dosage, PPM (Total—Natural)} \times \text{Rate of Flow, MGD}}{\text{Purity of Compound in Per Cent}}$$

$$= 1.98 \times \frac{\text{Desired Dosage, PPM (Total—Natural)} \times \text{Rate of Flow, GPM}}{\text{Purity of Compound in Per Cent}}$$

$$\text{Feeding Rate of Sodium Silicofluoride in Pounds Per Hour} = 57.3 \times \frac{\text{Desired Dosage, PPM (Total—Natural)} \times \text{Rate of Flow, MGD}}{\text{Purity of Compound in Per Cent}}$$

$$= 0.0825 \times \frac{\text{Desired Dosage, PPM (Total—Natural)} \times \text{Rate of Flow, GPM}}{\text{Purity of Compound in Per Cent}}$$

Expressed as the Fluoride ion, the total dosage will be:

Pounds of Fluoride Added as the Fluoride Ion = 60.6 x (Pounds of Sodium Silicofluoride Fed) x (Purity of Sodium Silicofluoride in Per Cent)

Special precautions in handling of fluoride compounds should require a mechanical dust collector on the fluoride equipment, and the operators use of a respirator, goggles, rubber gloves, and rubber apron.

### 7. Records
### A. Ground Water Supplies

Records are a must for all water systems regardless of size of the system. First of all, a layout plan giving in detail, the location of all pipelines and fittings must be kept on hand and must be current with improvements made on the system. As new services are made, such information should be added with accuracy to this plan. Not only should this plan show detailed locations, but rights-of-way and other vital information. These plans should be stored in a safe and fireproof location.

Records on wells should consist of a complete well log indicating types of underground strata and flow of the different water aquifers at specific depths. It is certainly desirable to acquire as much data on water quality from each acquifer as possible during the drilling process. Permanent information should also consist of static water level, pumping water level (draw-down), discharge, and times of recovery and draw-down.

Concerning pumps, controls, etc., files should be kept on manufacturers manuals on operation and maintenance, parts list, etc. Records should be kept on pump and control operation and maintenance.

If chemical treatment is used on the system, it is necessary not only to record the amount of chemicals added in terms of dosage rate, but regarding effectiveness, tests should be made to determine if these dosages rates are adequate. Permanent records should be kept on test results.

For large water systems, it is necessary to periodically flush sediment out of the system. This can be accomplished by flushing or blowing off fire hydrants. It is also necessary to drain the sediment from elevated or ground storage tanks and to inspect these facilities for corrosion and protective coatings. Records should be kept on all this type work. Regarding the fire hydrant flushing, it should be the established policy that each hydrant within the system be flushed at least once per year. Each hydrant should be numbered and a record maintained of each time the hydrant was operated.

All valves within the system should be operated on a yearly basis and maintained at that time. For each valve, a record should be kept of the number of turns to open and close the valve, and a record should be kept of each operation. Such information as this will assume that each valve is properly operating and completely open or closed during operation.

Records should be kept on daily, monthly, and yearly water consumption. If there are no meters on the individual wells, the water usage should be estimated from the length of the pump operation each day. Future planning of the system can best be made from such records on water consumption.

Complete cost of operation is a must where records are concerned. By comparing cost of operation each month with revenue received, it is possible to determine if the system is being operated efficiently. This will also provide other important information for estimating future operation costs, rates, and connection fees.

## B. Surface Treatment Plants

The records required for a surface treatment plant in addition to those recommended for a ground water supply involve the treatment plant operation.

Records for treatment plant operation must be so complete that it is possible to evaluate plant operation to the extent of determining efficiencies of operation, unaccounted water, power usage, personnel records, and inventories of material. From these reports, it is possible to predict future plant costs and factors concerning operation.

Required in plant operation are daily and monthly reports. Fluoride inventory should be calculated separately and on a weekly basis so that a close check of dosage, chemical used, and inventory may be had.

*(1). Daily Reports.* Daily records should be kept on all plant operation, water quality, inventory, and personnel working hours. The plant operation report should include complete analysis of water quality, chemical feeding rates and dosages, chemical inventory, bacteriological results, filter operation, and power consumption. Figure 45 is a suggested form for a daily log to record complete plant operation.

Evaluation of plant operation is based upon plant economics and efficiency of operation. Plant operational efficiency can be based upon the percentage of total water used in the filter washing and the general maintenance of the plant equipment. The wash water for the filters should not exceed three per cent of the total water treated and usually should be one per cent or less.

*(2) Monthly Reports.* Monthly reports should be a compilation of daily reports. These reports should include the total, maximum, minimum, and

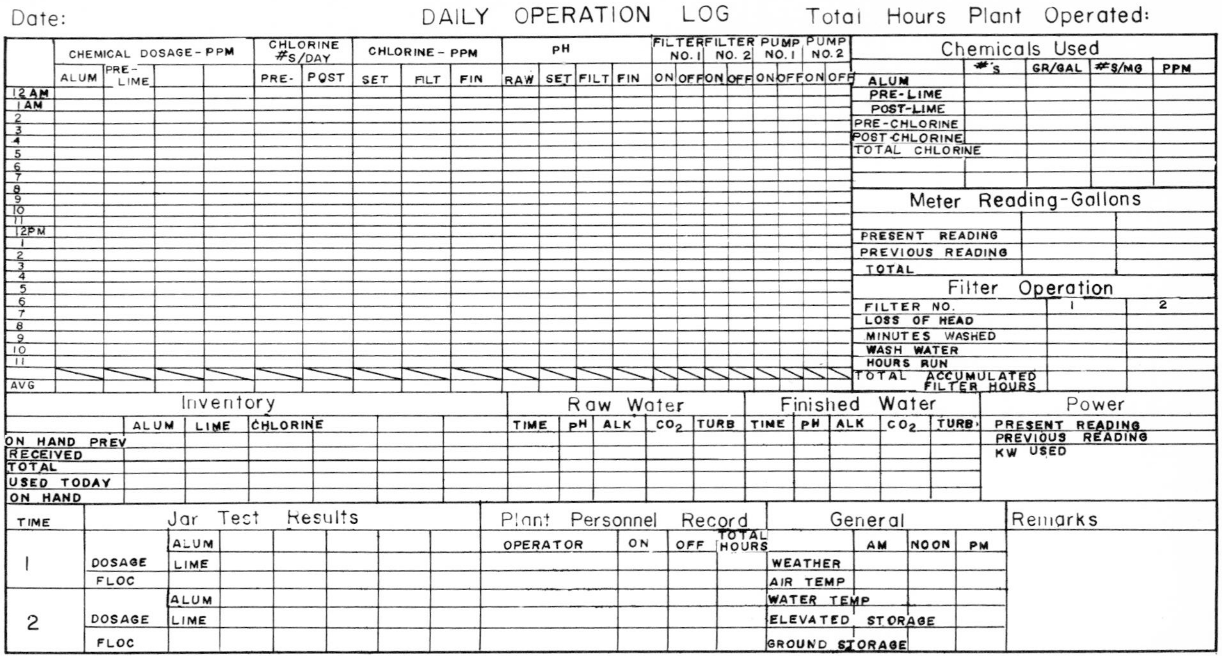

Date: _____

# DAILY OPERATION LOG

Total \_\_\_\_ Hours \_\_\_\_ Plant Operated: \_\_\_\_

**CHEMICAL DOSAGE - PPM**
ALUM | PRE-LIME

**CHLORINE #'S/DAY**
PRE- | POST

**CHLORINE - PPM**
SET | POST

**PH**
RAW | SET | FILT | FIN

**FILTER PUMP / PUMP**
NO. 2 NO. 1 NO. 2
ON OFF ON OFF ON OFF ON OFF

**Chemicals Used**
ALUM | #'S | GR/GAL | #'S/MG | PPM
PRE-LIME
POST-LIME
PRE-CHLORINE
POST-CHLORINE
TOTAL CHLORINE

Time rows: 12 AM, 1 AM, 2, 3, 4, 5, 6, 7, 8, 9, 10, 11, 12 PM, 1, 2, 3, 4, 5, 6, 7, 8, 9, 10, 11, AVG

**Meter Reading-Gallons**
PRESENT READING
PREVIOUS READING
TOTAL

**Filter Operation**
FILTER NO. | 1 | 2
LOSS OF HEAD
MINUTES WASHED
WASH WATER
HOURS RUN
TOTAL ACCUMULATED FILTER HOURS

**Inventory**
ALUM | LIME | CHLORINE
ON HAND PREV
RECEIVED
TOTAL
USED TODAY
ON HAND

**Jar Test Results**
1 — DOSAGE ALUM / LIME; FLOC
2 — DOSAGE ALUM / LIME; FLOC

**Raw Water**
TIME | pH | ALK | CO2 | TURB

**Plant Personnel Record**
OPERATOR | ON | OFF | TOTAL HOURS

**Finished Water**
TIME | pH | ALK | CO2 | TURB

**Power**
PRESENT READING
PREVIOUS READING
KW USED

**General**
AM | NOON | PM
WEATHER
AIR TEMP
WATER TEMP
ELEVATED STORAGE
GROUND STORAGE

**Remarks**

FIGURE 45. Daily Log Of Plant Operation.

— 158 —

# CITY OF HOMETOWN
## DEPARTMENT OF UTILITIES
HOMETOWN, U.S.A.

HOMETOWN WATER PURIFICATION PLANT

Cost of Operation for the Month of_____19_____

Total Amount of Water Treated (Gallons) . . . . . . . . . . . . . . _____
Total Amount of Water Pumped to City (Gallons) . . . . . . . _____
Total Amount of Water Used for Washing Filters (Gallons) _____
Average Gallons Treated per Day . . . . . . . . . . . . . . . . . . . . _____
Maximum Gallons Treated per Day . . . . . . . . . . . . . . . . . . . _____
Minimum Gallons Treated per Day . . . . . . . . . . . . . . . . . . . _____
Per Cent Wash Water Used . . . . . . . . . . . . . . . . . . . . . . . . . _____
Hours Plant in Operation . . . . . . . . . . . . . . . . . . . . . . . . . . _____

Cost of Chemicals:
_____ lbs. Aluminum Sulphate @ $_____ per hund. $_____
_____ lbs. Lime @ $_____ per hund. . . . . . . . . . . . $_____
_____ lbs. Chlorine @ $_____ per hund. . . . . . . . . $_____
_____ lbs. Activated Carbon @ $_____ per hund. . . . $_____
_____ lbs. _____ @ $_____ per hund. . . $_____

Total Cost of Chemicals . . . . . . . . . . . . . . . . . . . . . . . . . $_____

Cost of Chemicals per Million Gallons Filtered . . . . . . . . $_____

Cost of Power:
Pumping Water to City . . . . . . . . . . . . . . . . . . . . . . . . . . . $_____
Pumping Raw Water . . . . . . . . . . . . . . . . . . . . . . . . . . . . . $_____
Pumping Wash Water . . . . . . . . . . . . . . . . . . . . . . . . . . . . $_____
Dry Feed Machines . . . . . . . . . . . . . . . . . . . . . . . . . . . . . . $_____
Flocculator . . . . . . . . . . . . . . . . . . . . . . . . . . . . . . . . . . . . $_____
Mechanical Mix . . . . . . . . . . . . . . . . . . . . . . . . . . . . . . . . $_____
Air Compressor . . . . . . . . . . . . . . . . . . . . . . . . . . . . . . . . $_____
Lights and Sand Pump (Approx.) . . . . . . . . . . . . . . . . . . . $_____

Total Cost of Power for Month . . . . . . . . . . . . . . . . . . . . $_____
Cost of Power per Million Gallons Pumped to City . . . . . $_____

Labor . . . . . . . . . . . . . . . . . . . . . . . . . . . . . . . . . . . . . . . . $_____
Incidental (Approx.) . . . . . . . . . . . . . . . . . . . . . . . . . . . . . $_____
Total Cost of Plant Operation . . . . . . . . . . . . . . . . . . . . . . $_____
Cost of Operation per Million Gallons to City . . . . . . . . . $_____

_____
Superintendent of Water Plant

**Figure 46. Monthly Report of Plant Operation and Cost.**

average of the following: Daily Water Treated, Hours Plant Operated Daily, Length of Filter Runs, Wash Water, Chemicals Used in Pounds and Parts Per Million, and chemical test results for the raw, filtered, and finished for carbon dioxide, turbidity, hardness, alkalinity, pH, and chlorine.

Monthly calculations for plant evaluation should include per cent of wash water used, wash water rate, filter yield and rate of filtration. (See Appendix for these formulas.)

A second monthly report should be a compilation of information to give the most pertinent information regarding plant operational cost. Figure 46 is a suggestive form for this purpose.

Cost data is most valuable on a total and breakdown basis. But for comparison figures, the data is valuable on a production basis such as cost per million gallons of water treated. This again should be broken down on individual cost for chemicals and power cost per million gallons.

It is advisable to keep daily and weekly records for a period of three years. Monthly records should be considered as permanent records so that trends and comparisons of water usage, etc., may be obtained.

# CHAPTER VII
# Water Quality

**General**

The quality of water is based upon three distinct characteristics, each of which may independently govern the desirable potability of a water. These characteristics are: physical quality, the bacterial quality, and the chemical quality of the water. The present day standards, set forth by the United States Public Health Service are as follows:

In the following discussions, the influence of each of these characteristics on water quality will be noted.

**1. Physical Quality of Water**

The physical quality of water is the appearance of the water to the consumer. Physical quality includes the clearness of the water, taste and odor, and temperature. For a water to be of attractive physical quality, it must be clear in appearance, that is, have a

## TABLE LIX
## Water Quality Standards[17]

| Characteristic | Permissible Concentrations in Milligrams Per Liter | Objections to Concentrations Beyond Permissible Limits |
|---|---|---|
| Turbidity | 5* | Esthetic |
| Color | 15* | Esthetic |
| Threshold Odor Number | 3* | Esthetic |
| Alkyl Benzene Sulfonate (ABS) | 0.5 | Taste, Foaming, Indicator of Pollution |
| Arsenic (As) | 0.01 | Toxic |
| Chloride (Cl) | 250 | Possible Laxative Effect |
| Copper (Cu) | 1.0 | Possible Physiological Effect |
| Carbon Chloroform Extract (CCE) | 0.2 | Toxicological Interest |
| Cyanide (CN) | 0.01 | Toxic |
| Fluoride (F) | See Below | Mottling of Teeth |
| Iron (Fe) | 0.3 | Esthetic, Staining of Laundry |
| Manganese (Mn) | 0.05 | Esthetic, Staining of Laundry |
| Nitrate | 45 | Methemoglobinemia |
| Phenols | 0.001 | Taste |
| Sulfates | 250 | Possible Laxative Effect |
| Total Dissolved Solids | 500 | Possible Laxative Effect |
| Zinc (Zn) | 5 | Possible Laxative Effect |
| Radium-226 | 3** | Radiation Damage |
| Strontium-90 | 10** | Radiation Damage |
| Gross Beta Radioactivity | 1000** | Radiation Damage |

Concentrations in excess of following should be re-examined before use (mg/l):

| | | | |
|---|---|---|---|
| Arsenic (As) | 0.05 | Fluoride (F) | See Below |
| Barium (Ba) | 1.0 | Lead (Pb) | 0.05 |
| Cadmium (Cd) | 0.01 | Selenium (Se) | 0.01 |
| Hexavalent Chromium(+6) | 0.05 | Silver (Ag) | 0.05 |
| Cyanide (CN) | 0.2 | | |

| Annual Average of Maximum Daily Air Temperature | Recommended Control Limits— Fluoride Concentrations in mg/l | | |
|---|---|---|---|
| | Lower | Optimum | Upper |
| 50.0 to 53.7 | 0.9 | 1.2 | 1.7 |
| 53.8 to 58.3 | 0.8 | 1.1 | 1.5 |
| 58.4 to 63.8 | 0.8 | 1.0 | 1.3 |
| 63.9 to 70.6 | 0.7 | 0.9 | 1.2 |
| 70.7 to 79.2 | 0.7 | 0.8 | 1.0 |
| 79.3 to 90.5 | 0.6 | 0.7 | 0.8 |

*Standard Units.        **Pico-curies Per Liter.

low turbidity preferably less than 5.0 units of turbidity. The color within the water must be low in concentration so as not distract the consumers attention. Color should be less than 15.0 units of color.

The water should be free of substances which may produce taste and odors upon the addition of chlorine or upon use of water for cooking purposes. It should also be free of trouble producing organisms such as aromatic oils of algae or higher bacteria.

The temperature of the water will effect the attractiveness to the extent that the use by consumers will decrease if the water is of extremely high temperature. Ground water temperature varies very slightly with seasonal change with the water temperature varying from around 40 to 55 degrees Fahrenheit. Such temperature changes are dependent upon well depth and storage facilities above ground. Surface waters will vary with seasonal change from around 40 to 80 degrees Fahrenheit.

## 2. Bacterial Quality of Water

The most important quality of water is that of bacterial quality. In the early twentieth century, disease outbreaks from water and food-borne bacteria prevailed throughout the world. Progress in the related fields of bacteriology and water treatment engineering has eliminated to an almost non-existent occurrance, the outbreaks of water-borne communicable diseases where such advances of progress prevail.

### A. Bacteria Found in Water

Bacteria found in water may be classified into two categories; first are those native or whose natural habitat is a water environment, and second, those which are foreign or whose natural habitat is not normally a water environment. Under the classification of native bacteria, are found the following types of bacteria:

1. Water Spirochaetes of the pathogenic and non-pathogenic type found in surface waters. These are protozoan-like, slender spirals.

2. Slime bacteria (Myxobacteriales) appearing in the form of stalked bacteria (Caulobacteria) such as iron bacteria (Gallionella) or as sheathed bacteria as iron forming bacteria (Leptotherix, Crenothrix, Clonothrix) or as non-sheathed filamentous bacteria such as sulphur forming bacteria (Beggiota). All these bacteria are non-pathogenic in water but create distinct problems of taste and odor. This group includes the algae-like, filamentous, sheathed, and unsheathed bacteria of the groups mentioned.

3. True bacteria such as nitrogen fixation bacteria. The baceria converts the ammonia in water to nitrites and the nitrites to nitrates in the nitrogen cycle. These bacteria are non-pathogenic.

Under the classification of foreign bacteria, are found the following types of bacteria:

1. Soil bacteria such as Streptomyces commonly found in soil.

2. Air bacteria such as Bacillus, Staphlococcus, Streptococcus, Molds, and Yeasts.

3. Pollution organisms from excreta. In this group are the Escherichia Coliforms, the index organism of laboratory analysis for water quality, commonly found in the intestines of man and animals. Within this group of bacteria are the Clostridium welchii, Streptococcus faecalis, Shigella, Salmonella, and Vibrio comma, all pathogenic.

### B. Pathogenic Bacteria Found in Water[18]

It should be noted from the above paragraphs, that all bacteria found in water are not harmful or pathogenic. However, there are many pathogenic bacteria which will thrive in a water and which may be transmitted through the water medium. A partial list of pathogenic organisms is as follows:

(1) *Pathogenic Bacteria:*

| Disease | Organism |
|---|---|
| Bacillary Dysentery | Shigella dysenteriae |
| Cholera | Vibrios comma |
| Paratyphoid | Salmonella paratyphi, schottmulleri |
| Typhoid | Eberthella typhi |
| Tularemia | Pasteurella tularensis |
| Brucellosis (?) | Brucella melitensis |
| Tuberculosis (?) | Tubercle bacilli |

(2) *Spirochaetals:*

| Disease | Organism |
|---|---|
| Haemorrhagic Jaundice (Weil's Disease) | Leptospira icterohaemorrhagiae |

(3) *Virus:*

| Disease |
|---|
| Infectious Hepatitis (?) |
| Poliomyelitis |

(4) *Parasitic:*

| Disease | Organism |
|---|---|
| Amoebic Dysentery | Endamoeba histolytica |
| Schistosomiasis | Schistosoma mansoni |
| Hookworm (?) | Ancylostomiasis |

## C. Bacterial Standards of Water Quality

For a water to be of the highest bacterial quality, it should be free of all harmful or pathogenic bacteria. The laboratory methods of determining the presence of pathogenic bacteria or organisms, are time consuming and expensive. Therefore, in lieu of a test for specific indentification of bacteria, the water works profession and public health authorities have adopted a simplified procedure for obtaining the bacterial quality of water. This adopted procedure calls for the identification of the presence of the Coliform bacteria group of bacteria as the indicator or index organism of pollution. Since the Coliform group is a common habitat of the intestines of man and animals, it is present in abundance where ever pathogenic bacteria or organisms are found. Therefore, its presence will indicate either the presence, potential presence, or possibility of future entrance of harmful organisms in a water supply. It should be remembered however, that the presence of Coliform bacteriae does *not* positively state that the harmful organisms are present, *but* that they may find entry into the source of supply.

In the interpretation of data concerning bacterial counts or concentrations, it must be realized that bacteria are single cell organisms which are extremely small, thus making it impossible to detect the individual organisms under the lens of a microscope. Therefore, in all laboratory procedures for water analysis, the bacteria are incubated at optimum tem-

— 163 —

peratures for selected periods of time in order to produce growths or colonies which may be seen or which may produce other measureable means by which they may be counted. By making use of gas fermentation of certain type of media, it is possible to produce a means of estimating bacterial populations. Three methods are used for determining the population of Coliform bacteria[16][17][30].

*(1) Standard Plate Count.* The standard plate counting method consists of planting a portion of water within a Petrie dish containing melted nutrient agar at 43 degrees centigrade. The agar is cooled to 37 degrees and incubated for a period of 24 hours at which time each visible colony is counted. The portion of water planted is measured in milliliters or portion thereof in the amount that the number of colonies appearing will number from 30 to 300. Reporting of such samples will be on the basis of Number of Bacteria per Milliliter. This count will have an extremely wide range and may be considered insignificant as far as water quality is concerned since the colonies will include all types of bacterial growths in addition to the Coliform group. It does however, have significance in determining the efficiency of the treatment units by comparing plate counts obtained on influents and effluents of the units.

*(2) Standard Coliform Tests.* Bacterial standards based upon a count of Coliform bacteria are expressed in terms of Most Probable Number of Coliforms per 100 milliliters. This method of analysis is a statistical procedure in which a series of tubes are used. This series, called a Standard Portion, should consist of five 10 milliliter portions or five 100 milliliters each. The test is carried to a confirmation of the presence of Coliform bac-

teria. The results of the test are based upon the number of tubes showing the presence of the Coliform bacteria group. Table XL sets forth the Most Probable Number of Coliform bacteria for a stated number of positive tubes.

Since the Most Probable Number is a statistical method of reporting presence and concentration of bacteria, a water supply may occasionally show the presence of bacteria, provided that portions of consecutive samples are not positive or that not more than five per cent of the total portions examined per month are positive. The Most Probable Number is usually referred to as MPN which signifies the number of bacteria per 100 milliliters. When all portions of a sample are negative, the results should be reported as *less than 2.0* and not as zero.

*(3) Standard Membrane Filter Method[20].* Recently the use of the membrane filter has been approved as a method of determining the bacterial quality of water. This procedure sets forth that the sample size shall not be less than 50 milliliters and shall be free of disinfecting agents. Individual samples should be interpreted as satisfactory when the counts do not exceed:

| | |
|---|---|
| 3 colonies per | 50 ml. Sample |
| 4 colonies per | 100 ml. Sample |
| 7 colonies per | 200 ml. Sample |
| 13 colonies per | 500 ml. Sample |
| 22 colonies per | 1,000 ml. Sample |

in any two consecutive standard samples, or in more than five per cent of the standard samples when 20 or more samples are examined per month, with the arithmetic mean density of all standard samples examined per month not exceeding one per 100 milliliters.

**TABLE LX**

**Most Probable Number of Coliform Bacteria**

**Per 100 Milliliters[17][19]**

| Number of 10 ml. Tubes Showing Presence of Coliform Group | When Only Five 10 ml. Portions Are Used | Most Probable Number of Coliforms per 100 ml. | | |
|---|---|---|---|---|
| | | When an Additional 1.0 ml. Portion is Used and is Positive in Addition to the Stated Number of 10 ml. Portions | When an Additional 0.1 ml. Portion is Used and is Positive in Addition to the Stated Number of 10 ml. Portions | When Both the 1.0 ml. and 0.1 ml. Portions are Positive in Addition to the Stated Number of 10 ml. Portions |
| 0 | less than 2.0 | 2.0 | 2.0 | 4.0 |
| 1 | 2.0 | 4.4 | 4.4 | 6.7 |
| 2 | 5.0 | 7.6 | 7.5 | 10.0 |
| 3 | 8.0 | 12.0 | 12.0 | 16.0 |
| 4 | 15.0 | 21.0 | 20.0 | 27.0 |
| 5 | 38.0 | 240.0 | 96.0 | 240.0 plus |

## D. Laboratory Equipment for Bacterial Examination[16]

Apparatus and materials required for making the standard plate count and the determination of Coliform bacteria (MPN) are listed as follows:

| Suggested Quantity | Article |
| --- | --- |
| 1 ea. | Autoclave (25 quart pressure cooker may be substituted). |
| 1 ea. | Hot Plate*. |
| 1 ea. | Electric Sterilizing Oven with Thermometer*. |
| 1 ea. | Refrigerator (Apartment Size). |
| 1 ea. | Incubator, 37 degree, with temperature control. |
| 2 gross | Test Tubes, Bacteriological, 75 x 10mm. |
| 2 gross | Test Tubes, Bacteriological, 150 x 20mm. |
| 6 ea. | Test Tube Baskets, rectangular, 5″ x 4″ x 6″ high. |
| 2 ea. | Culture Dish Holders with inside tray. |
| 2 ea. | Pipette Boxes, copper 2″ x 17″. |
| 36 ea. | Bottles, wide mouth 250 ml. ground glass stoppers. |
| 36 ea. | Flasks, Pyrex Erlenmeyer, 100 cc. |
| 3 ea. | Flasks, Pyrex Erlenmeyer, 1,000 cc. |
| 60 ea. | Culture Dishes, 100 x 10mm. |
| 2 ea. | Inoculating needles (3″ chromel wire fused in glass handle). |
| 6 ea. | Wax Pencils, blue or red. |
| 2 lbs. | Cotton Batting for Plugging Tubes (Metal caps may be used). |
| 1 | Harvard Balance with weights. |
| 3 | Graduated Cylinders, 1,000 cc. |
| 3 | Graduated cylinders, 100 cc. |
| 1 | Clamp, Chaddock. |
| 2 | Test Tube Support, 24 holes. |
| 1 doz. | Tube Brushes, 9″ x 2¼″. |
| ½ doz. | Flask Brushes. |
| 3 doz. | Pipettes 1 ml. graduated to 0.1 ml. |
| 3 doz. | Pipettes 10 ml. graduated to 0.1 ml. |
| 1 lb. | Nutrient Agar, dehydrated. |
| 1 lb. | Lactose Broth, dehydrated. |
| ½ lb. | Brilliant Green Bile, dehydrated. |
| 1 ea. | Alcohol Burner. |

*A small electric stove (apartment size) may be substituted for the hot plate and the hot air sterilizer.

## E. Laboratory Procedures for Bacteria Examinations[16][30]

Laboratory procedures which are applicable in the determination of bacteria presence in a water, are described in the following paragraphs.

*(1) Cleaning of Glassware.* Glassware should be thoroughly cleaned using soap and water. If additional cleaning is necessary, dissolve about 100 grams of commercial potassium dichromate in 375 milliliters of distilled water and make up to one liter with concentrated acid. Care must be taken in mixing because of the heat produced in the reaction.

*(2) Sterilization.* Sterilization is accomplished by two methods, dry heat and steam pressure.

(a) Dry Heat Sterilization. Used for glassware. Heat at 170 degrees for 1½ hours. Cool gradually before removing. All pipettes should be sterilized in containers in which they will be stored. All glass bottles with glass stoppers should have a small piece of paper placed between stopper and bottle to prevent vacuum from forming.

(b) Pressure Sterilization for Liquids, Culture Media, and Dilution Water. Operate steam sterilizer at 15 pounds pressure for 15 to 20 minutes. Proper procedure is to exhaust all air before building up pressure. After sterilization period, allow pressure to drop slowly. Remove media, etc., as soon after pressure drops as possible.

*(3) Preparation of Culture Media.*
(a) Nutrient Agar. Dissolve 23 grams of dehydrated nutrient agar powder in one liter. Heat to dissolve. Transfer 50 ml. into small flasks. Plug with cotton and sterilize in pressure sterilizer.

(b) Lactose Broth. It is necessary to have two strengths of Lactose Broth, single strength and double strength. For the single strength, dissolve 13 grams of dehydrated broth powder into one liter. For the double strength, dissolve 26 grams of powder into one liter. Transfer seven milliliters of broth into the 150 x 20 mm tubes, carefully keeping the two strengths separate. Then place, inverted, the 75 x 10 mm tubes within the larger tubes. (After sterilization, these inverted tubes should be completely filled with broth.) Plug each large tube with cotton and sterilize with steam pressure. Repeat sterilization on all tubes in which gas appears within the inverted tubes.

(c) Brilliant Green Bile. Since Brilliant Green Bile is only used for confirmation of the positive Lactose Broth tubes, it is unnecessary to make this in large portions as the liter, but in 100 milliliter portions. Therefore, four grams of Brilliant Green Bile dehydrated powder is dissolved in 100 milliliters of water. If necessary, heat to dissolve. Pipette seven milliliters into each of the 150 x 20 mm tubes. Place the 75 x 10 mm tubes inverted within the larger tubes. Plug with cotton and sterilize in steam sterilizer.

*(4) Storage of Media.* Upon sterilization of media, it should be stored in a refrigerator. Pipettes and Petrie dishes should remain stored in proper containers.

*(5) Procedure for Standard Plate Count.* Nutrient Agar is used for making the standard plate count. The agar is placed in a beaker of hot water until melted, then the temperature is adjusted to around 42 degrees centigrade. At that time, one ml. of sample is placed in a sterilized Petrie dish (100 x 10 mm). Then 10 ml. of the agar is transferred by a sterile pipette to the Petrie dish by lifting the

lid of the dish. A slow circular movement is used to mix the sample and agar. After cooling, the dish is inverted and placed in the 37-degree incubator for 24 hours. In cases where the plate counts exceed 300 bacteria colonies, it is necessary to use dilutions.

(6) *Procedure for Standard Coliform Test.* The identification of the Coliform group of bacteria is based upon its ability to ferment the lactose culture media in the formation of gas. In the absence of gas in this test, it is assumed that Coliform Bacteria is not present. The test is divided into the presumptive, the confirmed, and the completed test. For the purpose of water examination, it is usually necessary to only confirm the presence of the Coliform group.

(a) The Presumptive Test. The presumptive test is made using Lactose Broth as prepared in (3) above. Three portions of sample are used, the 10 ml. portions, one ml. portions, and 0.1 ml. portions in the following series:

> 10.0 ml. is added to each of five tubes of double strength broth;
> 1.0 ml. is added to one tube of single strength broth; and
> 0.1 ml. is added to one tube of single strength broth.

The tubes are incubated at 37 degrees centigrade for 24 to 48 hours at which time the results are observed as follows: results are positive if the fermentation tubes have gas formation or the results are negative if there is no gas formation within the fermentation tubes.
(b) The Confirmed Test. All of the presumptive positive tubes (those tubes which have gas formation), must be confirmed to state that the gas producing organisms are Coliforms before the Most Probable

Number is calculated. Portions of the presumptive position tubes are transferred by using a wire loop, sterilized by flaming, from these tubes to the tubes containing the Brilliant Green Bile. During this Procedure, it is necessary to flame the mouths of each tube prior to the transfer of the media. The Brilliant Green Bile tubes are incubated for 24 to 48 hours and then observed. Gas formation within the fermentation or inverted tubes, indicates the presence of Coliform bacteria. The absence of gas formation indicates the absence of Coliform bacteria.
(c) Calculation of the Most Probable Number of bacteria per 100 milliliters from this series of positive tubes is obtainable from the table given on Page 165.

### 3. Water Chemistry

When one speaks of water, he has in mind its chemical composition as being $H_2O$. He is certainly correct because water is composed of those two constitutents by combining two parts of Hydrogen and one part of Oxygen. From the standpoint of the water supplier, this concept cannot be accepted in its entirety because the water which he deals with contains many other constitutents, some of which are of extreme importance. One may wonder what these constituents are and where they come from. In Chapter II the water cycle was described stating that water is continuously being re-cycled from the earth's bodies of water and plant transpiration to the clouds, then returning as rains, snow, sleet, etc.

It is during this cycle of water movement that water picks up many solid and gaseous components. As the rain drops fall to the earth, the many gases of the atmosphere act upon the spherical shaped raindrops. These gases, acting upon the gas-liquid interface of the raindrop, soon reach a state of equilibrium. Gases within the atmosphere are the many carbon, sulphur, and nitrogen compounds. Also picked up from the atmosphere are many microscopic particles of solids known as particulates. Many of the particulates are soluble in water and will dissolve within the raindrop.

In the other portion of the hydrological cycle, other constitutents are added to the water cycle from surface or ground water flow. Many and varied constitutents are added to the water from dissolution of rocks and minerals which come in contact with the water in its movement. Of particular importance to the water supplier are the following constitutents: acidity and alkalinity, calcium, carbon compounds, chlorides, fluorides, iron, magnesium, manganese, nitrogen compounds, silica, and sulphur compounds. All of these and many others, combined in water, determine the chemical quality of the water. Each of these constitutents will be discussed in detail.

## A. Acidity, Alkalinity, Carbon Compounds

Acidity is an expression of the concentration of the Hydrogen Ion concentration within a water or, in reverse, it may be considered a measure of the hydroxide or alkaline quality of the water.

$$H_2O \longrightarrow H^+ + OH^-$$

It is usually expressed as pH which is defined as the negative logarithm of the Hydrogen Ion concentration. The pH is a mere number and has no units. In stating this concentration in terms of pH, the interpretation is that a pH of 7.0 is assumed to be neutral. At this pH, the concentration of the Hydrogen Ion or acid

forming ion is in balance with the $OH^-$ or Hydroxide Ion concentration which is the alkaline forming ion. As the pH value decreases from 7.0 to 1.0, the acidity increases or in other words the Hydrogen Ion concentration increases to a maximum. As the pH value increases from 7.0 to 14.0, the acidity decreases or in other words the Hydrogen Ion concentration decreases to a minimum. Even though a pH value of 7.0 is considered neutral, it is not accepted as such in the field of water works because of the corrosive nature of the water at this pH. A water is considered to be neutral or non-corrosive around a pH of 8.2 because at this pH it is free of carbon dioxide which combines with water to form carbonic acid. Natural waters will fall within a pH range of five to 10. It is common to find most well waters within a pH range of 5.8 to 7.4. Thus it may be stated that most well waters are slightly acid in nature.

Alkalinity is closely tied into pH as an expression of chemical quality of water. It is an expression in terms of calcium carbonate of the carbonates, and carbon dioxide as measured by titrating with a known strength of acid to a pH of 4.7, which is known as the end point of methyl orange or methyl purple. Knowing the alkalinity of a water is of significance because it is possible from a knowledge of pH and alkalinity to determine the corrosiveness of the water.

Carbonaceous content of the water is an important part in the stability or aggressiveness of the water toward metal surfaces. Carbon compounds appear in water in the form of carbon dioxide, the bicarbonates, and the carbonate. The reaction which takes place in water is as follows:

Water + Carbon Dioxide $\longrightarrow$ Carbonate Acid + Bicarbonate.

It is possible to have any of the following three combinations of the carbon compounds in a water:

1. Carbon Dioxide and Bicarbonate.
2. Bicarbonate and Carbonate.
3. Carbonate.

Each of these phases will occur at times and it is impossible for carbon dioxide and the carbonate to occur at the same time within a water. The pH is the determining factor for the occurrence of these three phases. As the pH becomes lower, the tendency is for all alkalinity to appear as the carbon dioxide. Then at pH 8.2 it is impossible to have Carbon Dioxide in the water and the Carbonate begins to form. As the pH increases toward 14, all of the alkalinity will appear as the Carbonate.

It can be easily understood that water having a low alkalinity will tend to be corrosive. This can be explained by the fact that with low alkalinity, the Carbon Dioxide concentration is greater.

To render a water of low pH and low alkalinity to be non-corrosive or aggressive to pipelines, pumps, and fittings, three methods are used.

1. Aeration. By spraying the water into the air in the form of fine sprays, it is possible to reduce the Carbon Dioxide concentration by the gas being released into the atmosphere. This release of Carbon Dioxide will raise the pH, Bicarbonate and Carbonate Alkalinity. Duplicate pumping is required for this type installation.

2. Neutralization. The addition of an alkali such as lime, soda ash, or sodium hydroxide to the water will raise the pH, increase the bicarbonate and carbonate alkalinity and at the same time reduce the Carbon Dioxide. The use of lime will increase the Calcium concentration to make the water harder.

3. Protective Coatings. The use of sodium hexametaphosphate or polyphosphate in a concentration of two parts per million (Table LVIII) will produce a microscopical coating on the metal surface and prevent the reaction of the water on these surfaces. For best results using this method of control, the pH of the water must be from 6.7 to 7.4. Therefore, such pH adjustments should be made. The stock solution as prepared either in the one per cent to the five per cent strength, is corrosive to the feeder pump and lines to the point of application. Therefore, it is recommended that 10 per cent by weight of soda ash be added to this stock solution to prevent such reactions.

A knowledge of the pH and alkalinity is of utmost importance in the selection of treatment and the reduction of corrosion in water. For suitable domestic waters, the pH range should be from 6.7 to 8.6 with an alkalinity within the range of 20 to 60 parts per million as carbonates (Calcium Carbonate). For generalization, it may be stated that if the pH is less than 6.7, sodium hydroxide, lime, or soda ash may be added to increase the pH to at least 8.2 but not greater than 8.6. If the pH is increased to 6.7 to 7.4, the polyphosphates may be used in concentration of two parts per million. The increase of pH above 8.2 will provide a carbonate coating on the pipeline.

### B. Calcium, Magnesium, Hardness

Calcium and Magnesium are the chief constitutents of Hardness in water. Designation of water Hardness is given in Table LXI. This Table is somewhat arbitrarily set but may be used to state this standard of water quality.

## TABLE LXI
## Hardness Standards for Water

| Hardness in PPM | Degree of Hardness |
|---|---|
| 0 - 35 | Soft |
| 36 - 100 | Medium |
| 100 - 150 | Hard |
| Over 150 | Extremely Hard |

The effects of hardness upon a water system and its consumers are as follows:

1. Soap Consumption. Soap lather in very soft water is difficult to remove from laundry, hands, etc. Hard water reacts opposite to this because additional amounts of soap are required to acquire a lather. For large soap users such as launderers, hard waters will create economic problems from the cost of soap standpoint. For the home owner, soap rings may be formed around bath tubs, sinks, and lavatories from hard waters because of the large amounts of soap required. From the standpoint of all consumers, waters should have a medium hardness.

2. Corrosiveness of Water. Extremely soft waters are highly corrosive in their natural tendency. This corrosiveness is due to the low concentration of the Calcium and Magnesium. Hard waters are not corrosive because of the coating tendency of the Calcium and Magnesium on the pipe walls.

3. Scaling Properties. In balancing the pH, Alkalinity, and Hardness of a water, one of the prime factors to be considered is that of scaling or scale formation within the pipe lines, pump, fittings, and hot water facilities. The high concentration of Calcium and Magnesium within hard waters will plate out during transmission of cold water through pipelines of the distribution system. When hard water is heated to high temperatures in heaters and boilers, the plating out of the Calcium and Magnesium ions is much more rapid forming a tough scale on the walls of the units, thus greatly reducing the efficiency. Such scales may also create hot spots in boilers and cause hazardous conditions because of possible failure at these locations.

It is possible to check to some extent the plating out of hardness within a water system by keeping constant check on the pH, alkalinity, and hardness. This is a crude method and in many instances does not indicate the seriousness of the problem.

The reduction of hardness in a water may be accomplished by several means. One method is the use of chemical coagulation and filtration. Coagulation used in removing hardness provides for the coagulation of Calcium as Calcium Carbonate and utilizies lime and soda ash as coagulants. This method is expensive because of the installation, equipment, and operation required for the treatment of the water. A second method for removal of hardness is the use of ion exchange resins through which the water is passed and the Calcium and Magnesium in the water are exchanged for Sodium which is not a constitutent of hardness. These resins may be recharged by the use of salt brine in which the reaction is reversed and the Calcium and Magnesium are removed from the resins and discharged to waste. The resin is ready for use again to treat the water.

### C. Fluorides

Small amounts of fluorides are found in ground water. Within certain areas of the United States, fluoride concentrations are extremely high. In most instances, the concentration will range from 0.1 to 0.8 parts per million. Dental authorities have discovered that Fluorides in concentrations of about 0.7 to 2.0 parts per million in drinking water are helpful in the prevention of dental caries or tooth decay[21]. This applies only to children who consume water of this concentration from birth to about the age of 10 to 12. The overall effectiveness is somewhat directly proportional to the length of time within this age range during which the child drinks this water. The reduction of tooth decay for children in study areas is found to be about 60 to 70 per cent. Fluoride concentrations above the 2.0 parts per million will mottle the teeth, that is, will cause permanent darkening or staining of the teeth. Concentrations of less than 0.7 parts per million appear to have no effectiveness.

The removal of Fluoride from water is a very expensive proposition in that it requires costly installations, qualified personnel, and closely controlled operations. It is not at all practical or economical for small water systems to provide for Fluoride removal.

Some communities desire to add or supplement the natural Fluorides within the water to give a total concentration of 1.0 parts per million. Saturator type solution feeders are usually used to feed Sodium Fluoride to the water. Such an installation requires accurate metering of the water and close supervision of operation.

## D. Chlorides

The Chloride ion is a common constituent found in water. It is highly significant in coastal areas because of its prevalent "salty" taste and odor in drinking water. Chlorides within the coastal plain will range from 50 to 200 parts per million. This concentration decreases to about one to five parts per million for the mountain area.

For many years the Chloride ion was used as the index of pollution. Contours of Chloride concentration were established from the coast inland giving specific chloride concentrations. Due to the high concentration of chloride in sewage, an increase in the natural content of chloride in water indicated that pollution was evident.

Testing for Chlorides is still an excellent test for pollution to rule out the possibility of sewage within a water supply.

## E. Iron and Manganese

Iron and Manganese are of significance in water supplies because of their ability to stain laundry and plumbing fixtures. For the prevention of such stains, health authorities recommended a maximum of 0.3 parts per million for combined Iron and Manganese concentrations.

High concentrarations of Iron and Manganese not only cause straining of laundry and fixtures, but will cause the water to be discolored and may cause slight taste and odor. Where high Iron concentrations exist, the Iron-Forming Bacteria known as Crenothrix, Gallionella, etc., usually become prevalent as a slime within the pipelines. Where this growth prevails, the water will develop a Hydrogen Sulphide odor and an oil-like appearance on the surface of the water when it is collected in a container.

Iron in many cases will be dissolved in water and will remain unnoticeable. However, as this water passes through the air, the Iron is oxidized to the insoluble state and will appear as a red precipitate or red clay. In testing for Iron in water, it is necessary to determine the actual concentration of Iron within the water and that picked up as corrosion products within the pipelines, storage tanks, and pump fittings. This can be easily done by the collection of several samples at different points such as at the pump discharge, storage tank discharge, and at selected points on the distribution system. Comparison of such results will determine what type of treatment is necessary.

The removal of Iron from water may be accomplished in one of several methods. The first is by aeration followed by sedimentation and filtration. This method is quite expensive because of the installation required. A second method is by the coagulation at high pH by the use of lime. This method is also quite expensive because of the equipment and controlled operation. Third is the use of an ion exchange resin such as Sodium Zeolite. Within the exchange column, the Iron is exchanged for the Sodium in a similiar process as Calcium. The resin may be recharged and reused.

If a slime or Iron Bacteria is present within the system, it is necessary to disinfect the system to rid the system of the growth. This may be done by using Chlorine to a dosage of 50 parts per million for a period of 24 hours. This is done by placing the Chlorine in the well and storage facilities and drawing throughout the distribution system and allowing to stand for a period of at least 24 hours. At the end of that period the system is entirely flushed with fresh water. During the treatment period, the consumers are advised not to drink the water. Upon the completion of this treatment period, continuous chlorination should be provided in a concentration of at least 0.5 parts per million.

## F. Nitrogen Compounds

Present in ground waters are nitrogen compounds such as nitrites and nitrates. Nitrogen, due to reactions in nature, will appear in a changing state from ammonia to nitrite to nitrate.

Ammonia ■■■■➤

Nitrite ■■■➤ Nitrate

Nitrogen compounds are significant in water because of their ability to indicate the extent of pollution. Sewage contains a high content of ammonia. This ammonia is unstable and will be oxidized to form nitrites. Finally the nitrites will form the stable nitrate. Therefore, if ammonia is found within a water source, a conclusion can be reached that recent pollution by sewage or some other organic in nature compound has found its way into the water. Nitrites will indicate past pollution within the water.

Nitrates are significant in water because of their metabolism within the body whereby the nitrate replaces the oxygen within the hemoglobin to cause what is called meth-hemoglobinemia. This is a poisoning resulting in the lack of oxygen in the blood stream thus causing the skin to become blue. Infants are usually affected at concentrations of nitrates above 10 parts per million.

## G. Silica

Silica compounds are important from the standpoint of scale formation within boilers. Silicia has a tendency to form a very hard scale thus reducing the efficiency of boilers. Hot spots within the boiler may be easily created ,thus constituting hazardous conditions because of boiler wall or tube failure at this point.

## H. Sulphur Compounds

Sulphur compounds are common constitutents found in waters. Sulphur, as Nitrogen, is unstable in many of its states. Briefly, it may be stated that Sulphur will proceed along the following path to stability:

Sulphide ➡

Sulphite ➡ Sulphate

Of extreme importance in water is the sulphide. The sulphide, combining with the Hydrogen in water, will form Hydrogen Sulphide which readily takes up the available Oxygen within the water. Hydrogen Sulphide is very unstable and very odorous. It is usually given off as a gas with a prevalent "rotten egg" odor. It is detectable in extremely small concentrations. Similiar to Iron, Sulphur will form slime growths known as Sulphur Bacteria along the walls of the pipes, storage tanks, and pump fittings. This growth will give the water a distinct Hydrogen Sulphur taste and odor. Treatment for removal of this growth is the same as given for Iron Bacteria. Small concentrations of Hydrogen Sulphide may be treated by the use of Chlorination at the well in concentration of about one part per million. Higher concentrations of Hydrogen Sulphide may be reduced by proper aeration followed by chlorination. In many instances, it has been possible to reduce the Hydrogen Sulphide by sealing off the water veins along the well column which bears this constitutent. This is accomplished by taking samples from each water vein and testing for the Sulphide. Then if it is found to enter from one specific vein, to seal off this vein.

### 4. Corrosion[22][23]

Corrosion is the oxidation of metals by the reaction of metals of the solution upon the metal, by the transfer of electrons from the metal to solution, or from metal to metal, or by the oxidation reduction potential of the metal and water contact. Essentials for corrosion are: chemical constitutent, moisture, oxygen, loose elec-

trons and voltage set up within the pipelines.

### A. Reaction of Solution on Metal

Waters of low pH and alkalinity are aggressive to metal. This aggressiveness is due to the reaction of the carbon dioxide with the water to form carbonic acid which attacks the bare metal, dissolves the protective lime coating from the water treatment process, and carries the metal into solution causing pitting or tuberculation in the pipe. The dissolved oxygen content of the water plays an important part within this reaction.

Prevention of the reaction on the pipe metal is achieved in several ways.

1. Adjustment of pH and alkalinity to a point where the pH is above 8.2 thus eliminating the presence of carbon dioxide and bringing the corresponding alkalinity to a concentration of greater than 25 parts per million. The hardness of the water should be within the range of 25 to 50 parts per million.

2. Adjustment of the pH to 6.9 to 7.4, and add approximately 2.0 parts per million of hexametaphosphate to provide a protective coating.

3. Use of pipe protective coatings of non-metallic substances such as coal tar, bitumastic enamel, or cement, or the use of non-metallic pipe which is not subject to corrosion.

### B. Oxidation Reduction Potential

A water-metal contact will tend to be in somewhat of an equilibrium state in which a voltage will be built up at this interface. This voltage is called the Oxidation Reduction Potential and is the required voltage to bring the metal into solution by the build up of the liberated hydrogen ions within the water. Corrosion will bring iron into solution as the Ferric oxide, zinc as the carbonate-hydroxide, and copper as the carbonate. Two factors involved in this process of corrosion are important. These factors are the hydrogen gas formation and the content of dissolved oxygen concentration. Again, the solution to this problem is the pH and alkalinity adjustment because such adjustment will influence the production of the hydrogen gas.

## C. Galvanic Corrision

When two dissimilar metals are connected together, an electro-potential voltage is created to the extent that an electric current or electron movement will occur and the flow of electrons will be from high to low potential. The process would react to form corrosion products of the metals as follows:

Copper — Iron (Ferrous) —
Iron (Ferric) — Zinc.

In the combination of these metals, the metal to the right would corrode.

Methods of preventing corrosion between disimilar metals may be accomplished by placing an insulator such as hard rubber, plastic or non-metal pipe between the two metals to stop the flow of electrons.

## D. Stray Currents

Stray currents will cause corrosion of a pipeline by the jumping on or off of electrons on the pipe from some source of current. Grounds for electrical circuits create this problem when tied to water pipes when there is electrical leakage from some electrical source. Direct current is a much greater source of trouble than alternating current because of the constant direction of electrical flow. This problem may be controlled by using non-metallic pipe, protective coatings on metallic pipe, or the use of cathodic protection of pipes by use of magnesium anodes, etc.

## 5. Laboratory Procedures for Chemical Analysis[16]

A certain number of basic tests should be conducted daily to determine the chemical quality of water. These tests are: pH, alkalinity, carbon dioxide, hardness, chlorine residual, and in filtration plants, the jar test for coagulation. Other tests such as iron, manganese, solids, chlorides, etc., are also desirable at frequent intervals.

## A. Laboratory Equipment

*(1) Chemical Solutions.*

| Quantity | Item |
|---|---|
| 32 oz. | Solution, Volumetric, Acid Sulphuric, 1/50 Normal. |
| 32 oz. | Solution, Volumetric, Sodium Hydroxide, 1/44 Normal. |
| 16 oz. | Solution, Volumetric, Phenolphthalein, ½% Neutral Alcohol. |
| 16 oz. | Solution, Methyl Orange or Methyl Purple, c.p., A.C.S. |
| 32 oz. | Solution, Tolidin, Ortho, APHA. |
| 500 ml. | Solution, Brom Thymol Blue, 0.04% Standardized Indicator*. |
| 500 ml. | Solution, Phenol Red, 0.02% Standardized Indicator*. |
| 500 ml. | Solution, Thymol Blue, 0.04% Standardized Indicator*. |
| 500 ml. | Solution, Standard Soap**. |
| 1 lb. | Sulphuric Acid, concentrated***. |
| 1 lb. | Potassium Dichromate (powdered). |

*Not necessary if electric pH meter is used.
* *The Versenate Method is alternate method for hardness.
* * *Included in list of bacteriological test equipment.

*(2) Laboratory Apparatus.*

| Quantity | Item | Remarks |
|---|---|---|
| 1 | Still, Water, ½ gal. per hr. cap. | |
| 1 | Stirrer, Water Analysis. | For Jar Test. |
| 6 | Battery Jars, round, clear glass. | For Jar Test, |
| 1 | Turbidimeter, electric or candle. | 4″ x 5″ high. |
| 1 | Carboy, five gallon. | |
| 1 | Balance, Harvard trip, with cover and weights***. | |
| 1 | pH Meter or Comparator. | Above solutions for comparator. |
| 1 | Chlorine Comparator. | Range 0.05 to |
| 1 ea. | File, rat tail and triangular. | 2.0 ppm. |
| | | Cutting length 6″. |
| 2 ea. | Beakers, pyrex, low form with spout 50 ml., 100 ml., 250 ml., 500 ml., 1,000 ml. size. | |
| 2 ea. | Burrettes, pyrex with stopcock, 25 ml. and 50 ml. size. | |
| 2 ea. | Cylinders, graduated, pyrex with spout. | |
| 2 ea. | Cylinders, graduated, pyrex with spout 10 ml., 25 ml., 100 ml., 500 ml., 1,000 ml. size. | |
| 12 | Tubes, Nessler, high form, matched, APHA, 50 ml. | |
| 1 | Support, Nessler Tube, 12 holes. | |
| 1 | Burrett Support with clamp for two burrettes. | |
| 2 | Flasks, Erlenmeyer, pyrex, 125 ml. | |
| 6 | Flasks, Erlenmeyer, pyrex, 250 ml. | |
| 4 | Flasks, Erlenmeyer, pyrex, 500 ml. | |
| 2 | Flasks, Erlenmeyer, pyrex, 1,000 ml. | |
| 1 | Flask, Erlenmeyer, pyrex, 2,000 ml. | |
| 18 | Bottles, eight ounce sampling, glass stoppered, salt mouth. | |
| 6 | Bottles, dropping, resistant glass with rubber bulb. | |
| 2 | Funnel, fluted, pyrex, 7½″. | |
| 6 | Pipettes, measuring, pyrex, 10 ml. | |
| 12 | Glass Rods. | |
| 1 lb. | Glass tubing, laboratory bending, 7mm O.D. | |
| 8 ft. | Rubber Tubing, F.S. pure gum, black, ¼″ bore. | |
| 6 | Pencils, wax, heat resistant, red. | |
| 1 tube | Grease, stopcock. | |
| 1 | Spatula, stainless steel, 6″ blade. | |
| 1 pkg. | Filter Paper, 100 sheets, 12.5cm. | |
| 3 doz. | Stoppers, rubber, assorted sizes. | |
| 6 | Clamps, day's pinchcock. | |

## B. Laboratory Procedures for Chemical Tests[16 30]

*(1) pH Determination:*

(a) Electric pH Meter. Let instrument warm up for five minuites. Adjust for temperature. Check calibration by using known buffer. Place electrodes in sample and read results.

(b) Colorimetric[16]. Use following indicators for pH ranges shown:

| Indicator | Acid Color | Basic Color | pH of Color Change |
|---|---|---|---|
| Methyl orange | Pink | Yellow | 3.1 — 4.4 |
| Bromthymol blue | Yellow | Blue | 6.0 — 7.6 |
| Phenol red | Yellow | Red | 6.4 — 8.0 |
| Cresol red | Yellow | Red | 7.2 — 8.8 |
| Phenolphthalein | Colorless | Pink | 8.0 — 9.8 |
| Thymol blue | Red | Yellow | 8.0 — 9.6 |

Fill 10 ml. vial with sample and add indicator dropwise to full color development. Place in comparator and read. If results are near end of scale, go to next indicator range.

(c) Alkalinity Determination. To 100 ml. sample, add 2-3 drops of Phenolphthalein indicator. If color appears, titrate with 0.02 Normal Sulphuric Acid to colorless. Number of milliliters of acid x 10 = Carbonate Alkalinity. If no color appears, the Carbonate Alkalinity is zero. In either case, add 2-3 drops of Methyl Orange or Methyl Purple, and add 0.02 Normal Sulphuric Acid to color change.
Total Alkalinity, ppm as $CaCO_3$ = No. mls. Acid x 10.

(d) Carbon Dioxide Determination. With as little agitation as possible, collect 50 ml. sample in a Nessler tube. Add 2-3 drops of Phenolphthalein indicator. Titrate with 1/44 Normal Sodium Hydroxide until pink color developes.
Carbon Dioxide, ppm as $CO_2$ = 20 x No. mls. of Sodium Hydroxide.

(e) Hardness. Pipette 50 milliliters of sample into an eight-ounce glass stoppered bottle. Add standard soap solution in small quantities from a burette. After each addition, shake sample vigorously. Continue same process until lather remains for a five-minute period.
Hardness, ppm = 20 x (mls. standard soap solution — mls. lather factor).

(f) Residual Chlorine. Using chlorine residual comparator, place five ml. sample in vial. Add Orthotolidine dropwise until full color development. Allow to stand for 30 seconds to one minute. Read color comparison.

(g) Coagulation Dosage Determination by Jar Test.

(1) Stock Solutions.

Alum: Add 10 grams of Alum to one liter of water.
Then one ml. added to one liter = dosage of 10 ppm.
Alkali: Add 10 grams of Alkali to one liter of water.
Then one ml. added to one liter = dosage of 10 ppm.

(2) Jar Test Procedure.

(a) Fill each of six battery jars with one liter of sample. Test must be conducted immediately after collection of sample to prevent change of temperature or other effects.

(b) Add varying dosages of coagulants at five ppm interval for Alum and two ppm for Alkali.

(c) Mix vigorously at above 60 rpm for a period of not less than three minutes.

(d) Reduce speed of stirrer to around 15-20 rpm for 15 minutes.

(e) Stop stirrer and observe settling rate.

(f) Repeat procedure with dosage at two ppm for Alum and one ppm for alkali near best floc dosage.

(g) From repeated test, set optimum dosages on plant feed machines.

# References

[1] Individual Water Supply Systems, PHS Publication No. 24, 1950.

[2] Design Criteria, Sanitary Engineering Division, N. C. State Board of Health.

[3] Purser, John R., Jr., North Carolina Water Works Operators Association Yearbook, 1952.

[4] Manual of Recommended Water Sanitation Practice, PHS Publication No. 296, 1946.

[5] National Board of Fire Underwriters, New York, N. Y.

[6] Lecture Notes, Sanitary Engineering Department, School of Public Health, University of North Carolina.

[7] Handbook of Cast Iron Pipe, Second Edition, 1952, Cast Iron Pipe Research Association, Chicago, Illinois.

[8] Technical Bulletins, Johns-Manville Corporation, New York, N. Y.

[9] Technical Bulletins, A. M. Byers Company, Pittsburgh, Pennsylvania.

[10] Technical Bulletins, Price Brothers Company, Dayton, Ohio.

[11] Catalogue, Water Works, Supplies, 1953, Grinnell Company, Providence, Rhode Island.

[12] Naugautuck Chemical Division, U. S. Rubber Company, Naugautuck, Conn.

[13] Reference Manual, Badger Meter Manufacturing Company, Milwaukee, Wisconsin.

[14] Hazen, Richard, North Carolina Water, Sewage, and Industrial Wastes Association, Vol. XXX, No. 1, 1954.

[15] North Carolina Plumbing Code, N. C. State Board of Health, Raleigh, N. C.

[16] The Operation of Water Filtration Plants of the Mechanical Gravity Type, N. C. State Board of Health.

[17] Drinking Water Standards, PHS, Publication No. 956, 1962.

[18] Control of Communicable Diseases, PHS, Publication No. 1697, 1954.

[19] State Laboratory of Hygiene, North Carolina State Board of Health.

[20] Drinking Water Standards, PHS, 42 CFR Part 72, 1956.

[21] Better Health Through Fluoridated Water, PHS, Publication No. 62, 1951.

[22] Tull, E. R., North Carolina Water Works Operators Association, Yearbook, 1957.

[23] Lesslie, J. N., Jr., North Carolina Water Works Operators Association, Yearbook, 1956.

[24] Radiological Health Handbook, Taft Engr. Center, PHS, Cincinnati, Ohio.

[25] Keep Sheet No. 22, Omega Machine Company, BIF, Providence, R. I.

[26] Johnson, E. M., Journal, North Carolina Section AWWA and North Carolina Sewage Association, Volume XXXIII, No. 1, 1957.

[27] Gore, D. J., Journal, North Carolina Section AWWA and North Carolina Sewage Association, Volume XXX, No. 1, 1954.

[28] Rates, City of Greensboro, North Carolina.

# References *(Continued)*

[29]Water Quality and Control, Second Edition, 1951, American Water Works Association.

[30]Standard Methods for the Examination of Water, Sewage, and Industrial Wastes, Tenth Edition, 1955, American Public Health Association.
Many references are taken from Lecture Notes of:
Chang, Shi Lu, Professor of Bacteriology, Harvard Graduate School.
Fair, Gordon M., Professor of Sanitary Engineering, Harvard Graduate School.
Moore, Edward W., Professor of Sanitary Chemistry, Harvard Graduate School.
Morris, Carroll, Professor of Chemistry, Harvard Graduate School.
Thomas, Harold A., Professor of Sanitary Engineering, Harvard Graduate School.

# Appendix

# Appendix

## 1. Abbreviations

| | |
|---|---|
| Eff. | Efficiency |
| Ft., ft. | Feet |
| Ft/min., ft/min. | Feet per minute |
| Ft/sec., ft/sec. | Feet per second |
| Gals., gals. | Gallons |
| GPCD, gpcd | Gallons per capita per day |
| GPD, gpd | Gallons per day |
| GPM, gpm | Gallons per minute |
| H.P., HP | Horsepower |
| Hr., hr. | Hour |
| In., in. | Inches |
| Kw., KW. | Wilowatt |
| KW-Hr., Kw-Hr. | Kilowatt-Hours |
| Lb. | Pounds |
| M | One Thousand |
| Mg/L, mg/l | Milligrams Per Liter |
| MGD | Mllion Gallons Per Day |
| M1/min., m1/min. | Milliliter per minute |
| Min., min. | Minute |
| MPN | Most Probable Number |
| Oz., oz. | Ounce |
| % | Per cent |
| PPM, ppm | Parts Per Million |
| PSI | Pounds Per Square Inch |

# Appendix

## 2. Basic Equations

Efficiency: $\text{Efficiency} = \dfrac{\text{Actual}}{\text{Theoretical}}$

Flow: gpm x 1,440 = gpd
gpd x 0.000694 = gpm

Pressure: Feet of Water = 2.31 x PSI
PSI = 0.434 x Feet of Water

Volume: 1 Cubic Foot = 7.48 gals. = 28.3 Liters = 28,300 milliliters
1 Gallon = 0.133 Cubic Feet = 3.785 Liters = 3,785 Milliliters

Weight: 1 Pound = 16 Ounces = 453.6 Grams = 453,000 Milligrams
1 Gram = 1,000 Milligrams = 0.0325 Ounces =
0.00221 Pounds

Dosage: PPM x 8.34 = Pounds Per Million Gallons
Pounds Per Million Gallons x 0.12 = PPM
Per Cent x 10,000 = Parts Per Million

Pounds of Chemical x $\dfrac{1}{\text{Per Cent Purity}}$ = Actual Amount of Chemical

$$\begin{array}{c}\text{Parts Per Million} \\ \text{of Stock Solution}\end{array} \text{x } 0.000264 \text{ x } \begin{array}{c}\text{Milliliters Per} \\ \text{Minute Stock Solution Fed} =\end{array}$$

$$\begin{array}{c}\text{Parts Per} \\ \text{Million Desired}\end{array} \text{x } \begin{array}{c}\text{Flow in GPM} \\ \text{of Water Treated}\end{array}$$

One Milligram Per Liter (or ppm) = 0.0548 Grains Per Gallon
One Grain Per Gallon = 17.12 Milligrams Per Liter (or ppm)

Power: $\text{Water HP} = \dfrac{\text{Flow, gpm x Total Head, Feet x 8.34}}{33,000}$

$\text{Shaft HP} = \dfrac{\text{Water HP}}{\text{Pump Efficiency}}$

$\text{Electrical HP} = \dfrac{\text{Shaft HP}}{\text{Motor Efficiency}}$

KW = Electric HP x 0.746
KW-Hour = KW x Time, Hours
Cost = KW-Hours x Cost/KW-Hour

# Appendix

## 3. Conversion Factors

### CONVERSION FACTORS FOR VARIOUS ENGINEERING UNITS

| Multiply | By | To Obtain |
|---|---|---|
| Acre-feet | 43,560 | Cubic feet |
| " | 325,851 | Gallons |
| Atmospheres | 76.0 | Cms. of mercury |
| " | 29.92 | Inches of mercury |
| " | 33.90 | Feet of water |
| " | 14.70 | Lbs./sq. inch |
| Board-feet | 144 sq. in. x 1 in. | Cubic inches |
| British Thermal Units | 777.5 | Foot-lbs. |
| " " " | $3.927 \times 10^{-4}$ | Horse-power-hrs. |
| " " " | $2.928 \times 10^{-4}$ | Kilowatt-hrs. |
| B.T.U./min. | 12.96 | Foot-lbs./sec. |
| " " | 0.02356 | Horse-power |
| " / " | 0.01757 | Kilowatts |
| " " | 17.57 | Watts |
| Centimeters | 0.3937 | Inches |
| Centimtrs. of mercury | 0.01316 | Atmospheres |
| " " " | 0.4461 | Feet of water |
| " " " | 27.85 | Lbs./sq. ft. |
| " " " | 0.1934 | Lbs./sq. inch |
| Centimeters/second | 1.969 | Feet/min. |
| " " | 0.03281 | Feet/sec. |
| Cms./sec./sec. | 0.03281 | Feet/sec./sec. |
| Cubic centimeters | $3.531 \times 10^{-5}$ | Cubic feet |
| " " | $6.102 \times 10^{-2}$ | Cubic inches |
| " " | $1.308 \times 10^{-6}$ | Cubic yards |
| " " | $2.642 \times 10^{-4}$ | Gallons |
| Cubic Cm./min. | $2.118 \times 10^{-3}$ | Cu. Ft./Hr. |
| " " | $2.641 \times 10^{-4}$ | Gal./min. |
| Cubic feet | 1728 | Cubic inches |
| " " | 7.48052 | Gallons |
| Cubic feet/minute | 0.1247 | Gallons /sec. 7.48 Gal./min. |
| Cubic feet/second | 0.646317 | Million gals./day |
| " " " | 448.831 | Gallons/min. |
| Cubic inches | $5.787 \times 10^{-4}$ | Cubic feet |
| " " | $2.143 \times 10^{-5}$ | Cubic yards |
| " " | $4.329 \times 10^{-3}$ | Gallons |
| Cubic meters | 35.31 | Cubic feet |
| " " | 61,023 | Cubic inches |
| " " | 1.308 | Cubic yards |
| " " | 264.2 | Gallons |
| Cubic yards | 27 | Cubic feet |
| " " | 46,656 | Cubic inches |
| " " | 202.0 | Gallons |
| Degrees (angle) | 60 | Minutes |
| " " | 0.01745 | Radians |
| " " | 3600 | Seconds |
| Degrees/sec. | 0.01745 | Radians/sec. |
| " / " | 0.1667 | Revolutions/min. |
| " / " | 0.002778 | Revolutions/sec. |
| Feet | 30.48 | Centimeters |
| " | 12 | Inches |
| " | 0.3048 | Meters |
| Feet of water | 0.02950 | Atmospheres |
| " " " | 0.8826 | Inches of mercury |
| " " " | 62.43 | Lbs./sq. ft. |
| " " " | 0.4335 | Lbs./sq. inch |
| Feet/min. | 0.01667 | Feet/sec. |
| " " | 0.01136 | Miles/hr. |
| Feet/sec. | 0.6818 | Miles/hr. |
| Foot-pounds | $1.286 \times 10^{-3}$ | British Thermal Units |
| " " | $5.050 \times 10^{-7}$ | Horse-power-hrs. |
| " " | $3.766 \times 10^{-7}$ | Kilowatt-hrs. |
| Foot-pounds/min. | $1.286 \times 10^{-3}$ | B. T. Units/min. |
| " " / " | 0.01667 | Foot-pounds/sec. |
| " " / " | $3.030 \times 10^{-5}$ | Horse-power |
| " " / " | $2.260 \times 10^{-5}$ | Kilowatts |
| Foot-pounds/sec. | $7.717 \times 10^{-2}$ | B. T. Units/min. |
| " " / " | $1.818 \times 10^{-3}$ | Horse-power |
| " " / " | $1.356 \times 10^{-3}$ | Kilowatts |
| Gallons | 3785 | Cubic centimeters |
| " | 0.1337 | Cubic feet |
| " | 231 | Cubic inches |
| Gallons, Imperial | 1.20095 | U.S. gallons |
| " U.S. | 0.83267 | Imperial gallons |
| Gallons water | 8.3453 | Pounds of water |
| Gallons/min. | $2.228 \times 10^{-3}$ | Cubic feet/sec. |
| " / " | 8.0208 | Cu. ft./hr. |
| Grams | 0.03527 | Ounces |
| " | $2.205 \times 10^{-3}$ | Pounds |
| Grams/cu. cm. | 62.43 | Pounds/cubic foot |
| " / " " | 0.03613 | Pounds/cubic inch |
| Grams/liter | 58.417 | Grains/gal. |
| " " | 8.345 | Pounds/1000 gals. |
| " " | 0.062427 | Pounds/cubic foot |
| " " | 1000 | Parts/million |
| Horse-power | 42.44 | B.T. Units/min. |
| " | 33,000 | Foot-lbs./min. |
| " | 550 | Foot-lbs./sec. |
| " | 0.7457 | Kilowatts |
| Horse-power (boiler) | 33.479 | B.T.U./hr. |
| " " " | 9.803 | Kilowatts |

| Multiply | By | To Obtain |
|---|---|---|
| Horse-power-hours | 2547 | British Thermal U |
| " " " | 0.7457 | Kilowatt-hours |
| Inches | 2.540 | Centimeters |
| Inches of mercury | 0.03342 | Atmospheres |
| " " " | 1.133 | Feet of water |
| " " " | 70.73 | Lbs./sq. ft. |
| " " " | 0.4912 | Lbs./sq. inch |
| Inches of water | 0.002458 | Atmospheres |
| " " " | 0.07355 | Inches of mercury |
| " " " | 5.202 | Lbs./sq. foot |
| " " " | 0.03613 | Lbs./sq. inch |
| Kilograms | 2.205 | Lbs. |
| Kgs./sq. meter | $3.281 \times 10^{-3}$ | Feet of water |
| " " " | 0.2048 | Lbs./sq. foot |
| " " " | $1.422 \times 10^{-3}$ | Lbs./sq. inch |
| Kilometers | 3281 | Feet |
| " | 0.6214 | Miles |
| " | 1094 | Yards |
| Kilometers/hr. | 54.68 | Feet/min. |
| " " | 0.9113 | Feet/sec. |
| " / " | 0.6214 | Miles/hr. |
| Kilowatts | 56.92 | B.T. Units/min. |
| " | $4.425 \times 10^{4}$ | Foot-lbs./min. |
| " | 737.6 | Foot-lbs./sec. |
| " | 1.341 | Horse-power |
| " | $10^{3}$ | Watts |
| Kilowatt-hours | 3415 | British Thermal U |
| " " | $2.655 \times 10^{6}$ | Foot-lbs. |
| " " | 1.341 | Horse-power-hrs. |
| Liters | 0.03531 | Cubic feet |
| " | 61.02 | Cubic inches |
| " | 0.2642 | Gallons |
| Meters | 100 | Centimeters |
| " | 3.281 | Feet |
| " | 39.37 | Inches |
| " | 1.094 | Yards |
| Meters/sec. | 196.8 | Feet/min. |
| Millimeters | 0.1 | Centimeters |
| " | 0.03937 | Inches |
| Milligrams/liter | 1. | Parts/million |
| Millon gals./day | 1.54723 | Cubic ft./sec. |
| Ounces | 437.5 | Grains |
| " | 28.349527 | Grams |
| Parts/million | 0.0584 | Grains/U.S. gal. |
| " / " | 8.345 | Lbs./million gal. |
| Pounds | 16 | Ounces |
| " | 7000 | Grains |
| " | 453.5924 | Grams |
| Pounds of water | 0.01602 | Cubic feet |
| " " " | 27.68 | Cubic inches |
| " " " | 0.1198 | Gallons |
| Pounds/cubic foot | $5.787 \times 10^{-4}$ | Lbs./cubic inch |
| Pounds/cubic inch | 1728 | Lbs./cubic foot |
| Pounds/sq. foot | 0.01602 | Feet of water |
| " / " " | $6.945 \times 10^{-3}$ | Pounds/sq. inch |
| Pounds/sq. inch | 2.307 | Feet of water |
| " / " " | 2.036 | Inches of mercury |
| Radians | 57.30 | Degrees |
| " | 3438 | Minutes |
| " | 0.637 | Quadrants |
| Radians/sec. | 57.30 | Degrees/sec. |
| " / " | 0.1592 | Revolutions/sec. |
| " / " | 9.549 | Revolutions/min. |
| Revolutions/min. | 6 | Degrees/sec. |
| " / " | 0.1047 | Radians/sec. |
| " / " | 0.01667 | Revolutions/sec. |
| Square feet | $2.296 \times 10^{-5}$ | Acres |
| " " | 144 | Square inches |
| Square kilometers | 247.1 | Acres |
| " " | $10.76 \times 10^{6}$ | Square feet |
| " " | 0.3861 | Square miles |
| " " | $1.196 \times 10^{6}$ | Square yards |
| Square meters | $2.471 \times 10^{-4}$ | Acres |
| " " | 10.76 | Square feet |
| " " | $3.861 \times 10^{-7}$ | Square miles |
| " " | 1.196 | Square yards |
| Square miles | 640 | Acres |
| " " | $27.88 \times 10^{6}$ | Square feet |
| Square millimeters | $1.550 \times 10^{-3}$ | Square inches |
| Square yards | $2.066 \times 10^{-4}$ | Acres |
| " " | 9 | Square feet |
| " " | $3.228 \times 10^{-7}$ | Square miles |
| Temp. (°C.)+ 273 | 1. | Abs. temp. (°C.) |
| " " + 17.78 | 1.8 | Temp. (°F.) |
| " (°F.) + 460 | 1. | Abs. temp. (°F.) |
| " " − 32 | 5/9 | Temp. (°C.) |
| Watts | 0.05692 | B. T. Units/min. |
| " | $1.341 \times 10^{-3}$ | Horse-power |
| " | $10^{-3}$ | Kilowatts |

# Appendix

## 4. Flow Rates Through Service Pipes

**NUMBER OF GALLONS OF WATER PER MINUTE DISCHARGED THROUGH SERVICE PIPES OF DIFFERENT DIAMETERS AND LENGTHS UNDER VARIOUS HEADS**

| Head in Feet | ½ in. Diameter | | ¾ in. Diameter | | 1 in. Diameter | | 1½ in. Diameter | | 2 in. Diameter | | 3 in. Diam. | 4 in. Diam. | 6 in. Diam. |
|---|---|---|---|---|---|---|---|---|---|---|---|---|---|
| | 50 Ft. | 100 Ft. | 50 Ft. | 100 Ft. | 50 Ft. | 100 Ft. | 50 Ft. | 100 Ft. | 50 Ft. | 100 Ft. | 1000 Ft. | 1000 Ft. | 1000 Ft. |
| 10 | 2.64 | 1.76 | 7.19 | 4.84 | 14.96 | 10.14 | 41.16 | 30.01 | 83.46 | 61.35 | 48.7 | 111.8 | 319.8 |
| 20 | 3.81 | 2.50 | 10.18 | 7.31 | 21.15 | 15.27 | 59.38 | 42.45 | 120.25 | 86.76 | 75.6 | 158.1 | 452.3 |
| 30 | 4.67 | 3.26 | 12.45 | 8.93 | 26.43 | 18.71 | 72.73 | 52.00 | 147.27 | 108.30 | 92.6 | 193.7 | 575.3 |
| 40 | 5.39 | 3.77 | 14.68 | 10.33 | 30.52 | 21.60 | 83.98 | 61.24 | 170.06 | 125.11 | 107.0 | 234.5 | 664.3 |
| 50 | 6.02 | 4.22 | 16.41 | 11.55 | 34.13 | 24.15 | 93.89 | 68.46 | 190.13 | 139.88 | 126.0 | 262.2 | 742.7 |
| 60 | 6.60 | 4.62 | 17.98 | 12.65 | 37.38 | 27.00 | 102.85 | 74.99 | 208.28 | 153.23 | 138.0 | 287.2 | 813.5 |
| 70 | 7.13 | 4.99 | 19.42 | 13.95 | 40.38 | 29.16 | 111.10 | 81.00 | 224.90 | 165.51 | 149.0 | 310.2 | 878.6 |
| 80 | 7.62 | 5.33 | 20.76 | 14.91 | 43.17 | 31.18 | 118.76 | 86.60 | 240.50 | 176.94 | 159.0 | 331.7 | 939.4 |
| 90 | 8.08 | 5.65 | 22.02 | 15.82 | 45.79 | 33.06 | 125.97 | 91.85 | 255.08 | 187.66 | 169.1 | 351.8 | 1014.8 |
| 100 | 8.52 | 6.09 | 23.21 | 16.68 | 48.25 | 34.85 | 132.78 | 96.82 | 268.89 | 197.82 | 178.3 | 370.0 | 1070.0 |
| 125 | 9.52 | 6.81 | 25.95 | 18.64 | 53.96 | 38.97 | 148.45 | 108.24 | 300.62 | 221.17 | 199.3 | 422.8 | 1196.0 |
| 150 | 10.43 | 7.46 | 28.42 | 20.43 | 59.11 | 42.69 | 162.63 | 118.57 | 329.31 | 242.29 | 218.0 | 462.8 | 1310.0 |
| 175 | 11.27 | 8.05 | 30.71 | 22.06 | 63.85 | 46.11 | 175.66 | 128.00 | 355.70 | 261.70 | 240.4 | 500.0 | 1415.0 |
| 200 | 12.04 | 8.61 | 32.83 | 23.59 | 68.25 | 49.29 | 187.80 | 136.92 | 380.26 | 279.76 | 257.0 | 534.4 | 1513.0 |
| 225 | 12.77 | 9.13 | 34.82 | 25.02 | 72.40 | 52.28 | 199.18 | 145.23 | 403.35 | 296.74 | 272.6 | 566.8 | 1605.0 |
| 250 | 13.47 | 9.63 | 36.70 | 26.37 | 76.31 | 55.11 | 209.95 | 153.08 | 425.15 | 312.79 | 287.3 | 597.5 | 1691.0 |
| 275 | 14.12 | 10.09 | 38.49 | 27.65 | 80.03 | 57.80 | 220.20 | 160.56 | 445.90 | 328.06 | 301.3 | 626.7 | 1744.0 |
| 300 | 14.75 | 10.54 | 40.20 | 28.88 | 83.59 | 60.37 | 230.00 | 167.70 | 465.72 | 342.64 | 314.7 | 654.5 | 1853.0 |

—From Permission of Badger Meter Manufacturing Company.

# Appendix

## 5. Atomic Weights of Common Elements[24]

| Element | Symbol | Atomic Weight (A.M.U.)* |
|---|---|---|
| Aluminum | Al | 25.9944 |
| Calcium | Ca | 39.9754 |
| Carbon | C | 12.0038 |
| Chlorine | Cl | 34.9800 |
| Copper | Cu | 63.957 |
| Fluorine | F | 19.0044 |
| Hydrogen | H | 1.0081 |
| Iron | Fe | 55.8527 |
| Lead | Pb | 207.0400 |
| Magnesium | Mg | 23.9926 |
| Manganese | Mn | 54.9558 |
| Nitrogen | N | 14.0075 |
| Oxygen | O | 16.0000 |
| Phosphorus | P | 29.9885 |
| Potassium | K | 38.9760 |
| Sodium | Na | 22.9970 |
| Sulphur | S | 31.9821 |
| Zinc | Zn | 63.957 |

*Reprinted from Radiological Health Handbook, U.S.P.H.S., 1954, Kinsman et al.

# Appendix

## 6. Selected Chemicals Used Water Treatment[25]

The following Table gives characteristics of selected chemicals used in the treatment of water for disinfection, corrosion control, pH adjustment, and Fluoridation. To properly interpret this data, the following symbols and abbreviations are used:

| | | | |
|---|---|---|---|
| And | & | Maximum | Max. |
| At | @ | Milliliter | ml |
| Barrel | Bbl | Minimum | Min. |
| Carload | C/L | Minute | min |
| Concentrated | Concd. | Per | / |
| Concentration | Conc. | Per Cent | % |
| Cubic Centimeter | cc | Pound | lb |
| Cubic Foot | cu ft | Pounds per Gallon | lb/gal |
| Degrees Baume' | °Be' | Pounds per Square Inch | psi |
| Degrees Centigrade | °C | Proportioning Pump | Prop. Pump |
| Degrees Fahrenheit | °F | Saturated | Sat. |
| Gallon | gal | Solution | Soln. |
| Gallons per Hour | gal/hr | Specific Gravity | Sp. G. |
| Gram | gm | Standard | Std. |
| Less than Carload | LCL | Tank Car | T/C |
| Loss-In-Weight | L-I-W | Tank Truck | T/T |

| CHEMICAL | SHIPPING DATA | | | CHARACTERISTICS | | | |
|---|---|---|---|---|---|---|---|
| FORMULA<br>COMMON NAME<br>USE | AVAILABLE FORMS | CONTAINERS and REQUIREMENTS | APPEARANCE AND PROPERTIES | WEIGHT lb./cu. ft. (Bulk Density) | COMMERCIAL STRENGTH | SOLUBILITY IN WATER gm./100ml. |
| **1. ACTIVATED CARBON**<br>C<br>(Aqua Nuchar, Norit, Hydrodarco)<br>—<br>Decolorizing, Taste and Odor Removal | Powder<br>Granules | Bags—35 lbs.<br>(3x21x39 in.)<br>Drums—5, 25 lb.<br>Bulk—C/L | Black Powder, About 400 Mesh<br>Dusty, Smoulders if Ignited<br>Arches in Hoppers; Floodable | Powder<br>8 to 28<br>Avg. 12 | 10% C Bone Charcoal to 90% C Wood Charcoal | Insoluble<br>(Slurry May Contain 1 lb./gal.) |
| **2. ALUMINUM SULFATE**<br>Al₂(SO₄)₃·14H₂O (Approx.)<br>(Alma, Filter Alum, Pickle Alum, Sulfate of Alumina)<br>—<br>Coagulation at pH 5.5 to 8.0, Sludge Conditioner | Ground<br>Rice<br>Powder<br>Lump | Bags—100, 200 lb.<br>Bbl.—325, 400 lb.<br>Drums—25, 100, 250 lb.<br>Bulk—C/L | Light Tan to Gray-Green<br>Dusty, Astringent<br>Only Slightly Hygroscopic<br>1% Soln.—pH 3.4 | 60 to 75<br>(Powder is Lighter)<br>To Calculate Hopper Capacities, use 60 | 17% Al₂O₃<br>(Min.) | 60.0 @ 0°C<br>65.3 @ 10°C<br>71.0 @ 20°C<br>78.8 @ 20°C |
| **3. CALCIUM HYDROXIDE**<br>Ca(OH)₂<br>(Hydrated Lime, Slaked Lime)<br>—<br>Coagulation, Softening, pH Adjustment | Powder | Bags—50 lb.<br>Bbl.—100 lb.<br>Bulk—C/L<br>(Store in dry place) | White, 200-400 Mesh Powder, Free from Lumps<br>Caustic, Irritant, Dusty<br>Sat. Soln.—pH 12.4 | 35 to 50<br>To Calculate Hopper Capacity, use 40 | Ca(OH)₂<br>82 to 99%<br>CaO<br>62 to 74%<br>(Std. 66% CaO) | 0.18 @ 0°C<br>0.16 @ 20°C<br>0.15 @ 30°C |
| **4. CALCIUM HYPOCHLORITE**<br>Ca(OCl)₂·4H₂O<br>(H.T.H., Perchloron, Pittchlor)<br>—<br>Disinfection, Slime Control, Deodorization | Granules<br>Powder<br>Tablet | Bbl.—415 lb.<br>Cans—5, 15, 100, 300 lb.<br>Drums—800 lb. | White, Non-hygroscopic, Corrosive, Strong Chlorine Odor | 50 to 55 | 70% Available Cl₂ | 21.88 @ 0°C<br>22.7 @ 20°C<br>23.4 @ 40°C |

—From Permission of Omega Machine Company, B-I-F Industries.

## FEEDING RECOMMENDATIONS

| BEST FEEDING FORM | CHEMICAL TO WATER RATIO FOR CONTINUOUS DISSOLVING | TYPES OF FEEDERS | ACCESSORY EQUIPMENT REQUIRED | SUITABLE HANDLING MATERIALS |
|---|---|---|---|---|
| **1. ACTIVATED CARBON** Powder—with Bulk Density of 12 lb./cu. ft. | 1 lb./gal.—Max. for Slurry Feeding. "Wetters", with Eluctors for Dry Feeders, Require 10 gpm up to 10 lb./hr., 20 gpm for 30 lb./hr., 150 gpm for 300 lb./hr. | GRAVIMETRIC *Loss-in-Weight*— Up to 300 lb./hr. VOLUMETRIC *Disc*—Up to 10 lb./hr. *Universal*—to 30 lb./hr. *Retolock*—to 300 lb./hr. LIQUID *Rotodip*—to 1000 lb./hr. *Precision*—to 32 gph | Washdown Type Wetting Tank Hopper Agitators Non-flood Rotors Dust Collectors Large Storage Capacity For Liquid Feed— Tank Agitators Transfer Pumps | DRY Iron, Steel WET Stainless Steel, Rubber, Duriron; Bronze Eluctors are OK |
| **2. ALUMINUM SULFATE** Ground or Rice About 60 lb./cu. ft. Powder is Very Dusty, Arches in Hoppers and is Troublesome | 0.5 lb./gal.—Max. Dissolver Detention Time 5 min.—Min. | GRAVIMETRIC *Loss-in-Weight*— 1 to 1000 lb./hr. *Belt*—20 lb./hr. up *Disc*—Up to 20 lb./hr. *Universal*— 10 lb./hr. up | Dissolver Scales for Volumetric Feeders Dust Collector | DRY Iron, Steel, Concrete WET Lead, Rubber, Duriron, Asphalt, Cypress, Stainless Steel, Type 316 |
| **3. CALCIUM HYDROXIDE** Finer Particle Sizes More Efficient, but More Difficult to Handle and Feed* | Dry Feed 0.5 lb./gal.—Max. Slurry 0.93 lb./gal., i.e. 10% Solution—Max. | GRAVIMETRIC *Loss-in-Weight*— 1 to 500 lb./hr. *Belt*—50 to 2000 lb./hr. VOLUMETRIC *Disc*—Up to 20 lb./hr. *Universal*— With Small Hopper *Rotolock*— With Large Hopper LIQUID *Precision, Sampler Pump, Rotodip, Prop. Wet Tank* | Hopper Agitators Non-flood Rotor Under Large Hoppers Dust Collectors | Rubber Hose, Iron, Steel, Asphalt, Concrete; *No Lead* |
| **4. CALCIUM HYPOCHLORITE** Up to 2% Soln. as Available Cl₂—Max. | 0.125 lb./gal. Makes 1% Soln. of Available Cl₂ | LIQUID *Prop. Pump*—Up to 57 gph at 100 psi *Precision*—Up to 32 gph at Gravity Feed | Dissolving Tanks in Pairs with Drains to Draw Off Sediment Injection Nozzle Foot Valve | Ceramics, Glass, Plastics, or Rubber Lined Tanks; *No Tin* |

*For small dosages of chlorine use calcium hypochlorite or sodium hypochlorite.

—From Permission of Omega Machine Company, B-I-F Industries.

| CHEMICAL FORMULA COMMON NAME USE | SHIPPING DATA AVAILABLE FORMS | CONTAINERS and REQUIREMENTS | CHARACTERISTICS APPEARANCE AND PROPERTIES | WEIGHT lb./cu. ft. (Bulk Density) | COMMERCIAL STRENGTH | SOLUBILITY IN WATER gm./100ml. |
|---|---|---|---|---|---|---|
| 5. CHLORINE $Cl_2$ (Chlorine Gas, Liquid Chlorine) Disinfection, Slime Control, Taste and Odor Control, Waste Treatment, Activation of Silica* | Liquefied Gas Under Pressure | Steel Cylinders—100, 150 lb. Ton Containers T/C—15-ton Containers T/C—16, 30, 55 tons Green Label | Greenish Yellow Gas Liquefied Under Pressure Pungent, Noxious, Corrosive Gas Heavier than Air, Health Hazard | Spec. Grav. with Respect to Air 2.49 | 99.8% $Cl_2$ | 1.46 @ 0°C 0.98 @ 10°C 0.716 @ 20°C 0.57 @ 30°C |
| 6. COPPER SULFATE $CuSO_4 \cdot 5H_2O$ (Blue Vitriol, Blue Stone, Cupric Sulfate) Algae Control in Reservoirs Root Control in Sewers | Ground Powder Lump | Bags—100 lb. Bbl.—450 lb. Drums | Clear Blue Crystals or Pale Blue Powder Slowly Efflorescing Poisonous | Ground 75 to 90 Powder 73 to 80 Lump 60 to 64 | 99% | 19.1 @ 0°C 25.2 @ 15°C 26.3 @ 20°C 31.1 @ 30°C |
| 7. SODIUM CARBONATE $Na_2CO_3$ (Soda Ash—58%) Water Softening, pH Adjustment | Dense Crystals Light Powder Extra Light | Bags—100 lb. Bbl.—100 lb. Drums—25, 100 lb. Bulk—C/L | White, Alkaline 1% Soln.—pH 11.2 | Dense 65 Light 40 Extra Light 30 | 99.2% $Na_2CO_3$ 58% $Na_2O$ | 7.0 @ 0°C 12.5 @ 10°C 21.5 @ 20°C 38.8 @ 30°C |
| 8. SODIUM FLUORIDE NaF (Fluoride) Fluoridation | Granules (Crystals) Powder | Bags—100 lb. Drums—25, 125, 375 lb. (Bags Shipped Only by Carload or Truck, LCL by Drums Only) White Label | White or Tinted Nile Blue for Identification Store Dry and Separately from Other Chemicals Poison 1% Soln. (98%)—pH 6.5 4% Soln. (95%)—pH 7.6 | Powder 66 to 100 Granules (Crystal) 90 to 106 (Depends on Source) | NaF 95 to 98% F 43 to 44% | 4.05 @ 20°C |

*When feeding rates exceed 175 lb. per hr. economic factors may dictate use of calcium oxide (quick lime).

—From Permission of Omega Machine Company, B-I-F Industries.

## FEEDING RECOMMENDATIONS

| BEST FEEDING FORM | CHEMICAL TO WATER RATIO FOR CONTINUOUS DISSOLVING | TYPES OF FEEDERS | ACCESSORY EQUIPMENT REQUIRED | SUITABLE HANDLING MATERIALS |
|---|---|---|---|---|
| **5. CHLORINE** Gas—Vaporized from Liquid | 1 lb. to 45-50 gal. or More | Gas Chlorinizers | Vaporizers for High Capacities Scales Gas Masks | DRY LIQUID or GAS Black Iron, Copper, Steel WET GAS Glass, Silver, Hard Rubber, Tantalum |
| **6. COPPER SULFATE** Ground (sugar) or Powder | 0.25 lb./gal. | VOLUMETRIC *Disc*—Up to 10 lb./hr. *Universal*—10 lb./hr. up GRAVIMETRIC *Loss-in-Weight* SOLUTION *Rotodip*—5 to 1800 sph *Proportioneer*— Up to 57 gph | Dissolving Tanks For Direct Application from Boats—Dissolving Tank, Pump, Spray or Crystal Spreader, or Bags | Stainless Steel, Asphalt, Duriron, Rubber, Plastics, Ceramics |
| **7. SODIUM CARBONATE** Dense | Dry Feed 0.25 lb./gal. for 10 min. Detention Time 0.5 lb./gal. for 20 min. Solution Feed 1.0 lb./gal. | GRAVIMETRIC *Loss-in-Weight*— Up to 500 lb./hr. *Belt*—20 lb./hr., up VOLUMETRIC *Disc*—to 20 lb./hr. *Universal*— 10 lb./hr., up SOLUTION *Precision*—To 32 gph *Prop. Pump*—To 57 gph | Rotolock for Light Forms to Prevent Flooding Large Dissolvers Bin Agitators for Light Forms | Iron, Steel, Rubber Hose |
| **8. SODIUM FLUORIDE** Granular (Powder Arches, Floods, is Dustier) | Dry Feed 1 lb. to 12 gal. Solution Feed 1 lb. to 3 gal. or More | GRAVIMETRIC *Loss-in-Weight* 1 to 500 lb./hr. VOLUMETRIC *Disc*—Up to 10 lb./hr. SOLUTION *Prop. Pump Precision for Grav. Feed* | Dust Control Equipment Large Dissolvers Softeners for Water Used in Making Solutions for Pumping | DRY Iron, Steel SOLUTION Rubber, Plastics, Stainless Steel, Asphalt, Cypress |

—From Permission of Omega Machine Company, B-I-F Industries.

| CHEMICAL FORMULA COMMON NAME USE | SHIPPING DATA | | CHARACTERISTICS | | | |
|---|---|---|---|---|---|---|
| | AVAILABLE FORMS | CONTAINERS and REQUIREMENTS | APPEARANCE AND PROPERTIES | WEIGHT lb./cu. ft. (Bulk Density) | COMMERCIAL STRENGTH | SOLUBILITY IN WATER gm./100ml. |
| **9. SODIUM HEXA-META PHOSPHATE** (NaPO₃)₆ (Calgon, Glassy Phosphate, Sodium Polyphos, Micromet) ___ Corrosion and Red Water Control, Stabilization, Water Well Yield Adjustment | "Glass" (Powder or Flake More Expensive) (Unadjusted Form Less Expensive) | Bag—100 lb. Drums—100, 300, 320 lb. | Like Broken Glass Slightly Hygroscopic 12% Soln.—pH 7.0 | 50 | 63% P₂O₅ | Infinitely Soluble: Syrupy Above 50 gm./100ml. |
| **10. SODIUM HYDROXIDE** NaOH (Caustic Soda, Soda Lye) ___ pH Adjustment, Neutralization | Flakes Lumps Powder Solution | Drums—25, 50, 350, 400, 700 lb. Bulk—Solution in T/C Liquid White Label | White Flakes or Lumps Showing Crystaline Fracture Hygroscopic, Caustic Poison, Dangerous to Handle 1% Soln.—pH 12.9 | 60 to 70 | Solid 98.9% NaOH 74.7% Na₂O Solution 12 to 50% NaOH | 42 @ 0°C 109 @ 20°C 119 @ 30°C |
| **11. SODIUM HYPOCHLORITE** NaOCl (Javelle Water, Bleach Liquor, Chlorine Bleach) ___ Disinfection, Slime Control | Solution | Carboys—5, 13 gal. Drums—30 gal. Bulk—1300, 1800, 2000 gal. T/T | Yellow Liquid, Strongly Alkaline Store in Cool Place, Protect from Light and Vent Containers at Intervals | | 13.1% NaOCl or 12.5% Available Chlorine | Completely Miscible |

—From Permission of Omega Machine Company, B-I-F Industries.

# Appendix

**FEEDING RECOMMENDATIONS**

| BEST FEEDING FORM | CHEMICAL TO WATER RATIO FOR CONTINUOUS DISSOLVING | TYPES OF FEEDERS | ACCESSORY EQUIPMENT REQUIRED | SUITABLE HANDLING MATERIALS |
|---|---|---|---|---|
| **9. SODIUM HEXA-META PHOSPHATE** <br> Solution | 1 lb./gal. in Solution Feeders | SOLUTION <br> *Precision*—Up to 32 gph <br> *Prop. Pump*— <br> Up to 57 gph <br> *Sampler Pump*— <br> Up to 7 gph <br> (Large Quantities Can be Fed by Dry Feeders) | Tray or Basket Below Surface of Dissolving Tank <br> Agitator After Solution | Stainless Steel, Rubber, Plastics, Ceramics, Asphalt Lining |
| **10. SODIUM HYDROXIDE** <br> Solution Feed Only | | SOLUTION <br> *Prop. Pump*— <br> Up to 57 gph <br> *Precision*— <br> Up to 32 gph <br> *Sampler Pump*— <br> Up to 7 gph | Goggles, Rubber Gloves and Aprons | Cast Iron, Steel, Rubber |
| **11. SODIUM HYPOCHLORITE** <br> Solution <br> Up to 12.5% Avail. Cl₂ Conc. <br><br> NaOCl Soln. May be Made by Adding Na₂CO₃ to Ca(OCl)₂ Soln. | 1.0 gal. of 12.5% (Avail. Cl₂) Soln. to 15.75 gal. of water Gives a 1% Available Cl₂ Soln. | SOLUTION <br> *Prop. Pump*— <br> Up to 57 gph at Press. up to 100 psi <br> *Precision*—Up to 32 gph Gravity Feed <br> *Sampler Pump*—Up to 7 gph, at 10 psi | Solution Tanks <br> Foot Valves <br> Water Meters <br> Injection Nozzles | Rubber, Plastics, Glass, Ceramics |

—From Permission of Omega Machine Company, B-I-F Industries.

# Appendix

### 7. ChlorinationDisinfection-Sterilization[2]

a. New Construction. It is desirable to disinfect or sterilize new waterwork structures and pipelines with a dosage of 50 parts per million of chlorine. This dosage should remain within the structure or pipeline for a period of not less than 24 hours at which time the chlorine residual should be determined. At the end of that period, the chlorine residual should be at least 10 parts per million.

Procedures for determining the amount of chlorine to produce a concentration of 50 parts per million is as follows:

(1) Calculate the volume of water within the structure or pipeline. (Refer to Appendix Number 8.)

(2) Determine the amount of chlorine to produce this required dosage by using the following formulas:

(a) When 100% available chlorine is used:
Ounces Required = 0.006672 x Number of Gallons
Pounds Required = 417.0 x Number of Million Gallons.
Pounds Required = 0.417 x Number of Thousand Gallons.

(b) When 70% available chlorine is used:
Pounds Required = 595.5 x Number of Million Gallons
Pounds Required = 0.5955 x Number of Thousand Gallons
Ounces Required = 0.009228 x Number of Gallons

b. Repairs: Same as for new construction.

c. Continuous Chlorination: Chlorine in dosage of 0.75 to 2.0 parts per million is added at the well in constant dosage and rate to provide for continuous chlorination. The control of this dosage should be based upon the residual maintained at the extremes of the distribution system where a trace or 0.15 parts per million is desired. This is practical for small water systems because it is possible to maintain such dose readings throughout the system. However, for large systems, it is impractical to maintain chlorine residuals throughout the system without the creating of taste and odor problems. Dosages of 1.0 to 2.0 parts per million should be maintained unless it is possible to use Chlorine Dioxide, Break-point Chlorination, or chlorine-ammonia combination (Chloramines).

# Appendix

## 8. Areas and Volumes

### a. Pipes:

| Pipe Diameter | Area (Square Inches) | Gallons Per Foot |
|---|---|---|
| 1½ | 1.76 | 0.0908 |
| 2 | 3.14 | 0.163 |
| 2½ | 4.90 | 0.254 |
| 3 | 7.06 | 0.367 |
| 4 | 12.96 | 0.672 |
| 6 | 28.27 | 1.47 . |
| 8 | 50.26 | 2.61 |
| 10 | 78.54 | 4.08 |
| 12 | 113.10 | 5.86 |
| 16 | 201.06 | 10.45 |
| 18 | 254.47 | 13.20 |
| 20 | 314.16 | 16.35 |
| 24 | 452.39 | 23.42 |

### b. Circular Tanks:

| Tank Diameter (Inches) | Vertical (Gallons Per Foot Depth) |
|---|---|
| 12 | 5.86 |
| 18 | 13.20 |
| 24 | 23.42 |
| 30 | 36.6 |
| 36 | 52.6 |
| 42 | 71.6 |
| 48 | 93.6 |
| 54 | 119.0 |
| 60 | 146.0 |
| 72 | 211.0 |

### For Horizontal Tanks:

| Ratio: Water Depth to Total Depth | Per Cent of Total Volume |
|---|---|
| 0.1 | 5.22 |
| 0.2 | 14.22 |
| 0.3 | 26.2 |
| 0.4 | 37.4 |
| 0.5 | 50.0 |
| 0.6 | 62.6 |
| 0.7 | 73.8 |
| 0.8 | 85.8 |
| 0.9 | 94.8 |
| 1.0 | 100.0 |

# Appendix

## TABLE SHOWING CONTENTS IN GALLONS OF ROUND TANKS AND CISTERNS

| Diameter in Feet | *Depth in Feet and Contents in Gallons | | | | | | | | | |
|---|---|---|---|---|---|---|---|---|---|---|
| | *1 | 4 | 5 | 6 | 7 | 8 | 9 | 10 | 11 | 12 |
| 4 | 93.99 | 376. | 470. | 564. | 658. | 752. | 846. | 940. | 1034. | 1128. |
| 5 | 146.87 | 588. | 734. | 881. | 1028. | 1175. | 1322. | 1469. | 1616. | 1763. |
| 6 | 211.50 | 847. | 1058. | 1269. | 1481. | 1692. | 1904. | 2115. | 2327. | 2538. |
| 7 | 287.86 | 1152. | 1439. | 1727. | 2015. | 2303. | 2591. | 2879. | 3167. | 3455. |
| 8 | 375.98 | 1504. | 1880. | 2256. | 2632. | 3008. | 3384. | 3760. | 4136. | 4512. |
| 9 | 475.85 | 1904. | 2379. | 2855. | 3331. | 3806. | 4283. | 4759. | 5235. | 5711. |
| 10 | 587.47 | 2350. | 2938. | 3525. | 4113. | 4700. | 5288. | 5875. | 6462. | 7050. |
| 11 | 710.84 | 2844. | 3554. | 4265. | 4976. | 5687. | 6398. | 7109. | 7819. | 8531. |
| 12 | 845.97 | 3384. | 4230. | 5076. | 5922. | 6768. | 7614. | 8460. | 9306. | 10152. |

*To ascertain contents of a round tank or cistern of the above diameters, and of depth not given, multiply the contents of tank one foot deep by the required depth in feet.

—From Permission of Badger Meter Manufacturing Company.

# Appendix

## TABLE SHOWING CONTENTS IN GALLONS OF SQUARE TANKS AND CISTERNS

*Depth in Feet and Contents in Gallons

| Dimensions of Bottom in Feet | *1 | 4 | 5 | 6 | 7 | 8 | 9 | 10 | 11 | 12 |
|---|---|---|---|---|---|---|---|---|---|---|
| 4 x 4 | 119.68 | 479. | 598. | 718. | 838. | 957. | 1077. | 1197. | 1316. | 1436. |
| 5 x 5 | 187.00 | 748. | 935. | 1202. | 1309. | 1516. | 1683. | 1870. | 2057. | 2244. |
| 6 x 6 | 269.28 | 1077. | 1346. | 1616. | 1885. | 2154. | 2424. | 2693. | 2968. | 3231. |
| 7 x 7 | 366.52 | 1466. | 1833. | 2199. | 2566. | 2922. | 3299. | 3665. | 4032. | 4398. |
| 8 x 8 | 478.72 | 1915. | 2394. | 2872. | 3351. | 3830. | 4308. | 4787. | 5266. | 5745. |
| 9 x 9 | 605.88 | 2424. | 3029. | 3635. | 4241. | 4847. | 5453. | 6059. | 6665. | 7272. |
| 10 x 10 | 748.00 | 2992. | 3740. | 4488. | 5236. | 5984. | 6732. | 7480. | 8228. | 8976. |
| 11 x 11 | 905.08 | 3620. | 4525. | 5430. | 6336. | 7241. | 8146. | 9051. | 9956. | 10861. |
| 12 x 12 | 1077.12 | 4308. | 5386. | 6463. | 7540. | 8617. | 9694. | 10771. | 11848. | 12925. |

*To ascertain the contents of a square tank or cistern of depth not given, multiply the contents of tank one foot deep as in table by the required depth in feet:

—From Permission of Badger Meter Manufacturing Company.

# Appendix

## AREAS AND CAPACITIES
### PER ONE FOOT OF DEPTH FOR VERTICAL CYLINDRICAL TANKS 1 FT. TO 100 FT. IN DIAMETER

| Diameter Ft. | In. | Area in Sq. Ft. Cu. Ft. per 1 Ft. of Depth | U.S. Gallons per 1 Ft. of Depth |
|---|---|---|---|
| 1 | | 0.785 | 5.87 |
| 1 | 1 | 0.922 | 6.89 |
| 1 | 2 | 1.069 | 8.00 |
| 1 | 3 | 1.227 | 9.18 |
| 1 | 4 | 1.396 | 10.44 |
| 1 | 5 | 1.576 | 11.79 |
| 1 | 6 | 1.767 | 13.22 |
| 1 | 7 | 1.969 | 14.73 |
| 1 | 8 | 2.182 | 16.32 |
| 1 | 9 | 2.405 | 17.99 |
| 1 | 10 | 2.640 | 19.75 |
| 1 | 11 | 2.885 | 21.58 |
| 2 | | 3.142 | 23.50 |
| 2 | 1 | 3.409 | 25.50 |
| 2 | 2 | 3.687 | 27.58 |
| 2 | 3 | 3.976 | 29.74 |
| 2 | 4 | 4.276 | 31.99 |
| 2 | 5 | 4.587 | 34.31 |
| 2 | 6 | 4.909 | 36.72 |
| 2 | 7 | 5.241 | 39.21 |
| 2 | 8 | 5.585 | 41.78 |
| 2 | 9 | 5.940 | 44.43 |
| 2 | 10 | 6.305 | 47.16 |
| 2 | 11 | 6.681 | 49.98 |
| 3 | | 7.069 | 52.88 |
| 3 | 1 | 7.467 | 55.86 |
| 3 | 2 | 7.876 | 58.92 |
| 3 | 3 | 8.296 | 62.06 |
| 3 | 4 | 8.727 | 65.28 |
| 3 | 5 | 9.168 | 68.58 |
| 3 | 6 | 9.621 | 71.97 |
| 3 | 7 | 10.08 | 75.44 |
| 3 | 8 | 10.56 | 78.99 |
| 3 | 9 | 11.04 | 82.62 |
| 3 | 10 | 11.54 | 86.33 |
| 3 | 11 | 12.05 | 90.13 |
| 4 | | 12.57 | 94.00 |
| 4 | 1 | 13.10 | 97.96 |
| 4 | 2 | 13.64 | 102.0 |
| 4 | 3 | 14.19 | 106.1 |
| 4 | 4 | 14.75 | 110.3 |
| 4 | 5 | 15.32 | 114.6 |
| 4 | 6 | 15.90 | 119.0 |
| 4 | 7 | 16.50 | 123.4 |
| 4 | 8 | 17.10 | 128.0 |
| 4 | 9 | 17.72 | 132.6 |
| 4 | 10 | 18.35 | 137.3 |
| 4 | 11 | 18.99 | 142.0 |
| 5 | | 19.63 | 146.9 |
| 5 | 3 | 21.65 | 161.9 |
| 5 | 6 | 23.76 | 177.7 |
| 5 | 9 | 25.97 | 194.3 |

| Diameter Ft. | In. | Area in Sq. Ft. Cu. Ft. per 1 Ft. of Depth | U.S. Gallons per 1 Ft. of Depth |
|---|---|---|---|
| 6 | | 28.27 | 211.5 |
| 6 | 3 | 30.68 | 229.5 |
| 6 | 6 | 33.18 | 248.2 |
| 6 | 9 | 35.78 | 267.7 |
| 7 | . | 38.48 | 287.9 |
| 7 | 3 | 41.28 | 308.8 |
| 7 | 6 | 44.18 | 330.5 |
| 7 | 9 | 47.17 | 352.9 |
| 8 | | 50.27 | 376.0 |
| 8 | 3 | 53.46 | 399.9 |
| 8 | 6 | 56.75 | 424.5 |
| 8 | 9 | 60.13 | 449.8 |
| 9 | | 63.62 | 475.9 |
| 9 | 3 | 67.20 | 502.7 |
| 9 | 6 | 70.88 | 530.2 |
| 9 | 9 | 74.66 | 558.5 |
| 10 | | 78.54 | 587.5 |
| 10 | 6 | 86.59 | 647.7 |
| 11 | | 95.03 | 710.9 |
| 11 | 6 | 103.9 | 777.0 |
| 12 | | 113.1 | 846.0 |
| 12 | 6 | 122.7 | 918.0 |
| 13 | | 132.7 | 992.9 |
| 13 | 6 | 143.1 | 1071. |
| 14 | | 153.9 | 1152. |
| 14 | 6 | 165.1 | 1235. |
| 15 | | 176.7 | 1322. |
| 15 | 6 | 188.7 | 1412. |
| 16 | | 201.1 | 1504. |
| 16 | 6 | 213.8 | 1600. |
| 17 | | 227.0 | 1698. |
| 17 | 6 | 240.5 | 1799. |
| 18 | | 254.5 | 1904. |
| 18 | 6 | 268.8 | 2011. |
| 19 | | 283.5 | 2121. |
| 19 | 6 | 298.6 | 2234. |
| 20 | | 314.2 | 2350. |
| 20 | 6 | 330.1 | 2469. |
| 21 | | 346.4 | 2591. |
| 21 | 6 | 363.1 | 2716. |
| 22 | | 380.1 | 2844. |
| 22 | 6 | 397.6 | 2974. |
| 23 | | 415.5 | 3108. |
| 23 | 6 | 433.7 | 3245. |
| 24 | | 452.4 | 3384. |
| 24 | 6 | 471.4 | 3527. |
| 25 | | 490.9 | 3672. |
| 25 | 6 | 510.7 | 3820. |
| 26 | | 530.9 | 3972. |
| 26 | 6 | 551.5 | 4126. |
| 27 | | 572.6 | 4283. |

| Diameter Ft. | In. | Area in Sq. Ft. Cu. Ft. per 1 Ft. of Depth | U.S. Gallons per 1 Ft. of Depth |
|---|---|---|---|
| 27 | 6 | 594.0 | 4443. |
| 28 | | 615.8 | 4606. |
| 28 | 6 | 637.9 | 4772. |
| 29 | | 660.5 | 4941. |
| 29 | 6 | 683.5 | 5113. |
| 30 | | 706.9 | 5288. |
| 31 | | 754.8 | 5646. |
| 32 | | 804.3 | 6016. |
| 33 | | 855.3 | 6398. |
| 34 | | 907.9 | 6792. |
| 35 | | 962.1 | 7197. |
| 36 | | 1018. | 7616. |
| 37 | | 1075. | 8043. |
| 38 | | 1134. | 8483. |
| 39 | | 1195. | 8940. |
| 40 | | 1257. | 9404. |
| 41 | | 1320. | 9876. |
| 42 | | 1385. | 10360. |
| 43 | | 1452. | 10860. |
| 44 | | 1521. | 11370. |
| 45 | | 1590. | 11900. |
| 46 | | 1662. | 12430. |
| 47 | | 1735. | 12980. |
| 48 | | 1810. | 13540. |
| 49 | | 1886. | 14110. |
| 50 | | 1964. | 14690. |
| 52 | | 2124. | 15890. |
| 54 | | 2290. | 17130. |
| 56 | | 2463. | 18420. |
| 58 | | 2642. | 19760. |
| 60 | | 2827. | 21150. |
| 62 | | 3019. | 22580. |
| 64 | | 3217. | 24060. |
| 66 | | 3421. | 25590. |
| 68 | | 3632. | 27170. |
| 70 | | 3848. | 28790. |
| 72 | | 4072. | 30450. |
| 74 | | 4301. | 32170. |
| 76 | | 4536. | 33930. |
| 78 | | 4778. | 35740. |
| 80 | | 5027. | 37600. |
| 82 | | 5281. | 39500. |
| 84 | | 5542. | 41450. |
| 86 | | 5809. | 43450. |
| 88 | | 6082. | 45490. |
| 90 | | 6362. | 47590. |
| 92 | | 6648. | 49720. |
| 94 | | 6940. | 51920. |
| 96 | | 7238. | 54140. |
| 98 | | 7543. | 56420. |
| 100 | | 7854. | 58750. |

—Courtesy of Darling Valve and Mfg. Co.

# Appendix

## 9. Pressure Conversion Table

Feet $\longleftarrow$————— Pounds Per Square Inch

Feet ————$\longrightarrow$ Pounds Per Square Inch

| Feet | Pounds Per Square Inch | Pounds Per Square Inch |
|---|---|---|
| 2.31 | 1 | 0.4335 |
| 4.62 | 2 | 0.8670 |
| 6.93 | 3 | 1.3005 |
| 9.24 | 4 | 1.7340 |
| 11.54 | 5 | 2.16 |
| 13.85 | 6 | 2.60 |
| 16.16 | 7 | 3.03 |
| 18.47 | 8 | 3.46 |
| 20.78 | 9 | 3.90 |
| 23.09 | 10 | 4.33 |
| 46.18 | 20 | 8.67 |
| 69.27 | 30 | 13.00 |
| 92.36 | 40 | 17.34 |
| 115.45 | 50 | 21.67 |
| 138.54 | 60 | 26.01 |
| 161.63 | 70 | 30.34 |
| 184.72 | 80 | 34.68 |
| 207.81 | 90 | 39.01 |
| 230.89 | 100 | 43.35 |
| 461.79 | 200 | 86.70 |
| 692.69 | 300 | 130.05 |
| 923.59 | 400 | 173.40 |
| 1,154.49 | 500 | 216.68 |

The components of this Table may be used for conversion of any value from Pounds Per Square Inch to Feet of Water or from Feet of Water to Pounds Per Square Inch. For example, a pressure of 75 pounds per square inch is equivalent to a head of water of 173.17 feet of water. To obtain this from the Table, the value of 75 pounds per square inch is broken into hundreds, tens, and unity values such as 0, 70, and five pounds per square inch. Then from the Table, obtain the values of 161.63 plus 11.54 to give 173.17 feet of water.

# Appendix

## 10. Flow Conversation Table

Gallons Per Day ◄─────── Gallons Per Minute

Gallons Per Minute ─────► Cubic Feet Per Second

| Gallons Per Day | Gallons Per Minute | Cubic Feet Per Second |
|---|---|---|
| 1,440 | 1 | 0.002228 |
| 2,880 | 2 | 0.004456 |
| 4,320 | 3 | 0.006684 |
| 5,760 | 4 | 0.008912 |
| 7,200 | 5 | 0.011140 |
| 8,640 | 6 | 0.013368 |
| 10,080 | 7 | 0.015596 |
| 11,520 | 8 | 0.017824 |
| 12,860 | 9 | 0.020052 |
| 14,400 | 10 | 0.022280 |
| 28,800 | 20 | 0.044560 |
| 43,200 | 30 | 0.066840 |
| 57,600 | 40 | 0.089120 |
| 72,000 | 50 | 0.111400 |
| 86,400 | 60 | 0.133680 |
| 100,800 | 70 | 0.155960 |
| 115,200 | 80 | 0.178240 |
| 128,600 | 90 | 0.200520 |
| 144,000 | 100 | 0.22280 |
| 288,000 | 200 | 0.44560 |
| 432,000 | 300 | 0.66840 |
| 576,000 | 400 | 0.89120 |
| 720,000 | 500 | 1.11400 |
| 864,000 | 600 | 1.33680 |
| 1,008,000 | 700 | 1.55960 |
| 1,152,000 | 800 | 1.78240 |
| 1,286,000 | 900 | 2.00520 |
| 1,440,000 | 1,000 | 2.2280 |

The components of this Table may be used for conversion of any value from Gallons Per Minute to either Gallons Per Day or Cubic Feet Per Second. For example, a well with a yield of 162 gallons per minute will produce 233,280 gallons per day. To obtain this form the Table, the value of 162 is broken into hundreds ,tens, and unity values such as 100, 60, and two gallons per minute. Then from the Table, obtain the values of 144,000 plus 86,400 plus 2,880 to give 233,280 gallons per day.

# Appendix

## 11. Volume Conversion Table

| Gallons ← Cubic Feet | Gallons → | Cubic Feet |
|---|---|---|
| 7.48 | 1 | 0.134 |
| 14.96 | 2 | 0.268 |
| 22.44 | 2 | 0.402 |
| 29.22 | 4 | 0.436 |
| 37.40 | 5 | 0.670 |
| 44.88 | 6 | 0.804 |
| 52.36 | 7 | 0.938 |
| 59.84 | 8 | 1.072 |
| 67.32 | 9 | 1.206 |
| 74.8 | 10 | 1.34 |
| 149.6 | 20 | 2.68 |
| 224.4 | 30 | 4.02 |
| 299.2 | 40 | 5.36 |
| 374.0 | 50 | 6.70 |
| 448.8 | 60 | 8.04 |
| 523.6 | 70 | 9.38 |
| 598.4 | 80 | 10.72 |
| 673.2 | 90 | 12.06 |
| 748.0 | 100 | 13.4 |
| 1,496.0 | 200 | 26.8 |
| 2,244.0 | 300 | 40.2 |
| 2,992.0 | 400 | 53.6 |
| 3,740.0 | 500 | 67.0 |
| 4,480.0 | 600 | 80.4 |
| 5,236.0 | 700 | 93.4 |
| 5,984.0 | 800 | 107.2 |
| 6,732.0 | 900 | 120.6 |
| 7,480.0 | 1,000 | 134.0 |

| Gallons ← Cubic Feet | Gallons → | Cubic Feet |
|---|---|---|
| 14,960 | 2,000 | 268 |
| 22,440 | 3,000 | 402 |
| 29,920 | 4,000 | 536 |
| 37,400 | 5,000 | 670 |
| 44,880 | 6,000 | 804 |
| 52,360 | 7,000 | 934 |
| 59,840 | 8,000 | 1,072 |
| 67,320 | 9,000 | 1,206 |
| 74,805 | 10,000 | 1,340 |
| 149,610 | 20,000 | 2,680 |
| 224,415 | 30,000 | 4,020 |
| 299,220 | 40,000 | 5,360 |
| 374,025 | 50,000 | 6,700 |
| 448,831 | 60,000 | 8,040 |
| 523,636 | 70,000 | 9,340 |
| 598,441 | 80,000 | 10,720 |
| 673,246 | 90,000 | 12,060 |
| 748,051 | 100,000 | 13,400 |

The components of this Table may be used for conversion of any value from Gallons to Cubic Feet or from Cubic Feet to Gallons. For example, 63,750 gallons would occupy 8,542.1 cubic feet. To obtain this from the Table, the value of 63,750 gallons is broken down into tens thousands, thtounsands, hundreds, tens and unity values such as 60,000 plus 3,000 plus 700 plus 50 gallons. Then from the Table, obtaine related cubic feet values for each such as 8,040 plus 402.0 plus 93.40 plus 6.70 to give 8,542.1 cubic feet.

# Appendix

## 12. Relative Carrying Capacities of Pipes

# RELATIVE CARRYING CAPACITIES

### OF STANDARD WEIGHT AND OUTSIDE DIAMETER
### WROUGHT PIPE FOR WATER

| Actual Inside Diameter Inches | 0.269 | 0.364 | 0.493 | 0.622 | 1.824 | 1.049 | 1.380 | 1.610 | 2.067 | 2.469 | 3.068 | 3.548 |
|---|---|---|---|---|---|---|---|---|---|---|---|---|
| **Nominal Size** | 1/8 | 1/4 | 3/8 | 1/2 | 3/4 | 1 | 1 1/4 | 1 1/2 | 2 | 2 1/2 | 3 | 3 1/2 |
| 1/8 | 1 | 0.475 | 0.222 | 0.122 | 0.0625 | 0.0333 | 0.0167 | 0.0114 | 0.0061 | 0.00392 | 0.00228 | 0.0015 |
| 1/4 | 2.1 | 1 | 0.475 | 0.263 | 0.130 | 0.0714 | 0.0357 | 0.0244 | 0.0130 | 0.00833 | 0.00485 | 0.0033 |
| 3/8 | 4.5 | 2.1 | 1 | 0.555 | 0.278 | 0.151 | 0.077 | 0.0526 | 0.0278 | 0.0178 | 0.0103 | 0.0072 |
| 1/2 | 8.2 | 3.8 | 1.8 | 1 | 0.500 | 0.270 | 0.139 | 0.091 | 0.050 | 0.0322 | 0.0185 | 0.0128 |
| 3/4 | 16 | 7.7 | 3.6 | 2 | 1 | 0.555 | 0.278 | 0.189 | 0.100 | 0.0645 | 0.0370 | 0.0263 |
| 1 | 30 | 14 | 6.6 | 3.7 | 1.8 | 1 | 0.500 | 0.344 | 0.182 | 0.1180 | 0.0666 | 0.0476 |
| 1 1/4 | 60 | 28 | 13 | 7.2 | 3.6 | 2 | 1 | 0.666 | 0.357 | 0.232 | 0.143 | 0.0910 |
| 1 1/2 | 88 | 41 | 19 | 11 | 5.3 | 2.9 | 1.5 | 1 | 0.526 | 0.345 | 0.200 | 0.139 |
| 2 | 164 | 77 | 36 | 20 | 10 | 5.5 | 2.8 | 1.9 | 1 | 0.625 | 0.370 | 0.256 |
| 2 1/2 | 255 | 120 | 56 | 31 | 15.5 | 8.5 | 4.3 | 2.9 | 1.6 | 1 | 0.588 | 0.400 |
| 3 | 439 | 206 | 97 | 54 | 27 | 15 | 7 | 5 | 2.7 | 1.7 | 1 | 0.715 |
| 3 1/2 | 632 | 297 | 139 | 78 | 38 | 21 | 11 | 7.2 | 3.9 | 2.5 | 1.4 | 1 |
| 4 | 867 | 407 | 191 | 107 | 53 | 29 | 15 | 9.9 | 5.3 | 3.4 | 2 | 1.4 |
| 5 | 1,525 | 716 | 335 | 188 | 93 | 51 | 26 | 17 | 9.3 | 6 | 3.5 | 2.4 |
| 6 | 2,414 | 1,133 | 531 | 297 | 147 | 80 | 41 | 28 | 15 | 9.5 | 5.5 | 3.8 |
| 8 | 4,795 | 2,251 | 1,054 | 590 | 292 | 160 | 80 | 54 | 29 | 19 | 10.9 | 7.6 |
| 10 | 8,468 | 3,976 | 1,862 | 1,042 | 516 | 282 | 142 | 97 | 52 | 33 | 19 | 13.4 |
| 12 | 13,292 | 6,240 | 2,923 | 1,635 | 809 | 443 | 223 | 152 | 81 | 52 | 30 | 21 |
| 14 OD | 17,028 | 7,994 | 3,745 | 2,094 | 1,037 | 567 | 286 | 194 | 104 | 67 | 39 | 27 |
| 16 OD | 24,199 | 11,361 | 5,322 | 2,976 | 1,474 | 806 | 406 | 276 | 148 | 95 | 55 | 38 |
| 18 OD | 31,750 | 14,906 | 6,982 | 3,905 | 1,933 | 1,057 | 533 | 362 | 194 | 124 | 72 | 50 |
| 20 OD | 41,928 | 19,685 | 9,221 | 5,157 | 2,553 | 1,396 | 703 | 478 | 256 | 164 | 95 | 66 |
| 24 OD | 67,599 | 31,737 | 14,866 | 8,315 | 4,116 | 2,251 | 1,134 | 771 | 413 | 265 | 154 | 107 |

| Actual Inside Diameter Inches | 4.026 | 5.047 | 6.065 | 7.981 | 10.02 | 12.00 | 13.25 | 15.25 | 17.00 | 19.00 | 23.00 |
|---|---|---|---|---|---|---|---|---|---|---|---|
| **Nominal Size** | 4 | 5 | 6 | 8 | 10 | 12 | 14 OD | 16 OD | 18 OD | 20 OD | 24 OD |
| 1/8 | 0.00115 | 0.000655 | 0.000415 | 0.000209 | 0.000118 | 0.000075 | 0.000059 | 0.000041 | 0.000032 | 0.000024 | 0.000015 |
| 1/4 | 0.00246 | 0.00139 | 0.000882 | 0.000445 | 0.000252 | 0.000160 | 0.000125 | 0.000088 | 0.000067 | 0.000051 | 0.000032 |
| 3/8 | 0.00523 | 0.00298 | 0.00188 | 0.000948 | 0.000536 | 0.000342 | 0.000267 | 0.000188 | 0.000143 | 0.000108 | 0.000067 |
| 1/2 | 0.00934 | 0.00532 | 0.00336 | 0.00169 | 0.000959 | 0.000611 | 0.000477 | 0.000336 | 0.000256 | 0.000193 | 0.000120 |
| 3/4 | 0.0189 | 0.01075 | 0.00680 | 0.00342 | 0.00194 | 0.00124 | 0.000965 | 0.000678 | 0.000517 | 0.000392 | 0.000243 |
| 1 | 0.0345 | 0.0196 | 0.0125 | 0.00625 | 0.00355 | 0.00226 | 0.00176 | 0.00124 | 0.000945 | 0.000716 | 0.000444 |
| 1 1/4 | 0.0666 | 0.0384 | 0.0244 | 0.0125 | 0.00705 | 0.00449 | 0.00350 | 0.00246 | 0.00188 | 0.00142 | 0.000881 |
| 1 1/2 | 0.1010 | 0.0588 | 0.0357 | 0.0185 | 0.0103 | 0.00657 | 0.00515 | 0.00362 | 0.00276 | 0.00209 | 0.001300 |
| 2 | 0.1887 | 0.1075 | 0.0666 | 0.0345 | 0.0192 | 0.0123 | 0.00961 | 0.00675 | 0.00515 | 0.00390 | 0.00242 |
| 2 1/2 | 0.294 | 0.1665 | 0.1050 | 0.0526 | 0.0303 | 0.0192 | 0.0149 | 0.0105 | 0.00805 | 0.00610 | 0.00377 |
| 3 | 0.500 | 0.296 | 0.182 | 0.0917 | 0.0526 | 0.0333 | 0.0256 | 0.0182 | 0.0159 | 0.01050 | 0.00650 |
| 3 1/2 | 0.715 | 0.417 | 0.263 | 0.1315 | 0.0746 | 0.0476 | 0.0370 | 0.0263 | 0.0200 | 0.01515 | 0.00935 |
| 4 | 1 | 0.555 | 0.357 | 0.1820 | 0.1020 | 0.0666 | 0.0500 | 0.0357 | 0.0270 | 0.0208 | 0.0128 |
| 5 | 1.8 | 1 | 0.625 | 0.322 | 0.1785 | 0.1150 | 0.0909 | 0.0625 | 0.0476 | 0.0370 | 0.0227 |
| 6 | 2.8 | 1.6 | 1 | 0.500 | 0.286 | 0.1820 | 0.1430 | 0.1000 | 0.0769 | 0.0555 | 0.0357 |
| 8 | 5.5 | 3.1 | 2 | 1 | 0.555 | 0.3570 | 0.278 | 0.2000 | 0.1515 | 0.1150 | 0.0714 |
| 10 | 9.8 | 5.6 | 3.5 | 1.8 | 1 | 0.6250 | 0.500 | 0.3450 | 0.2630 | 0.2000 | 0.1250 |
| 12 | 15 | 8.7 | 5.5 | 2.8 | 1.6 | 1 | 0.769 | 0.500 | 0.416 | 0.322 | 0.196 |
| 14 OD | 20 | 11 | 7 | 3.6 | 2 | 1.3 | 1 | 0.714 | 0.526 | 0.400 | 0.250 |
| 16 OD | 28 | 16 | 10 | 5.0 | 2.9 | 1.8 | 1.4 | 1 | 0.769 | 0.588 | 0.357 |
| 18 OD | 37 | 21 | 13 | 6.6 | 3.8 | 2.4 | 1.9 | 1.3 | 1 | 0.769 | 0.476 |
| 20 OD | 48 | 27 | 18 | 8.7 | 5 | 3.1 | 2.5 | 1.7 | 1.3 | 1 | 0.625 |
| 24 OD | 78 | 44 | 28 | 14 | 8 | 5.1 | 4 | 2.8 | 2.1 | 1.6 | 1 |

The carrying capacity for water varies as the square root of the fifth power of the actual inside diameter.
*Example.*—A 2-in. pipe has a water-carrying capacity equal to ten 3/4-in. pipes, or 0.1887 that of a 4-in. pipe.

—Courtesy of Darling Valve and Mfg. Co.

# Appendix

### 3. Measurement of Well Water Depth, Air Line Method

To determine the distance to water in a well, install ¼-inch pipe or copper tube of known length, 10 to 20 feet below the low pumping level. Make all joints air tight with white lead or piping compound. Connect through a tube to an air gauge a tire valve and air pump.

Pump air into the line until the indicated air pressure is constant. This indicates that all the water has been expelled from the pipe. The gauge reading shows the pressure necessary to support a column of water of a height equal to the depth that the pipe is submerged.

X = depth of water in feet (required).

Y = length of air line in feet (known).

Z = Air line water pressure (pressure gauge reading). This must be in feet of water.

Should gauge read in pounds, then convert to feet by multiplying by 2.31.

X = Y — Z.

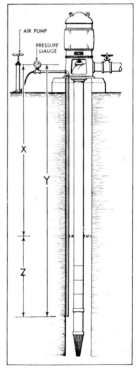

*Example:* Assume air pipe is 100 feet long from center of gauge to bottom end of pipe. Also that the highest gauge reading is 20 lbs.

*Then,*

Y = 100 feet
Z = 20 x 2.31 = 46.2 feet
X = Y — Z    100 — 46.2 = 53.8
feet, depth of water.

—Courtesy of Peerless Pump Company.

# Appendix

## 14. Methods of Determining Chemical Dosages for Solution Fed Chemicals

An accurate measurement and determination of chemicals fed by solution feeders into a pump discharge is sometimes tedious and burdensome to calculate. Below are simplified methods of determination of dosage of chemical per volume of water treatment:

1. When it is possible to measure the volume of solution fed by feeder into the pump discharge which is metered:

$$\text{Dosage, Parts Per Million} = \frac{\% \text{ Solution x Gallons of Solution Fed x 10,000}}{\text{Total Gallons of Water Treated}}$$

Example: A 4% solution of Phosphate is used for treatment of water and is fed by solution pump into well pump discharge. At the end of certain period, two gallons of solution is used and the well meter indicates that 40,000 gallons of water has been treated. What dosage of chemical was fed?

$$\text{Dosage in PPM} = \frac{\% \text{ Solution x Gallons Solution Fed x 10,000}}{\text{Total Volume of Water Treated}}$$

$$= \frac{4 \quad \text{x} \quad 2 \quad \text{x 10,000}}{40,000}$$

$$= 2 \text{ parts per million}$$

2. When it is more desirable to mix solution in earthenware crocks and by means of a calibrated ruler or yardstick, to read directly in pounds, the amount of solution fed. For example, a 30-gallon crock measures 20 inches in depth. If two pounds of chemical were dissolved in this crock, then each inch of depth would be equivalent to 0.1 pounds or a dosage of:

$$\text{Dosage in Parts Per Million} = \frac{119,900 \text{ x Pounds of Chemical Fed}}{\text{Total Water Treated}}$$

In the above example where 1.2 pounds of chemical is fed into a total volume of 40,000 gallons of water, the dosage would be:

$$\text{Dosage in PPM} = \frac{119,900 \text{ x Pounds of Chemical Fed}}{\text{Total Water Treated}}$$

$$= \frac{119,900 \text{ x} \quad 1.2}{40,000}$$

$$= 3.57 \text{ parts per million}$$

3. In many instances, the chemical used is not of 100% purity, but some other per cent such as 70% for powdered chlorine. In such cases, the dosage as found in (1) and (2) above is corrected by this purity factor such that the results as found in (1) and (2) are multiplied by the factor, per cent purity, to give actual dosage. For example, if 70% available chlorine is used, the dosage as found in (1) and (2) would be corrected by multiplying by 0.70.

# Appendix

## 15. Recommendations for Quality Concrete

To give maximum protection against pollution of water supplies and to be assured of permanent watertight structures, it is particularly important that concrete used be of high quality.

*Water.* Mixing water for concrete should be clean enough to drink.

*Portland Cement.* Portland cement should be dry. Any cement containing lumps so hard that they do not readily pulverize in the hand should not be used.

*Sand and Gravel.* Sand should be clean, hard and well graded; that is, with particles of many sizes from very fine to those which will pass through a No. 4 screen (four openings per lin. in.). Gravel should be clean and hard and range in size from ¼ in. up to about one in. for most work. Only sand and gravel known to make good concrete should be used. Crushed stone is sometimes used in place of gravel.

### Mixing and Placing Concrete

All materials—cement, water, sand, gravel—should be measured for each batch of concrete. It is especially important that the cement and water be accurately measured. When too much water is added the concrete will be weak and porous.

There are several ways to measure materials for concrete. On small concrete jobs one of the most practical ways to measure cement and water is to use pails. Sand and gravel too can be measured in this way, although they are sometimes more conveniently measured in a one-cubit-foot box.

When pails are used for measuring the cement and water, the proper level should be marked on the inside as a guide in mixing. Shovels can be used for the sand and gravel but the proper number of shovelfuls should first be determined by measuring the sand and gravel in buckets. It is important to keep the shovelfuls uniform.

Suggested mixes are given under "Suggested Concrete Mixes." The proportions recommended should result in a mushy, workable mix. It should be

### Suggested Concrete Mixes*

| Type of Concrete | Gallons of Water Per Sack Cement (Average Wet Sand) | Sand and Gravel Per Sack Cement | | Largest Size of Gravel (In.) |
|---|---|---|---|---|
| | | Sand (Cu. Ft.) | Gravel (Cu. Ft.) | |
| All Concrete 4 in. to 8 in. Thick | 5 | 2¼ | 3 | 1 |
| All Concrete 2 in. to 4 in. Thick | 5 | 2¾ | 2¾ | ¾ |

*These are trial mixes for average conditions. It is particularly important to use no more water per sack of cement than shown in the table, unless sand is very wet, in which case decrease amount of water one gallon per sack of cement, or unless sand is dry, in which case increase amount of water ½ gallon.

*Note:* When five gallons of water is used per sack of cement and a one-third-bag mixer is used, 10 quart of cement and seven quart of water are mixed per batch. When one-half-bag mixer is used, 15 quarts of cement and 10 quarts of water are mixed.

# Appendix

somewhat sticky when worked with a shovel or trowel and smooth enough to finish readily. If the mix is soupy or sloppy, or if an appreciable amount of water comes to the top while spading the concrete, the amounts of sand and gravel in following batches should be increased. If the mix is too stiff, the amounts of sand and gravel should be decreased.

*Construction joints,* caused by stopping work temporarily, should be avoided if possible. In building watertight concrete structures it is best to complete the concrete work in one continuous operation. Should it be necessary to interrupt concreting, however, it is best to roughen the surface of the concrete with a stiff broom before it hardens. Before placing concrete again, wet the surface; then cover it with a layer of cement mortar about ½ inch thick. This helps to insure a tight joint between old and new concrete. The cement mortar is made by mixing one part of portland cement to 2½ parts of sand with sufficient water to make a mushy workable mix.

## Finishing and Curing Concrete

Newly placed concrete is leveled off in the forms with a strikeboard or a woodfloat; then the woodfloat is used to make an even surface. Further finishing, as may be required for well platforms and pump pit floors, is delayed until the concrete has lost its watery sheen. If a smooth, dense surface is desired, a steel trowel is then used. Stony spots or "homeycomb" found when forms are removed from wall surfaces may be neatly filled by working a stiff cement

### Approximate Amounts of Materials Required per Cubic Yard of Concrete

| Type of Concrete | Sacks of Cement | Sand (Cu. Yd.) | Gravel (Cu. Yd.) | Maximum Size of Gravel |
|---|---|---|---|---|
| All Concrete 4 in. to 8 in. Thick (1 : 2¼ : 3 mix) | 6¼ | ½ | ¾ | 1 in. |
| All Concrete 2 in. to 4 in. Thick (1 : 2¾ : 2¾ mix) | 6½ | ¾ | ¾ | ¾ in. |

mortar into them with a woodfloat. The mortar should be one part portland cement to 2½ parts sand with enough water to make a workable mix.

Concrete needs moisture to harden properly, that is, to cure. New concrete should, therefore, be protected from drying out for at least seven days by covering with burlap, earth, straw, etc., and keeping this material wet for the required time. Proper curing increases the strength and watertightness of concrete.

# Appendix

*How to Estimate Materials Needed**

Table 8 shows the amount of materials required to make a cubic yard (27 cubic feet) of concrete. The procedure in estimating the materials needed for a particular job is shown in the following example:

Suppose a water tank is to be built with 750-gallon capacity.

Outside dimensions: 4½ x 5-5/6 x 8½ feet.
    Overall volume = 223 cubic feet.

Inside dimensions: 3½ x 5 x 7½ feet.
    Inside volume = 131 cubic feet.

Subtract inside volume from overall volume:

Volume of concrete = 92 cubic feet ÷ 27 = 3½ cubic yards (approximately).

Table 8 shows that one cubic yard of 1 : 2¼ : 3 concrete mix requires approximately 6¼ sacks of cement, ½ cubic yard of sand and ¾ cubic yard of gravel.

Then for the 3½ cubic yard of concrete needed for the water tank one would need:

3½ x 6¼ sacks cement = 22 sacks of cement
3½ x ½ cubic yard sand = 1¾ cubic yard sand
3½ x ¾ cubic yard gravel = 2¾ cubic yard gravel

---

*If concrete aggregates are sold in your locality by weight, you may assume for estimating purposes that a ton contains approximately 22 cubic feet of sand or crushed stone, or about 20 cubic feet of gravel. For information on local aggregates consult your building material dealer.

# Appendix

**16. Storage Facilities, Low Pressure, Concrete**

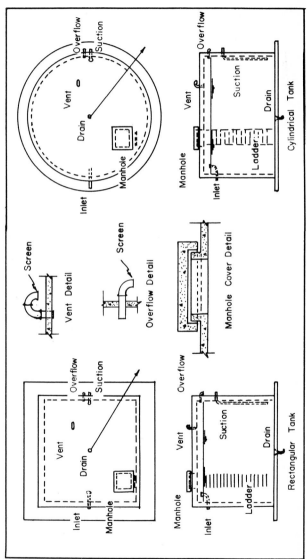

APPENDIX 16. Storage Facilities, Low Pressure, Concrete.

## 17. Additional Hydraulic Data (Measurement of Flows)
### Orifices

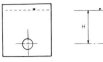

$Q = 7.25\ C\ A\ H^{0.5}$ Where $Q$ = Flow in gallons per minute
$C$ = Coefficient of orifice plate
= 0.60 for sharp-edged orifice
= 0.82 for standard short tube orifice
$A$ = Area of orifice in square inches
$H$ = Total head in inches on center of orifice

### Weirs

**Triangular or V-Notched Weir***

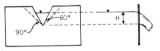

**Rectangular Weir***

| For 60° Notch | For 90° Notch | For Rectangular Weir (Francis Formula) |
|---|---|---|
| $Q = 1.284\ H^{2.5}$ | $Q = 2.24\ H^{2.5}$ | $Q = 2.97\ L\ H^{1.5}$ |

Where $Q$ = Flow in gallons per minute
$H$ = Head in inches over weir and measured at point prior to curvature of water surface
$L$ = Length of weir in inches

| Depth of Water Over Weir, Inches | Flow in GPM For V-Notch Weir, 60° Weir | 90° Weir | Flow in GPM for Rectangular Weir For Weir Lengths in Inches as Shown 6" | 8" | 10" | 12" |
|---|---|---|---|---|---|---|
| 1 | 1 | 2 | 18 | 24 | 30 | 36 |
| 1½ | 4 | 6 | 32 | 43 | 54 | 65 |
| 2 | 7 | 13 | 51 | 67 | 84 | 103 |
| 2½ | 13 | 22 | 70 | 94 | 118 | 141 |
| 3 | 20 | 35 | 92 | 122 | 154 | 186 |
| 3½ | 30 | 51 | 115 | 154 | 193 | 232 |
| 4 | 41 | 71 | 142 | 190 | 238 | 285 |
| 4½ | 56 | 96 | 169 | 226 | 282 | 339 |
| 5 | 72 | 125 | 198 | 266 | 332 | 396 |
| 5½ | 91 | 159 | 230 | 307 | 383 | 460 |
| 6 | 113 | 198 | 263 | 351 | 439 | 527 |

*For sharp edged weirs.

## 18. Additional Hydraulic Data — Resistance of Fittings

Resistance of Fittings — Equivalent Length of Pipe — Feet
For Cast Iron Pipe — C = 100

| Nominal Diameter of Standard Pipe, Inches | Type of Fitting | | | |
|---|---|---|---|---|
| | Sudden Enlargement $\frac{d}{D} = \frac{1}{2}$ | Sudden Contraction $\frac{d}{D} = \frac{1}{2}$ | Ordinary Entrance | Borda Entrance |
| ½ | 1.0 | 0.6 | 0.9 | 1.6 |
| ¾ | 1.4 | 0.8 | 1.3 | 2.0 |
| 1 | 1.7 | 1.0 | 1.5 | 2.5 |
| 1¼ | 2.3 | 1.3 | 2.0 | 3.4 |
| 1½ | 2.7 | 1.5 | 2.4 | 4.0 |
| 2 | 3.5 | 1.9 | 3.0 | 5.0 |
| 2½ | 4.2 | 2.2 | 3.6 | 6.0 |
| 3 | 5.2 | 2.8 | 4.5 | 7.8 |
| 4 | 7.0 | 3.8 | 6.0 | 10.7 |
| 5 | 9.0 | 4.7 | 7.5 | 13.5 |
| 6 | 11.0 | 5.8 | 9.0 | 15.4 |
| 8 | 14.0 | 7.5 | 13.0 | 19.9 |
| 10 | 17.0 | 10.0 | 15.0 | 24.5 |
| 12 | 20.0 | 12.0 | 18.0 | 29.8 |
| 14 | 24.0 | 13.0 | 20.0 | 34.9 |
| 16 | 26.0 | 15.0 | 23.0 | 40.0 |

—From Permission of Worthington Pump and Machinery Corporation.

# Glossary of Terms

*Actual Horsepower*—Often referred to as Line to Water Horsepower. It is the overall theoretical divided by the overall efficiency. It may also be described as the total horsepower required to overcome all frictional and other losses to produce a specified discharge.

*Commercial*—Business establishments, shopping centers, office, etc.

*Density*—Weight per unit volume as compared with water at standard temperature and pressure.

When referring to population, indicates persons per unit of area as acre, square mile, etc.

*Discharge*—Flow from any outlet expressed in some unit of time as second, minute, etc.

*Draw-down*—Distance which water is drawn down in a well during pumping cycle. It is the actual distance from the static water level to the water level during the pumping cycle. Expressed in Feet.

*Gallons Per Day*—Rate of flow expressed in period of 24 hours, or total water used per daily period.

*Gallons Per Minute*—The rate of flow expressed in period of one minute or volume per minute.

*Head of Water*—Expression referring to height of water in feet above a certain datum plane.

*High Pressure Storage*—Also known as high service storage, or if in pressure storage tank is called pneumatic storage. This is the storage which maintains constant pressure on distribution system and which is readily available for use by consumers.

*Industrial*—Manufacturing plants, processing plants, etc.

*Instantaneous Flow*—That flow which occurs during a relatively short period of time.

*Low Pressure Storage*—Often called clear water storage. This storage is under atmospheric pressure, that is, it exerts no pressure head upon the distribution system. By means of a high service pump, this storage readily accessible to the distribution system.

*Milligram Per Liter*—Equivalent to a part per million.

*Parts Per Million*—An expression of dosage which infers a milligram per liter or 8.34 pounds per million gallons of water.

*Pounds Per Square Inch*—An expression of pressure head on the basis of 2.31 feet of water will provide a pressure of one pound per square inch.

*Residential*—Refers to domestic consumption in residential areas.

*Suction*—Water under negative pressure. Considered that water below pump datum plane.

*Theoretical Horsepower*—Calculated horsepower neglecting pump and motor efficiencies and piping friction losses. Neglecting losses, is the foot-pounds of energy to lift a certain quality of water to a specified height above a datum plane.

*Total Head*—Sum of individual heads which include friction losses in pipes, fittings, pumps, etc. Expressed in Feet.

*Yield*—An expression for wells which state the output in terms of gallons per minute. This is the actual discharge without depletion of well input.

# Index

# Index

# Index

# Notes

# Notes